FRONTIERS IN SUPERCONDUCTIVITY RESEARCH

FRONTIERS IN SUPERCONDUCTIVITY RESEARCH

BARRY P. MARTINS
EDITOR

Nova Science Publishers, Inc.
New York

Senior Editors: Susan Boriotti and Donna Dennis
Coordinating Editor: Tatiana Shohov
Office Manager: Annette Hellinger
Graphics: Magdalena Nunez
Editorial Production: Vladimir Klestov, Matthew Kozlowski, Alexandra Columbus and Maya Columbus
Circulation: Ave Maria Gonzalez, Vera Popovic, Luis Aviles, Raymond Davis, Melissa Diaz, Marlene Nunez and Jeannie Pappas
Communications and Acquisitions: Serge P. Shohov
Marketing: Cathy DeGregory

Library of Congress Cataloging-in-Publication Data

Frontiers in superconductivity research / Barry P. Martins (editor).
p. cm.
Includes index.
ISBN 1-59454-005-5
1. Superconductivity--Research. 2. Superconductors--Research. I. Martins, Barry P.
QC611.96.F63 2004
537.6'23--dc22 2004005555

400 Oser Ave, Suite 1600
Hauppauge, New York 11788-3619
Tele. 631-231-7269 Fax 631-231-8175
e-mail: Novascience@earthlink.net
Web Site: http://www.novapublishers.com

Printed in the United States of America

Contents

Preface

Superconductivity is the ability of certain materials to conduct electrical current with no resistance and extremely low losses. High temperature superconductors, such as La2-xSrxCuOx (Tc=40K) and YBa2Cu3O7-x (Tc=90K), were discovered in 1987 and have been actively studied since. In spite of an intense, worldwide, research effort during this time, a complete understanding of the copper oxide (cuprate) materials is still lacking. Many fundamental questions are unanswered, particularly the mechanism by which high-Tc superconductivity occurs. More broadly, the cuprates are in a class of solids with strong electron-electron interactions. An understanding of such "strongly correlated" solids is perhaps the major unsolved problem of condensed matter physics with over ten thousand researchers working on this topic.

High-Tc superconductors also have significant potential for applications in technologies ranging from electric power generation and transmission to digital electronics. This ability to carry large amounts of current can be applied to electric power devices such as motors and generators, and to electricity transmission in power lines. For example, superconductors can carry as much as 100 times the amount of electricity of ordinary copper or aluminum wires of the same size. Many universities, research institutes and companies are working to develop high-Tc superconductivity applications and considerable progress has been made. This volume brings together leading research in this growth field.

Efforts to unify the Bardeen, Cooper & Schrieffer (BCS) and the Bose-Einstein condensation (BEC) formalisms in terms of a "*complete* boson-fermion (BF) model" (CBFM) are surveyed by M. de Llano. A vital distinction is that Cooper pairs (CPs) are indeed bosons that suffer BEC, in contrast with BCS pairs that are not bosons. Another crucial ingredient (particularly in 2D where ordinary BEC does not occur) is the *linear* dispersion relation of "ordinary" CPs, at least in leading order in the center-of-mass momentum (CMM) power-series expansion of the CP energy. This arises because CPs propagate not *in vacuo* but in the Fermi "sea." A many-body Bethe-Salpeter equation treatment of CPs based on the ideal Fermi gas (IFG) sea yields the familiar negative-energy, two-particle bound-state *if* 2h-CPs are ignored as in the ordinary CP problem. But it gives purely-imaginary energies, and is thus meaningless, if 2h-CPS are included as completness requires. However, when based on the BCS ground state instead of the IFG, in addition to the familiar trivial solution (or Anderson-Bogoliubov-Higgs) sound mode, legitimate two-particle *moving* "generalized CPs" emerge but as positive-energy, finite-lifetime, resonant nontrivial solutions for nonzero-CMM. This amounts to replacing the purely-kinetic-energy unperturbed Hamiltonian by the BCS one. The moving CPs again have a *linear* dispersion leading term. BEC of such pairs may thus occur in exactly 2D (as it cannot with quadratic dispersion) and in fact all the way down to $(1+\epsilon)$D where ϵ can be infinitesimally small, thus encompassing all empirically known superconductors. The unified theory reduces in limiting cases to all the main continuum (as opposed to "spin") statistical theories of superconductivity. These include both the BCS and BEC theories. The unified BF theory is "complete" in that not only two-electron (2e) but also two-hole (2h) CPs are allowed, and in arbitrary proportions. In contrast, BCS theory can be deduced from the CBFM but allows only equal (50%-50%) mixtures of them, a fact rarely if ever stressed. The CBFM shows that the BCS condensate is precisely a BE condensate of a mixture of kinematically independent electrons coexisting with weakly-coupled zero CMM 2e- and 2h-CPs in *equal* proportions. Without abandoning the electron-phonon mechanism, the CBFM has been applied in 2D and 3D. The BCS model interaction in moderately weak coupling is sufficient to reproduce the unusually high values of T_c (in units of the Fermi temperature) of $0.01-0.1$ empirically exhibited by the so-called "exotic" superconductors, including cuprates. This range is high relative to the low values of $\leq 10^{-3}$ more or less correctly reproduced by BCS theory for conventional (mostly elemental) superconductors. Also accounted for is the empirical fact that "hole superconductors" systematically have higher T_c's. Room temperature superconductors are predicted to be possible but only via 2h-CP BE condensates.

D. Dominguez, H. Kawamura and Mai Suan Li present a review of the results of their simulations on equilibrium and dynamic properties of the *d*-wave ceramic high-T_c superconductors. They represent disordered superconductors by a three-dimensional lattice model of randomly distributed π Josephson junctions with finite self-inductance. The paramagnetic Meissner effect observed experimentally in ceramic high-T_c superconductors is well reproduced by this model. In equilibrium, one can show that there is a low temperature chiral glass phase, which is characterized by chiralities frozen in time and in space. Experimental attempts on the search for the chiral glass phase are discussed. Dynamical phenomena such as anomalous microwave absorption, AC resistivity and enhancement of critical current by external electric fields are also considered by Langevin dynamics simulations. A satisfactory agreement of the simulations with several experiments in ceramic high T_c superconductors was obtained.

In order to analyze pairing symmetry of an intrinsic superconducting true gap for inhomogeneous high-T_c superconductors, Hyun-Tak Kim explains the intrinsic inhomogeneity of high-T_c superconductors on the basis of the metal-insulator instability and the extended Brinkman-Rice picture explaining the first-order metal-insulator transition, and justify a relation between a fractional effective charge and band filling ($e' = \rho e$; $0< \rho \leq 1$ is band filling) by means of measurement. An observed superconducting gap is given as a function of band-filling and intrinsic true gap ($\triangle_{obs}=\frac{\triangle_i}{\rho}$)

and is the effect of measurement when $0< \rho <1$. The true gap is observed only when $\rho=1$. The peak width of conductance curve as the density of states determines pairing symmetry. The identity of the observed superconducting gap anisotropy for $Bi_2Sr_2CaCu_2O_8+x$ (Bi-2212)is also revealed that the gap anisotropy is attributed to inhomogeneity of a d-wave insulating phase and a metal phase in the measurement region and is not evidence of the d-wave symmetry. The Ambegaokar-Baratoff (AB) theory based on the BCS theory is extended. Small I_cR_n values observed by experiments are explained by the extended AB theory. The magnitude of the true gap deduced from I_cR_n values for Bi-2212 is $8.5< \triangle_i <17$ meV. In addition, the half-flux quantum ($\Phi_0/2$) as evidence of the d-wave symmetry observed by the triple-π-junction experiments, is caused by flux trap. Comments on a flux trap of the magnetic modulation experiment using Pb-YBCO dc SQUIDs are also given on the ground of experimental results for the observation of paramagnetic Meissner effect of $Ba_{0.6}K_{0.4}BiO_3$. Recent researches on tunnel effect as well as proximity effect are discussed by means of measurement. Finally, it is concluded that an analyzed pairing symmetry is s-wave.

Adriana C. Serquis and Xiaozhou Liao review their recent progress on the processing, structures and properties of MgB_2. In particular,they have used a *magnesium vapor infiltration process* (MVIP) to make high quality MgB_2 powder. Serquis and Liao present detailed studies of the field and temperature dependence of the magnetization as well as scanning and transmission electron microscopy characterizations of samples prepared under different conditions. They compare the environmental stability, the critical current densities (J_c) and the creep relaxation rates of MgB_2 samples with different microstructures. The MgB_2 samples synthesized by MVIP were found to contain nanometer-sized $Mg(B,O)_2$ precipitates. Magnetization data show that such precipitates act as effective flux pinning centers, without deteriorating other superconducting properties such as T_c. The sizes and distribution of these precipitates can be controlled through processing, providing an attractive way to introduce flux pinning centers. They also review their results on the effect of heat treatments on the microstructure, magnetization and transport properties of MgB_2 wires prepared by the powder-in-tube method. They discuss the optimization of the annealing conditions that strongly improve the connectivity by eliminating most of the microcracks present in the un-annealed wires. On the other hand, hot isostatic pressed (HIPed) wires have a higher J_c than the annealed wires, especially at high temperatures and magnetic fields, and higher irreversibility field. The improvement is attributed to a high density of structural defects, which are the likely source of vortex pinning.

In the present work, R. Di Capua et al. report on the thin films fabrication and characterization of the recently discovered magnesium diboride (MgB_2) intermetallic superconducting compound. High-quality c-axis oriented thin films were grown by a d.c. planar magnetron sputtering technique in a UHV system (10^{-7} Pa) equipped with 3 focused 2" magnetron sources. A precursor deposition step was followed by an in-situ annealing, in Mg atmosphere, at about 800C in a In sealed Nb box. Superconducting samples were obtained both on MgO and Al_2O_3 (sapphire) single crystal substrates, 10 mm x 10 mm wide. The process is highly reproducible and can be easily scaled to produce large area films. The best films showed maximum Tc = 35 K (onset), a transition width of 0.5 K, a residual resisitivity ratio up to 1.6, a low temperature critical current density Jc > 10_6 A/cm_2, with a thickness ranging between 0.5μm and 1μm. The films were characterized by a variety of structural and electronic measurements. Structural characterizations included profilometer, X-rays diffraction, SEM and AFM measurements. From them, a wide c-axis orientation was revealed, together with a granular structure of the surface. Resistivity measurements in external magnetic field up to 8 T have been performed both in parallel and perpendicular configuration. The upper critical magnetic field vs. temperature behavior has been determined from the experimental data. Measurement of upper critical field showed, for the best samples, an anisotropy ratio of about 2.5, very close to the values observed for single crystals. Di Capua et al. measured the temperature and magnetic field dependencies of the critical current density Jc(H,T). Three-dimensional point like normal core pinning was evidenced by measurements of the magnetic dependence of the pinning forces independently from the superconducting and structural quality of the investigated films. The analysis of the experimental data in terms of the collective pinning model has pointed out the presence of a crossover magnetic field from a single vortex to a small vortex bundle pinning regime. A ΔTc pinning mechanism, i.e., a pinning associated with spatial fluctuations of the transition temperature, has been evidenced by the temperature dependence of this crossover field, in agreement with previous observations performed on MgB_2 bulk materials. In view of possible device applications, the microwave response has been studied in detail. They report and discuss the dependence of the surface impedance on temperature and r.f. field amplitude at 20 GHz and the temperature dependence of the penetration depth via a dielectric resonator technique.

An experimental review on the influence of nonlocal electrodynamics in the vortex pinning properties of non-magnetic borocarbide superconductors is presented by A. V. Silhanek, J. R. Thompson, L. Civale, S. L. Bud'ko, and P. Canfield. They show that the pinning force density F_p exhibits a rich and complex anisotropic behavior that sharply contrast with the small mass anisotropy of these compounds. For magnetic fields $\mathbf{H}$ applied parallel to the crystallographic c-axis, the first order reorientation transition between two rhombic lattices manifests itself as a kink in $F_p(H)$. For $\mathbf{H}\perp$c-axis, a much larger $F_p(H)$ and a slower relaxation rate is observed. In this field configuration, nonlocality induces a fourfold periodicity in F_p when $\mathbf{H}$ is rotated within the square basal plane. Unlike the out-of-plane anisotropy, which persists for increasing impurity levels, the in-plane fourfold anisotropy can be strongly suppressed by reducing the electronic mean free path. This result unambiguously demonstrate that the in-plane anisotropy is a consequence of nonlocal effects. The unique combination of superconducting and material parameters of the cuprate high-temperature superconductors gives rise to tremendously rich vortex phase diagrams and raises many fundamentally and technologically important questions. Complex structured low-temperature superconductors may exhibit similarly intricate phase diagrams and can offer alternative and sometimes advantageous ways of addressing some of the unsolved problems.

Amorphous films of alternating Ta_xGe_{1-x} superconducting and Ge insulating layers provide such a system with arbitrary layer thicknesses and thus full control over anisotropy and coupling between adjacent superconducting layers. Extensive dc-conductance measurements over a large part of the H-T phase diagram were performed by Andreas Engel and Benjamin J. Ruck on a number of films, where in some cases the layering was augmented with a columnar microstructure. This columnar structure results in a network of extended strong pinning sites comparable to twin boundaries in twinned $YBa_2Cu_3O_{7-\delta}$. For the films presented $T_c(0)$ values were in the range from 1.7 to 2.8 K. They are strongly type-II superconductors with $\kappa \equiv \lambda/\xi \approx 90$ or higher and the full range from weak to strong anisotropy. The current-voltage (I-V) curves measured from non-columnar samples can be collapsed according to the vortex glass scaling laws. However, a lack of universality in the critical exponents indicates that the scaling analysis may simply be highlighting a continuous crossover between strong pinning at low T and H and much weaker pinning at high T and H, with no actual phase transition separating the two regimes. For the most anisotropic samples, with essentially two-dimensional decoupled layers, the strongly pinned phase is absent, and the low T and H regime is characterized by thermally activated plastic vortex flow. The micro-structured columnar films show strongly enhanced vortex pinning for magnetic fields co-aligned with the extended pinning sites. The T and H range for which dissipation-free current transport was observed was considerably expanded relative to non-columnar films. For these films a critical scaling analysis clearly identified the pinned vortex phase as a Bose-glass, lending support to the notion that the Bose-glass is a universal phase exhibited by superconductors containing extended defects. It was noted, however, that for the most anisotropic of the micro-structured samples Bose-glass scaling was successful only at relatively low magnetic fields. The high-field vortex phase in this sample was instead best described as a very viscous vortex liquid, with no phase transition to a glass upon lowering the temperature. Further analysis of the I-V characteristics taken in the Bose-glass phase allowed for the extraction of the field, temperature and current dependent glass exponent μ. A markedly different T and H dependence of μ for films with different anisotropy suggests different mechanisms for vortex creep within the pinned vortex phases. Variable-range hopping of vortices and collective flux creep are considered as models to describe the experimental data.

High-T_c Superconductivity via BCS and BEC Unification: A Review

M. de Llano
Instituto de Investigaciones en Materiales, UNAM, 04510 México, DF, Mexico

Abstract

Efforts to unify the Bardeen, Cooper & Schrieffer (BCS) and the Bose-Einstein condensation (BEC) formalisms in terms of a "*complete* boson-fermion (BF) model" (CBFM) are surveyed. A vital distinction is that Cooper pairs (CPs) are indeed bosons that suffer BEC, in contrast with BCS pairs that are not bosons. Another crucial ingredient (particularly in 2D where ordinary BEC does not occur) is the *linear* dispersion relation of "ordinary" CPs, at least in leading order in the center-of-mass momentum (CMM) power-series expansion of the CP energy. This arises because CPs propagate not *in vacuo* but in the Fermi "sea." A many-body Bethe-Salpeter equation treatment of CPs based on the ideal Fermi gas (IFG) sea yields the familiar negative-energy, two-particle bound-state *if* 2h-CPs are ignored as in the ordinary CP problem. But it gives purely-imaginary energies, and is thus meaningless, if 2h-CPS are included as completness requires. However, when based on the BCS ground state instead of the IFG, in addition to the familiar trivial solution (or Anderson-Bogoliubov-Higgs) sound mode, legitimate two-particle *moving* "generalized CPs" emerge but as positive-energy, finite-lifetime, resonant nontrivial solutions for nonzero-CMM. This amounts to replacing the purely-kinetic-energy unperturbed Hamiltonian by the BCS one. The moving CPs again have a *linear* dispersion leading term. BEC of such pairs may thus occur in exactly 2D (as it cannot with quadratic dispersion) and in fact all the way down to $(1+\epsilon)$D where ϵ can be infinitesimally small, thus encompassing all empirically known superconductors.

The unified theory reduces in limiting cases to all the main continuum (as opposed to "spin") statistical theories of superconductivity. These include both the BCS and BEC theories. The unified BF theory is "complete" in that not only two-electron (2e) but also two-hole (2h) CPs are allowed, and in arbitrary proportions. In contrast, BCS theory can be deduced from the CBFM but allows only equal (50%-50%) mixtures of them, a fact rarely if ever stressed. The CBFM shows that the BCS condensate is precisely a BE condensate of a mixture of kinematically independent electrons coexisting with weakly-coupled zero

CMM 2e- and 2h-CPs in *equal* proportions. Without abandoning the electron-phonon mechanism, the CBFM has been applied in 2D and 3D. The BCS model interaction in moderately weak coupling is sufficient to reproduce the unusually high values of T_c (in units of the Fermi temperature) of $0.01 - 0.1$ empirically exhibited by the so-called "exotic" superconductors, including cuprates. This range is high relative to the low values of $\leq 10^{-3}$ more or less correctly reproduced by BCS theory for conventional (mostly elemental) superconductors. Also accounted for is the empirical fact that "hole superconductors" systematically have higher T_c's. Room temperature superconductors are predicted to be possible but only via 2h-CP BE condensates.

1 Introduction

Boson-fermion (BF) models of superconductivity (SC) as a Bose-Einstein condensation (BEC) [1][2] go back to the mid-1950's [3]-[6], pre-dating even the BCS-Bogoliubov theory [7]-[9]. Although BCS theory only contemplates the presence of "Cooper correlations" of single-particle states, BF models [3]-[6],[10]-[18] posit the existence of actual bosonic CPs. Such pair charge carriers have been observed in magnetic flux quantization experiments on elemental [19, 20] as well as on cuprate [21] superconductors (SCs). Larger clusters than pairs are *not* observed, apparently because the clustering occurs not *in vacuo* but in the Fermi sea. However, no experiment has yet been done, to our knowledge, that distinguishes between electron and hole CPs. CPs appear to be the single most important universally accepted ingredient of SC, whether conventional or "exotic" and whether of low- or high-transition-temperatures T_c. And yet, inspite of their centrality they are poorly understood. The fundamental drawback of early [3]-[6] BF models, which took 2e bosons as analogous to diatomic molecules in a classical atom-molecule gas mixture, is the notorious absence of an electron energy gap $\Delta(T)$. "Gapless" models cannot describe the superconducting state at all, although they are useful in locating transition temperatures if approached from above, i.e., $T > T_c$. Even so, we are not aware of any calculations with the early BF models attempting to reproduce any empirical T_c values. The gap first began to appear in later BF models [10]-[15]. With two [13][14] exceptions, however, all BF models neglect the effect of *hole* CPs included on an equal footing with electron CPs to give a "complete" BF model (CBFM) consisting of *both* bosonic CP species coexisting with unpaired electrons.

For 13 years the highest T_c value for any superconductor was 23 K, until the discovery [22] in 1986 of the first so-called "high-T_c" cuprate superconductor $LaBaCuO$ having a $T_c \simeq 35$ K. A feverish search for materials with even higher T_c's lead within just seven years to the highest-T_c superconductor known to date, the $HgBaCaCuO$ cuprate [23] with a $T_c \simeq 164$ K under very high pressure ($\simeq 310,000$ atm). The embarrassing fact is that since 1993 this record has not been broken, very probably because there is yet no *predictive* microscopic theory of superconductivity that can provide orientation in a search that until now has proceeded on a trial-and-error basis.

We submit that progress in developing such a theory has been held back by too many common myths or false dogmas firmly entrenched in the theoretical community.

2 Some false dogmas

The false theoretical dogmas just mentioned can be summarized in the following assertions:

1. With the electron-phonon dynamical mechanism transition temperatures (as given by the BCS formula) $T_c = 1.13\Theta_D e^{-1/\lambda} \lesssim 45$ K at most, since a typical Debye temperature $\Theta_D \sim 300K$ and $\lambda \lesssim \frac{1}{2}$. For higher T_c's one needs to invoke magnons or excitons or plasmons or other electronic mechanisms to provide pairing [24].

2. Superconductivity is unrelated to Bose-Einstein condensation (BEC) [25].

3. BEC is impossible in 2D [26][27].

4. Cooper pairs:

a) are such that "there is a very strong preference for singlet, zero-momentum pairs, so strong that one can get an adequate description of SC by treating these correlations alone [28]."

b) consist of negative-energy stable (i.e., stationary) bound states [29].

c) propagate in the Fermi sea with an energy $\hbar^2K^2/2(2m)$, where m is the effective electron (or hole) mass and $\hbar K$ the CP center-of-mass momentum (CMM) [30], hence assertion # 3 above.

d) with the linear dispersion $E \propto v_F\hbar K$, where v_F is the Fermi velocity, simply represent the sound mode of the ideal Fermi gas (+ interactions), with sound speed $v_F/\sqrt{d}$ in any dimensionality d [31].

e) "...with $K \neq 0$ represent states with net current flow" [32].

f) and BCS pairs are the same thing [33].

g) are *not* bosons, Ref. [34] p. 38, hence assertion # 2 above.

3 Ordinary Cooper pairing

For bosons with excitation (e.g., kinetic) energy for small CMM K given by

$$\varepsilon_K = C_s K^s + o(K^s), \tag{1}$$

with C_s some coefficient and $s > 0$, BEC occurs in a box of length L if and only if $d > s$, since $T_c \equiv 0$ for all $d \leq s$. The commonest example is $s = 2$ as in the textbook case of ordinary bosons with exactly $\varepsilon_K = \hbar^2 K^2/2m_B$, with m_B the boson mass, giving the familiar result that BEC is not allowed for $d \leq 2$. The general theorem for any $s > 0$ is stated as follows. The total boson number is

$$N = N_0(T) + \sum_{\mathbf{K}\neq\mathbf{0}} [\exp\beta(\varepsilon_K - \mu_B) - 1]^{-1} \tag{2}$$

with $\beta \equiv k_B T$. Since $N_0(T_c) \simeq 0$ while the boson chemical potential μ_B also vanishes at $T = T_c$, in the thermodynamic limit the (finite) boson number density becomes

$$N/L^d \simeq A_d \int_{0^+}^{\infty} \mathrm{d}K K^{d-1} [\exp\beta_c(C_s K^s + \cdots) - 1]^{-1} \tag{3}$$

where A_d is a finite coefficient. Thus

$$N/L^d \simeq A_d (k_B T_c/C_s) \int_{0^+}^{K_{\max}} \mathrm{d}K K^{d-s-1} + \int_{K_{\max}}^{\infty} \cdots, \tag{4}$$

where $K_{\max}$ is small and can be picked arbitrarily so long as the integral $\int_{K_{\max}}^{\infty} \cdots$ is finite, as is N/L^d. However, if $d = s$ the first integral gives $\ln K \mid_0^{K_{\max}} = -\infty$; and if $d < s$ it gives $1/(d-s)K^{s-d} \mid_0^{K_{\max}} = -\infty$. Hence, T_c must vanish if and only if $d \leq s$, but is otherwise finite. This conclusion hinges *only* on the leading term of the boson dispersion relation ε_K.

The case $s = 1$ emerges in both the "ordinary" CP problem [29] to be recalled now, as well as in the "generalized" case of the next section. The question of whether or not CPs are bosons or not is resolved in Appendix A. For $s = 1$ BEC occurs for all $d > 1$. Striking experimental confirmation of how superconductivity is "extinguished" as dimensionality d is diminished towards unity has been reported by Tinkham and co-workers [35][36]. They report conductance *vs.* diameter curves in superconducting nanowires consisting of carbon nanotubes sputtered with amorphous $Mo_{79}Ge_{21}$ ($T_c \simeq 5.5\ K$) and of widths from 22 to 10 nm. The conductance diminishes to zero, implying the nanotube becomes an insulator below a certain diameter, thus exposing how T_c vanishes for the thinnest nanotubes.

The CP equation for the energy $\mathcal{E}_K$ of two fermions above the Fermi surface with momentum wavevectors $\mathbf{k}_1$ and $\mathbf{k}_2$ (and arbitrary CMM wavenumber K where $\mathbf{K} \equiv \mathbf{k}_1 + \mathbf{k}_2$) is given by

$$[\hbar^2 k^2/m - 2E_F - \mathcal{E}_K + \hbar^2 K^2/4m]\psi_\mathbf{k} = -\sum_\mathbf{q}{}' V_{\mathbf{kq}}\psi_\mathbf{q}, \tag{5}$$

where $\mathbf{k} \equiv \frac{1}{2}(\mathbf{k}_1 - \mathbf{k}_2)$ is the CP relative momentum and $\psi_\mathbf{q}$ its wave function in momentum space. The prime on the summation implies restriction to states *above* the Fermi surface with energy $E_F \equiv \hbar^2 k_F^2/2m$, viz., $|\mathbf{k} \pm \mathbf{K}/2| > k_F$, and $V_{\mathbf{kq}}$ is the double Fourier transform of the interaction defined as

$$V_{\mathbf{kq}} \equiv \frac{1}{L^d}\int d\mathbf{r}\int d\mathbf{r}' e^{-i\mathbf{q}\cdot\mathbf{r}} V(\mathbf{r},\mathbf{r}') e^{i\mathbf{k}\cdot\mathbf{r}'}, \tag{6}$$

with $V(\mathbf{r},\mathbf{r}')$ the (possibly nonlocal) interaction in real d-dimensional space.

3.1 Delta interaction

If the interfermion interaction $V(\mathbf{r},\mathbf{r}')$ is local, then $V(\mathbf{r},\mathbf{r}') = V(\mathbf{r})\delta(\mathbf{r}-\mathbf{r}')$ in (6). Moreover, if $V(r) = -v_0\delta(\mathbf{r})$ with $v_0 > 0$, this gives $V_{\mathbf{kq}} = v_0/L^d$ and (5) becomes, for any d,

$$\frac{1}{L^d}\sum_\mathbf{k}{}' \frac{1}{\hbar^2 k^2/m - 2E_F - \mathcal{E}_K + \hbar^2 K^2/4m} = \frac{1}{v_0}. \tag{7}$$

In $d = 1$ where the δ-well supports a single bound state, the problem is quite tractable [37]. In either 2D or 3D, however, the δ-well supports an infinite set of bound levels with the lowest level in each case being infinitely bound. This in turn leads to a rigorous collapse of the many-fermion system [38]. To prevent this unphysical collapse the δ-wells must be "regularized," i.e., constructed, say, from square wells [39] such that the remaining δ-well possesses only one bound level. This leaves an infinitesimally small strength parameter v_0 which would make the rhs of (7) diverge (so as to cancel the lhs that also diverges in 2D and 3D but not in 1D). Combining (7) for 2D with the vacuum two-body momentum-space Schrödinger equation for the same δ-potential well allows eliminating [40] v_0 in favor of the (positive) binding energy B_2 of the single bound level of the regularized δ-well. One arrives at

$$\sum_\mathbf{k} \frac{1}{B_2 + \hbar^2 k^2/m} = \sum_\mathbf{k}{}' \frac{1}{\hbar^2 k^2/m - 2E_F - \mathcal{E}_K + \hbar^2 K^2/4m}, \tag{8}$$

where $B_2 \geq 0$ now serves as a coupling constant. A small-K power-series expansion for $\mathcal{E}_K$ gives the analytic expression *valid for any dimensionless coupling* $B_2/E_F \geq 0$,

$$\varepsilon_K \equiv \mathcal{E}_K - \mathcal{E}_0 = \frac{2}{\pi}\hbar v_F K + \left[1 - (2 - [4/\pi]^2)\frac{E_F}{B_2}\right]\frac{\hbar^2 K^2}{2(2m)} + O(K^3), \tag{9}$$

where a nonnegative *CP excitation energy* ε_K has been defined, and the Fermi velocity v_F comes from $E_F/k_F = \hbar v_F/2$. The leading term in (9) is linear in K, followed by a quadratic term. It is clear that the leading term in (9) is quadratic, namely

$$\varepsilon_K = \hbar^2 K^2/2(2m) + O(K^3), \tag{10}$$

provided v_F and hence E_F vanish, i.e., there is no Fermi sea. This is just the familiar nonrelativistic kinetic energy in vacuum of the composite (so-called "local") pair of mass $2m$ and CMM K. The same result (10) is also found to hold in 3D but not analytically as here in 2D. Figure 1 shows exact numerical results of a dimensionless CP excitation energy $\varepsilon_K/(-\mathcal{E}_0)$ (in figure, Δ_0 means present $-\mathcal{E}_0 > 0$) as function of K/k_F for different couplings B_2. Note that ordinary CPs *break up* whenever $\mathcal{E}_K$ turns from negative to positive, i.e., when $\mathcal{E}_K$ vanishes, or by (9) when $\varepsilon_K/(-\mathcal{E}_0) \equiv \varepsilon_K/\Delta_0 = 1$. These points are marked in the figure by dots. In addition to the exact results (full curves) also shown are some results for the linear approximation [first term on the right-hand side of (9), dot-dashed lines (virtually coinciding with the exact curve for all $B_2/E_F \lesssim 0.1$)], as well as for the quadratic approximation (dashed parabolas) as given by the leading term in (10) for stronger couplings. For weak enough coupling the exact dispersion relation is virtually linear—*in spite of the divergence* of the quadratic term in (9) as $B_2/E_F \to 0$. As E_F decreases the quadratic dispersion relation (10) very slowly begins to dominate. A result unique to 2D (and associated with the fact that in 2D the fermionic density of states is *independent* of energy) is that $-\mathcal{E}_0 \equiv \Delta_0 = B_2$.

In 3D [41] instead of (8) similar procedures for two-component fermions give

$$\sum_{\mathbf{k}} \frac{1}{\hbar^2 k^2/m} - \sum_{\mathbf{k},(|\mathbf{k}\pm\mathbf{K}/2|>k_F)} \frac{1}{\hbar^2 k^2/m - \mathcal{E}_K - 2E_F + \hbar^2 K^2/4m} = \frac{mL^3}{4\pi\hbar^2}\frac{1}{a} \tag{11}$$

where a is the s-wave scattering length associated with the regularized δ-well, which corresponds with weak to strong coupling according as $-\infty < 1/k_F a < +\infty$. One finds for weak coupling ($k_F a \to 0^-$, e.g., prior to the well-known first-bound-state singularity as the depth of a 3D potential well is increased) that

$$\mathcal{E}_0/E_F \to -(8/e^2)\exp(-\pi/k_F|a|), \tag{12}$$

a result first reported by Van Hove [42]. For strong coupling ($k_F a \to 0^+$, beyond the single-bound-state resonance) one gets

$$\mathcal{E}_0/E_F \to -2/(k_F a)^2. \tag{13}$$

Numerical results in 3D very similar to those in Fig. 1 for 2D are obtained. Namely, for weak coupling the CP dispersion curves are very nearly linear while for smaller

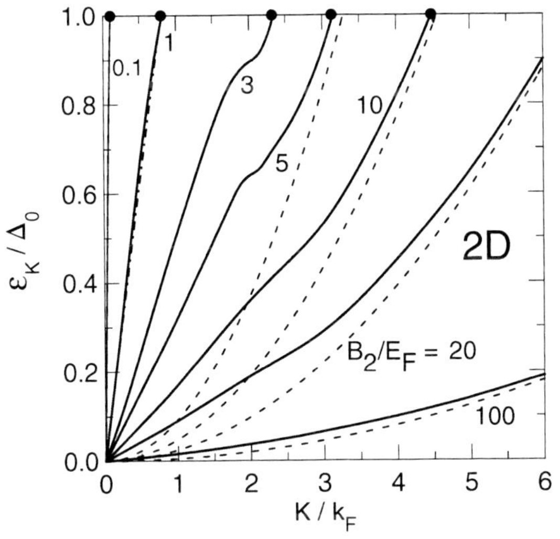

Figure 1: Dimensionless CP excitation energy $\varepsilon_K/(-\mathcal{E}_0) \equiv \varepsilon_K/\Delta_0$ *vs* K/k_F , numerically determined from (8) for different couplings B_2/E_F, full curves, for the delta interaction in 2D. The dot-dashed line is the linear approximation (virtually coincident with the exact curve for $B_2/E_F \lesssim 0.1$) while the dashed curve is the pure quadratic term of (9). Dots denote values of CMM wavenumber where the CP breaks up, i.e., where $\mathcal{E}_K \equiv 0$.

density they very slowly tend to the quadratic. The limit given by (9) in 2D was found too complicated in 3D to be evaluated analytically, except for weak coupling. Repeating the 2D analysis without attempting to explicitly determine the coefficient of the quadratic term one gets, for the δ-well interfermion interaction in weak coupling,

$$\varepsilon_K \equiv \mathcal{E}_K - \mathcal{E}_0 = \frac{1}{2}\hbar v_F K + O(K^2). \tag{14}$$

This is the same result cited without proof by Schrieffer in 1964 (Ref. [34], p. 33) for the BCS model interaction, to which we now turn.

3.2 BCS model interaction

The BCS model interaction is of the simple form

$$V_{\mathbf{kk}'} = \begin{cases} -V & \text{if } k_F < |\mathbf{k} \pm \frac{1}{2}\mathbf{K}|,\ |\mathbf{k}' \pm \frac{1}{2}\mathbf{K}| < \sqrt{k_F^2 + k_D^2} \\ 0 & \text{otherwise,} \end{cases} \tag{15}$$

where $V_{\mathbf{kk}'}$ is defined in (6). Here $V > 0$, and $\hbar\omega_D \equiv \hbar^2 k_D^2/2m$ is the maximum energy of a vibrating-ionic-lattice phonon. This means that two fermions interact with a constant attraction $-V$ when the tip of their relative-momentum wavevector $\mathbf{k}$ points anywhere inside the overlap volume in k-space of the two spherical shells in Figure 2. Inserting (15) into (5) and converting sums over $\mathbf{k}$ into energy integrals by introducing the electronic density of states (DOS) $g(\epsilon)$ gives

$$1 = V \sum_{\mathbf{k}}{}' [2\epsilon_k - 2E_F - \mathcal{E}_K + \hbar^2 K^2/4m]^{-1} = V \int_{E_F}^{E_F + \hbar\omega_D} \frac{g(\epsilon) d\epsilon}{2\epsilon - 2E_F - \mathcal{E}_K + \hbar^2 K^2/4m}. \tag{16}$$

From this one immediately obtains the familiar result for $K = 0$,

$$\mathcal{E}_0 = -\frac{2\hbar\omega_D}{e^{2/\lambda} - 1} \underset{\lambda \to 0}{\longrightarrow} -2\hbar\omega_D e^{-2/\lambda}. \tag{17}$$

Here $\lambda \equiv g(E_F)V$ is a dimensionless coupling constant and $g(E_F)$ the DOS for each spin evaluated at the Fermi energy. The equality in (17) is *exact* in 2D for all coupling—as well as in 1D or 3D provided only that $\hbar\omega_D \ll E_F$ so that $g(\epsilon) \simeq g(E_F)$, a constant that can be taken outside the integral in (16).

For a 2D system (16) gives [43] for weak coupling

$$\mathcal{E}_K \underset{K \to 0}{\longrightarrow} \mathcal{E}_0 + (2/\pi)\hbar v_F K + O(K^2). \tag{18}$$

The exact dispersion relation obtained numerically from (16) for $\lambda = \frac{1}{2}$ and $\hbar\omega_D/E_F = 10^{-2}$ shows that the linear approximation (18) is very good for moderately small λ and $\hbar\omega_D/E_F$, over the entire range of K values for which $\mathcal{E}_K \leq 0$. Note that the linear term carries the *same* coefficient as (9) for a *different* interfermion interaction. Pair breakup, specifically $\mathcal{E}_K > 0$ for these values of λ and $\hbar\omega_D/E_F$, occurs at a relatively small value of K, about four orders of magnitude smaller than the maximum value $2\sqrt{k_F^2 + k_D^2}$ allowed by the interaction (15).

In 3D, assuming $\hbar\omega_D/E_F << 1$ so that the 3D DOS $g(\varepsilon) = (L^3/\pi^2\hbar^3)\sqrt{m^3\varepsilon/2}$ can be replaced by $g(E_F)$ and then taken outside the integral sign, the result cited in Ref. [34], p. 33, (see also Ref. [44], p. 336, Prob. 10.4 but note here an erroneous coeffcient) follows, namely

$$\mathcal{E}_K \underset{K \to 0}{\longrightarrow} \mathcal{E}_0 + \frac{1}{2}\hbar v_F K + O(K^2). \tag{19}$$

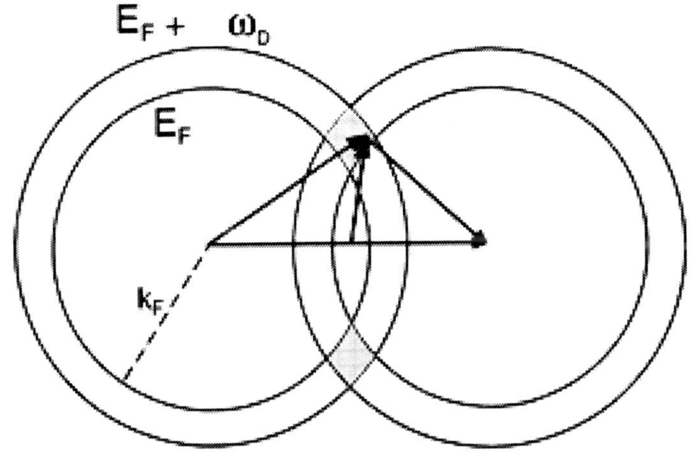

Figure 2: Cross-section of overlap volume in k-space (shading) where the tip of the relative CP wavevector $\mathbf{k} \equiv \frac{1}{2}(\mathbf{k_1} - \mathbf{k_2})$ must point for the attractive BCS model interaction (15) to be nonzero for a CP of CMM $\hbar\mathbf{K} \equiv \hbar(\mathbf{k}_1 + \mathbf{k}_2)$.

Exact numerical results in 3D are qualitatively similar [43] to those in 2D as regards goodness of the linear approximation for weak coupling.

4 Generalized Cooper pairing

The "ordinary" CP problem just summarized for two distinct interfermion interactions (the δ-well and the BCS model interaction) neglects the effect of two-hole (2h) CPs treated on an equal footing with two-particle (2p) CPs—as Green's functions [44] can naturally guarantee. On the other hand, the BCS condensate consists [13] of *equal numbers of 2p and 2h Cooper "correlations."* This was already evident, though scarcely emphasized, from the perfect symmetry about μ, the electron chemical potential, of the well-known Bogoliubov [45] $v^2(\epsilon)$ and $u^2(\epsilon)$ coefficients [see just below (30) later on], where ϵ is the electron energy. the prime motivation here rests on the recently established remarkable fact [13] that a BCS condensate is precisely a BE condensate with equal numbers of 2p and 2h zero-CMM CPs, in the limit of weak coupling. Further motivation comes from the unique but unexplained role played by *hole* charge carriers in the normal state of superconductors [46] in general (see also Ref. [47]). Final motivation stems from the ability of the "complete (in that both 2h- and 2p-CPs are allowed in varying proportions) BF model" of Refs. [13]-[15] to "unify" both BCS and BEC theories as special cases, and to predict substantially higher T_c's than BCS theory without abandoning electron-phonon dynamics. The latter is important as compelling evidence for a significant, if not sole, presence of it in high-T_c cuprate superconductors from angle-resolved photoemission spectroscopy data has recently been reported [48].

In this section we sketch how the Bethe-Salpeter (BS) many-body equation (in the ladder approximation) treating both 2p and 2h pairs on an equal footing shows that, while the ordinary CP problem [based on an ideal Fermi gas (IFG) ground state (the usual "Fermi sea")] does *not* possess stable energy solutions, but that it does so when the IFG ground state is replaced by the BCS one. This is equivalent to starting from an unperturbed Hamiltonian that is the BCS ground state instead of the pure-kinetic-energy operator corresponding to the IFG. We discuss how: i) CPs based not on the IFG-sea but on the BCS ground state survive in a *nontrivial* solution as "generalized" or "moving" CPs which are *positive* energy resonances with an imaginary energy term leading to finite-lifetime effects; ii) as in the "ordinary" CP problem of the previous section, their dispersion relation in leading order in the total (or center-of-mass) momentum (CMM) $\hbar\mathbf{K} \equiv \hbar(\mathbf{k}_1 + \mathbf{k}_2)$ is also *linear* rather than the quadratic $\hbar^2K^2/2(2m)$ of a composite boson (e.g., a deuteron) of mass $2m$ moving not in the Fermi sea but in vacuum; and iii) this latter "moving CP" solution, though often confused [31] with it, is physically *distinct* from another more common *trivial* solution sometimes called, even though Bogoliubov [8] was the first to derive it, the Anderson-Bogoliubov-Higgs (ABH) [49], ([9] p. 44), [50]-[52] collective excitation. The ABH mode is also linear in leading order and goes over into the IFG ordinary sound mode in zero coupling. All this occurs in both 2D [53] as well as in the 3D study outlined earlier in Ref. [54]. We focus here on 2D because of its interest [55]-[57] for quasi-2D high-T_c cuprate superconductors. In general, the results will be crucial for BEC scenarios employing BF models of superconductivity, not only *in exactly 2D* as with the Berezinskii-Kosterlitz-Thouless [58][59] transition, but also down to $(1+\epsilon)$D which characterize the quasi-1D organo-metallic (Bechgaard salt) superconductors [60]-[62]. These results also apply, albeit with a different interaction, to neutral-atom superfluidity as in liquid ^{3}He [63] and very probably also in ultracold trapped alkali Fermi gases such as ^{40}K [64] and ^{6}Li [65] atoms.

In dealing with the many-electron system we again assume the BCS model interaction (6) in 2D with double Fourier transform

$$\begin{aligned} \nu(k_1,k_1') &= -(k_F^2/k_1k_1')V \quad \text{if } k_F-k_D<k_1,k_1'<k_F+k_D, \\ &= 0 \quad \text{otherwise.} \end{aligned} \tag{20}$$

Here $V > 0$, $\hbar k_F \equiv m v_F$ the Fermi momentum, m the effective electron mass, v_F the Fermi velocity, and $k_D \equiv \omega_D / v_F$ with ω_D the Debye frequency; note difference with previous definition just below (15). The usual physical constraint $\hbar\omega_D \ll E_F$ then implies that $k_D/k_F \equiv \hbar\omega_D/2E_F \ll 1$. Assuming perfect ph symmetry about the Fermi surface, we set

$$\epsilon_k \simeq E_F + \hbar v_F (k - k_F) \tag{21}$$

as it simplifies all calculations when very near the Fermi surface.

The bound-state BS wavefunction equation [54] in the ladder approximation with both particles and holes for the original IFG-based CP problem is

$$\Psi(\mathbf{k},E) = -\left(\frac{i}{\hbar}\right)^2 G_0\left(\mathbf{K}/2+\mathbf{k}, \mathcal{E}_K/2+E\right) G_0\left(\mathbf{K}/2-\mathbf{k}, \mathcal{E}_K/2-E\right) \times \\ \times \frac{1}{2\pi i}\int_{-\infty}^{+\infty} dE' \frac{1}{L^d}\sum_{\mathbf{k}'} v(|\mathbf{k}-\mathbf{k}'|)\Psi(\mathbf{k}',E'). \tag{22}$$

Here L^d is the "volume" of the d-dimensional system; $\mathbf{K} \equiv \mathbf{k}_1 + \mathbf{k}_2$ is the CMM and $\mathbf{k} \equiv \frac{1}{2}(\mathbf{k}_1 - \mathbf{k}_2)$ the relative wavevectors of the 2e bound state whose wavefunction is $\Psi(\mathbf{k},E)$; $\mathcal{E}_K \equiv E_1 + E_2$ is the energy of this bound state while $E \equiv (E_1 - E_2)/2$, and $G_0\left(\mathbf{K}/2+\mathbf{k}, \mathcal{E}/2+E\right)$ is the bare one-fermion Green's function given by

$$G_0(\mathbf{k}_1, E_1) = \frac{\hbar}{i}\left\{\frac{\theta(k_1 - k_F)}{-E_1 + \epsilon_{\mathbf{k}_1} - E_F - i\varepsilon} + \frac{\theta(k_F - k_1)}{-E_1 + \epsilon_{\mathbf{k}_1} - E_F + i\varepsilon}\right\} \tag{23}$$

where $\epsilon_{\mathbf{k}_1} \equiv \hbar^2 k_1^2/2m$ and $\theta(x) = 1$ for $x > 0$ and $= 0$ for $x < 0$, so that the first term refers to *electrons* and the second to *holes*. Figure 3 shows all Feynman diagrams for the 2p, 2h and ph wavefunctions ψ_+, ψ_- and ψ_0, respectively, that emerge in the general (BCS-ground-state-based) problem to be discussed later. For the present IFG-based case, diagrams in shaded rectangles do *not* contribute as they involve factors of $\theta(k_1 - k_F)\theta(k_F - k_1) \equiv 0$. Since the energy dependence of $\Psi(\mathbf{k}, E)$ in (22) is only through the Green's functions, the ensuing energy integrals (22) can be evaluated directly in the complex E'-plane and yield, for interaction (20), an equation for the wavefunction $\psi_{\mathbf{k}}$ in momentum space for CPs with *zero* CMM $\mathbf{K} \equiv \mathbf{k}_1 + \mathbf{k}_2 = 0$ that is

$$(2\xi_k - \mathcal{E}_0)\psi_{\mathbf{k}} = V\sum_{\mathbf{k}'}{}' \psi_{\mathbf{k}'} - V\sum_{\mathbf{k}'}{}'' \psi_{\mathbf{k}'}. \tag{24}$$

Here $\xi_k \equiv \hbar^2 k^2/2m - E_F$ while $\mathcal{E}_0$ is the $\mathbf{K} = 0$ eigenvalue energy, and $\mathbf{k} \equiv \frac{1}{2}(\mathbf{k}_1 - \mathbf{k}_2) = \mathbf{k}_1$. The single prime over the first (2p-CP) summation term denotes the restriction $0 < \xi_{k'} < \hbar\omega_D$ while the double prime in the last (2h-CP) term means $-\hbar\omega_D < \xi_{k'} < 0$. Without this latter term we have Cooper's

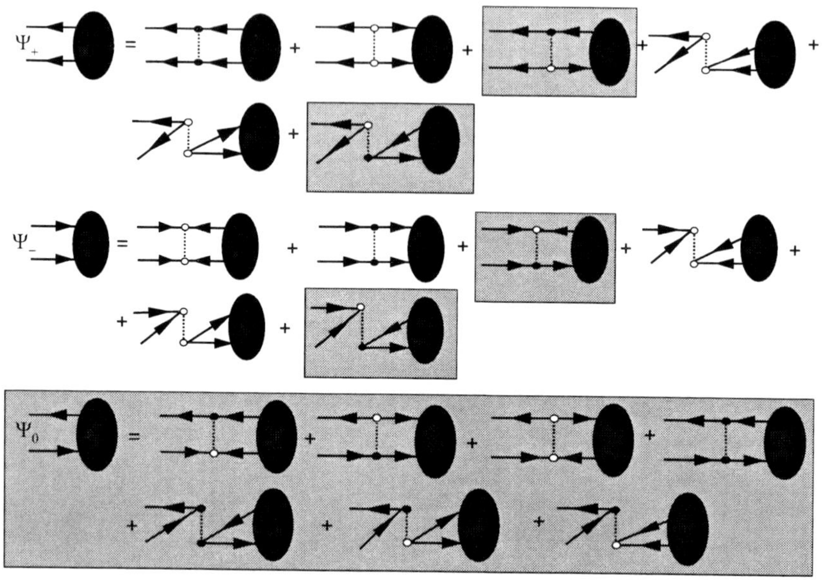

Figure 3: Wavefunction Feynman diagrams for 2p (ψ_+), 2h (ψ_-) and ph (ψ_0) bound states arising from the BS equations. Shaded rectangles designate diagrams that do not contribute in the IFG-based case.

Schrödinger-like equation [29] for 2p-CPs whose implicit solution is clearly $\psi_{\mathbf{k}} = (2\xi_k - \mathcal{E}_0)^{-1} V \sum'_{\mathbf{k}'} \psi_{\mathbf{k}'}$. Since the summation term is constant, performing that summation on both sides allows canceling the $\psi_{\mathbf{k}}$-dependent terms, leaving the eigenvalue equation $\sum'_{\mathbf{k}} (2\xi_k - \mathcal{E}_0)^{-1} = 1/V$. This is one equation in one unknown $\mathcal{E}_0$; transforming the sum to an integral over energies gives the familiar solution (17) exact in 2D, and to a very good approximation otherwise if $\hbar\omega_D \ll E_F$, where $\lambda \equiv VN(E_F)$ with $N(E_F)$ the electronic DOS for one spin. This corresponds to a negative-energy, stationary-state bound pair. For $K \geqslant 0$ the 2p-CP eigenvalue equation becomes

$$\sum_{\mathbf{k}}{}' (2\xi_k - \mathcal{E}_K + \hbar^2 K^2/4m)^{-1} = 1/V. \tag{25}$$

Note that a 2p CP state of energy $\mathcal{E}_K$ is characterized only by a definite K but *not* definite $\mathbf{k}$, in contrast to a "BCS pair" defined [Ref. [7], Eqs. (2.11) to (2.13)] with fixed $\mathbf{K}$ and $\mathbf{k}$ (or equivalently definite $\mathbf{k}_1$ and $\mathbf{k}_2$); see Appendix A. Without the first summation term in (24) the same expression (17) for $\mathcal{E}_0$ for 2p-CPs follows for 2h-CPs, apart from an overall sign change.

The *complete* equation (24) *cannot* be derived from an ordinary (non-BS) Schrödinger-like equation in spite of its simple appearance. To solve it for the unknown energy $\mathcal{E}_0$, let the rhs of (24) be defined as $A - B$, with A relating to the 2p term and B to the 2h one. Solving for the unknown $\psi_{\mathbf{k}}$ gives

$$\psi_{\mathbf{k}} = (A - B)/(2\xi_k - \mathcal{E}_0) \quad \text{or equivalently} \quad \psi(\xi) = (A - B)/(2\xi - \mathcal{E}_0) \tag{26}$$

whence

$$A \equiv \lambda \int_0^{\hbar\omega_D} d\xi \psi(\xi) = \frac{1}{2}(A - B)\lambda \int_{-\mathcal{E}_0}^{2\hbar\omega_D - \mathcal{E}_0} dz/z \equiv (A - B)x \tag{27}$$

$$B \equiv \lambda \int_{-\hbar\omega_D}^{0} d\xi \psi(\xi) = \frac{1}{2}(A - B)\lambda \int_{-2\hbar\omega_D - \mathcal{E}_0}^{-\mathcal{E}_0} dz/z \equiv (A - B)y. \tag{28}$$

The integrals are readily evaluated giving $x \equiv \frac{1}{2}\lambda \ln(1 - 2\hbar\omega_D/\mathcal{E}_0)$ and $y \equiv -\frac{1}{2}\lambda \ln(1 + 2\hbar\omega_D/\mathcal{E}_0)$. As A and B still contain the unknown $\psi(\xi)$ let us eliminate them. Note that (27) and (28) are equivalent to *two* equations in two unknowns A and B, namely

$$\begin{aligned} (1 - x)A + xB &= 0 \\ -yA + (1 + y)B &= 0. \end{aligned}$$

This leads immediately to the equation $1 - x + y = 0$, which on inserting the definitions of x and y becomes

$$1 = \frac{1}{2}\lambda \ln[1 - (2\hbar\omega_D/\mathcal{E}_0)^2],$$

which finally yields

$$\mathcal{E}_0 = \pm i 2\hbar\omega_D/\sqrt{e^{2/\lambda} - 1}. \tag{29}$$

As the CP energy is pure-imaginary there is an obvious instability of the CP problem when both particle- and hole-pairs are included. This was reported in Refs. [9] p. 44 and [66], who did not, however, stress the pure 2p and 2h special cases just discussed. Clearly then, the original CP picture *is meaningless if particle- and hole-pairs are treated on an equal footing*, as consistency demands.

5 BCS-based BS treatment of Cooper pairing

However, a BS treatment not about the IFG sea but about the BCS ground state *vindicates the CP concept* as a nontrivial solution. This is equivalent to starting not from the IFG unperturbed Hamiltonian but from the BCS one. Its physical justification lies in recovering three expected items: ABH sound mode, the BCS

$T = 0$ gap equation and finite-lifetime effects of the "moving CPs." In either 2D [53] or 3D [54] the BS equation yields a 4×4 determinant which reduces to a 3×3 and a 1×1 determinant representing, respectively, *two distinct solutions*: a) the trivial ABH sound solution and b) a highly *nontrivial* moving CP solution, respectively. In either case the BS formalism gives a set of three coupled equations, one for each (2p, 2h and ph) channel wavefunction for any spin-independent interaction such as (20). However, the ph channel decouples, leaving only two coupled wavefunction equations for the ABH solution in 2D which we consider first. We note that in Ref. [67] the hh channel was ignored, leading to a 3×3 determinant from which only the trivial ABH solution emerges, but the nontrivial moving CP one was missed entirely. Thus, the IFG Green function (23) is replaced by the BCS one

$$\mathbf{G}_0(\mathbf{k}_1, E_1) = \frac{\hbar}{i}\left\{\frac{v_{k_1}^2}{-E_1 + E_{k_1} - i\varepsilon} + \frac{u_{k_1}^2}{-E_1 + E_{k_1} + i\varepsilon}\right\} \tag{30}$$

where $E_{\mathbf{k}} \equiv \sqrt{\xi_k{}^2 + \Delta^2}$ with Δ the $T = 0$ fermionic gap, $v_k^2 \equiv \frac{1}{2}(1 - \xi_k/E_{\mathbf{k}})$ and $u_k^2 \equiv 1 - v_k^2$ are the Bogoliubov functions [68]. As $\Delta \to 0$ these three quantities become $|\xi_k|$, $\theta(k_1 - k_F)$ and $\theta(k_F - k_1)$, respectively, so that (30) reduces to (23), as expected. Substituting $G_0(\mathbf{k}_1, E_1)$ by $\mathbf{G}_0(\mathbf{k}_1, E_1)$ corresponds to rewriting the total Hamiltonian so that the pure-kinetic-energy unperturbed Hamiltonian is replaced by the BCS one. The remaining Hamiltonian terms are then assumed suitable to a perturbation treatment. We focus in this section only on 2D.

5.1 ABH sound (trivial) solution

The equations involved are too lengthy even in 2D and will be derived in detail elsewhere, but for the trivial ABH sound solution the aforementioned 3×3 determinant boils down to the single expression

$$\begin{aligned}\frac{1}{2\pi}\lambda\hbar v_F \int_{k_F-k_D}^{k_F+k_D} dk \int_0^{2\pi} d\varphi\{u_{\mathbf{K}/2+\mathbf{k}}\, u_{\mathbf{K}/2-\mathbf{k}} + v_{\mathbf{K}/2+\mathbf{k}}\, v_{\mathbf{K}/2-\mathbf{k}}\}\times \\ \times\left[\frac{v_{\mathbf{K}/2+\mathbf{k}} v_{\mathbf{K}/2-\mathbf{k}}}{\mathcal{E}_K + E_{\mathbf{K}/2+\mathbf{k}} + E_{\mathbf{K}/2-\mathbf{k}}} + \frac{u_{\mathbf{K}/2+\mathbf{k}}\, u_{\mathbf{K}/2-\mathbf{k}}}{-\mathcal{E}_K + E_{\mathbf{K}/2+\mathbf{k}} + E_{\mathbf{K}/2-\mathbf{k}}}\right] = 1\end{aligned} \tag{31}$$

where φ is the angle between $\mathbf{K}$ and $\mathbf{k}$. Here $k_D \equiv \omega_D/v_F$; note difference with definition just below (15). As before $\lambda \equiv VN(E_F)$ with $N(E_F) \equiv m/2\pi\hbar^2$ the constant 2D electronic DOS and $V > 0$ is the interaction strength defined in (20). Angle-resolved photoemission spectral studies of $BiSrCaCuO$ have shown evidence [69] in this cuprate for the Bogoliubov functions u_k^2 and v_k^2, both above and below the Fermi energy.

The *ABH collective excitation mode* energy $\mathcal{E}_K$ must then be extracted from this equation. For $\mathbf{K} = 0$ it is just $\mathcal{E}_0 = 0$ (Ref. [9] p. 39). Then (31) rewritten as an integral over $\xi \equiv \hbar^2 k^2/2m - E_F$ reduces to

$$\int_0^{\hbar\omega_D} d\xi/\sqrt{\xi^2 + \Delta^2} = 1/\lambda, \tag{32}$$

or the familiar BCS $T = 0$ gap equation for interaction (20). The integral is exact and gives

$$\Delta = \hbar\omega_D/\sinh(1/\lambda). \tag{33}$$

Returning to the ABH energy $\mathcal{E}_K$ equation (31) and Taylor-expanding $\mathcal{E}_K$ about $K = 0$ and small λ leaves

$$\mathcal{E}_K = \frac{\hbar v_F}{\sqrt{2}} K + O(K^2) + o(\lambda), \tag{34}$$

where $o(\lambda)$ denote interfermion interaction correction terms that vanish as $\lambda \to 0$. Note that the leading term is just the ordinary sound mode in an IFG whose sound speed $c = v_F/\sqrt{d}$ in d dimensions.

The latter also follows elementarily on solving for c in the familiar thermodynamic relation $dP/dn = mc^2$ involving the zero-temperature IFG pressure

$$\begin{aligned} P &= n^2[d(E/N)/dn] = 2nE_F/(d+2) \\ &= 2C_d n^{2/d\,+1}/(d+2) \end{aligned} \tag{35}$$

where the constant C_d will drop out. Here the IFG ground-state (internal) energy per fermion $E/N = dE_F/(d+2) = C_d n^{2/d}$ was used along with $E_F \equiv \hbar^2 k_F^2/2m$ and

$$n \equiv N/L^d = k_F^d/d2^{d-2}\pi^{d/2}\Gamma(d/2) \tag{36}$$

for the fermion-number density n. The derivative of (35) with respect to n finally gives $c = \hbar k_F/m\sqrt{d} \equiv v_F/\sqrt{d}$, which in 2D is just the leading term in (34).

5.2 Moving CP (nontrivial) solution

The nontrivial *moving CP* solution of the BCS-ground-state-based BS treatment, which is *entirely new*, comes from the remaining 1×1 determinant. It leads to the pair energy $\mathcal{E}_K$ which in 2D is contained in the equation

$$\begin{aligned} &\frac{1}{2\pi}\lambda\hbar v_F \int_{k_F-k_D}^{k_F+k_D} dk \int_0^{2\pi} d\varphi\, u_{\mathbf{K}/2+\mathbf{k}} v_{\mathbf{K}/2-\mathbf{k}} \times \\ &\times \{u_{\mathbf{K}/2-\mathbf{k}} v_{\mathbf{K}/2+\mathbf{k}} - u_{\mathbf{K}/2+\mathbf{k}} v_{\mathbf{K}/2-\mathbf{k}}\} \frac{E_{\mathbf{K}/2+\mathbf{k}} + E_{\mathbf{K}/2-\mathbf{k}}}{-\mathcal{E}_K^2 + (E_{\mathbf{K}/2+\mathbf{k}} + E_{\mathbf{K}/2-\mathbf{k}})^2} = 1. \end{aligned} \tag{37}$$

In addition to the pp and hh wavefunctions (depicted diagrammatically in Ref. [54] Fig. 2), diagrams associated with the ph channel give zero contribution at $T = 0$. A third equation for the ph wavefunction describes the ph bound state but turns out to depend only on the pp and hh wavefunctions. Taylor-expanding $\mathcal{E}_K$ in (37) in powers of K around $K = 0$, and introducing a possible damping factor by adding an imaginary term $-i\Gamma_K$ in the denominator, yields to order K^2

$$\pm\mathcal{E}_K \simeq 2\Delta + \frac{\lambda}{2\pi}\hbar v_F K + \frac{1}{9}\frac{\hbar v_F}{k_D}e^{1/\lambda}K^2 \\ - i\left[\frac{\lambda}{\pi}\hbar v_F K + \frac{1}{12}\frac{\hbar v_F}{k_D}e^{1/\lambda}K^2\right] + O(K^3) \tag{38}$$

where the upper and lower signs refer to 2p- and 2h-CPs, respectively. A linear dispersion in leading order again appears, but now associated with the bosonic moving CP. Hence the *positive*-energy 2p-CP resonance has a width Γ_K and a lifetime

$$\tau_K \equiv \hbar/2\Gamma_K = \hbar/2\left[(\lambda/\pi)\hbar v_F K + (\hbar v_F/12k_D)e^{1/\lambda}K^2\right]. \tag{39}$$

This diverges only at $K = 0$, falling to zero as K increases. Thus, "faster" moving CPs are shorter-lived and eventually break up, while "non-moving" ones are infinite-lifetime stationary states. The linear term $(\lambda/2\pi)\hbar v_F K$ in (38) contrasts sharply with the *coupling-independent* leading-term in (18) [or 1/2 in 3D in (19), Ref. [34] p. 33, instead of $2/\pi$] that follows from the *original* CP problem (25) neglecting holes. This holds for either interaction (20) [43] *or* for an attractive delta interfermion potential well in 2D [40] or in 3D [41]. These δ-wells are imagined regularized [39] to possess a single bound level whose binding energy (in 2D) or scattering length (in 3D) serve as the coupling parameter. Figure 4a shows the exact moving CP (mCP) energy (full curves) extracted from (37), along with its leading linear-dispersion term (thin short-dashed lines) and this plus the next (quadratic) term (long-dashed curves) from (38). The interaction parameter values used with (20) were $\hbar\omega_D/E_F = 0.05$ (a typical value for cuprates) and the two values $\lambda = \frac{1}{4}$ and $\frac{1}{2}$. Using (33) in (38) gives

$$\mathcal{E}_0/E_F \equiv 2\Delta/E_F = 2\hbar\omega_D/E_F \sinh(1/\lambda), \tag{40}$$

having the values $\simeq 0.004$ and 0.028, respectively (marked as dots on the figure ordinate). Remarkably enough, the linear approximation (thin short-dashed lines in figure) is better over a wider range of K/k_F values for weaker coupling (lower set of three curves) in spite of a larger and larger (because of the factor $e^{1/\lambda}$) partial contribution from the quadratic term in (38). This peculiarity also emerged from the ordinary CP treatment of Sec. 3, Refs. [40][41][43]. It suggests the expansion in powers of K to be an asymptotic series that should be truncated after the linear term. For reference we also plot the linear leading term $\hbar v_F K/\sqrt{2}$ of the sound solution (34). We note that the *coupling-independent* leading-term [43] $(2/\pi)\hbar v_F K$ from the *original* CP problem neglecting holes, if graphed in Fig. 4, would almost coincide with the ABH term $\hbar v_F K/\sqrt{2}$ and have a slope about 90% smaller.

Empirical evidence for the *linearly-dispersive* nature of Cooper pairs in cuprates has been argued by Wilson [70] to be suggested by the scanning tunneling microscope conductance scattering data in BSCCO obtained by Davis and coworkers [71][72]. More suggestive direct evidence is shown in Figure 5 [73] with experimental data (mostly from penetration-depth measurements) for two 3D SCs [74][75], two quasi-2D cuprates [76]-[78], and a quasi-1D SC [79]. The data are seen to agree quite well, at least for $T \gtrsim 0.5T_c$, with the *pure-phase* (only 2e- *or* 2h-CP) BEC condensate fraction formula $1-(T/T_c)^{d/s}$ for $d = 3$, 2 and 1, respectively, *provided one assumes* $s = 1$. For lower T's, one can argue on the basis of Fig. 9 below that a *mixed* BEC phase containing both 2e- and 2h-CPs becomes more stable (i.e., has lower Helmholtz free energy) so that the simple pure-phase $1-(T/T_c)^{d/s}$ formula is no longer strictly valid.

As in Cooper's [29] original equation (25), the BS moving CPs are characterized by a definite $\mathbf{K}$ and *not* also by definite $\mathbf{k}$ as the pairs discussed by BCS [7]. Hence, the objection does not apply that CPs are not bosons because BCS pairs with definite $\mathbf{K}$ and $\mathbf{k}$ (or equivalently definite $\mathbf{k}_1$ and $\mathbf{k}_2$) have creation/annihilation operators that do *not* obey the usual Bose commutation relations [Ref. [7], Eqs. (2.11) to (2.13)]. In fact, either (25) or (37) shows that a given "ordinary" or "generalized" CP state labeled by either $\mathbf{K}$ or $\mathcal{E}_K$ can accommodate (in the thermodynamic limit) an indefinitely many possible BCS pairs with different $\mathbf{k}$'s; see Ref. [82] or Appendix A. A recent electronic analog [83] of the Hanbury Brown-Twiss photon-effect experiment suggest electron pairs in a SC to be definitely bosons.

To conclude this section, hole pairs treated on a par with electron pairs play a vital role in determining the precise nature of CPs even at zero temperature—only when based not on the usual IFG "sea" but on the BCS ground state. Their treatment with a Bethe-Salpeter equation gives purely-imaginary-energy CPs when based on the IFG, and positive-energy resonant-state CPs with a finite lifetime for nonzero CMM when based on the BCS ground state—instead of the more familiar negative-energy stationary states of the original IFG-based CP problem that neglects holes, as sketched just below (24). The BS "moving-CP" dispersion relation (38), on the other hand, resembles the plasmon dispersion curve in 3D. It is gapped by twice the BCS energy gap, followed by a *linear* leading term in the CMM expansion about $K = 0$, instead of the quadratic for the 3D plasmon curve. This linearity is

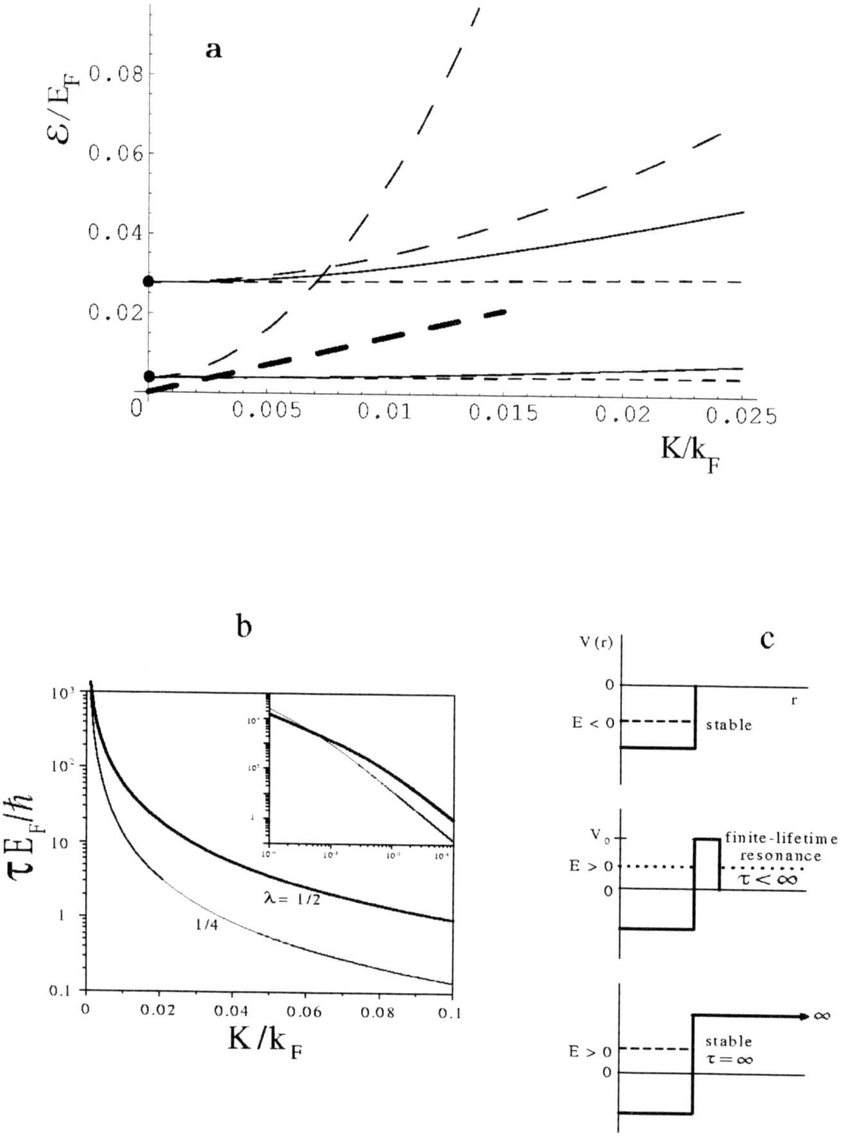

Figure 4: a) Exact "moving" 2p-CP (real) energy $\mathcal{E}_K$ (in units of E_F) in 2D from (37) (full curves), compared with its linear leading term (thin short-dashed lines) and its linear plus quadratic expansion (long-dashed curves) both from (38), *vs.* CMM wavenumber K (in units of k_F), for interaction (20) parameters $\lambda = \frac{1}{4}$ (lower set of curves) and $\frac{1}{2}$ (upper set of curves), and $\hbar\omega_D/E_F = 0.05$. For reference, leading linear term (34) of trivial ABH sound mode is also plotted (lower thick dashed line). b) 2p-CP lifetime as defined in (39). c) Analogy of ordinary and BCS-based-BS 2p-CPs with various confined states in a 3D potential problem.

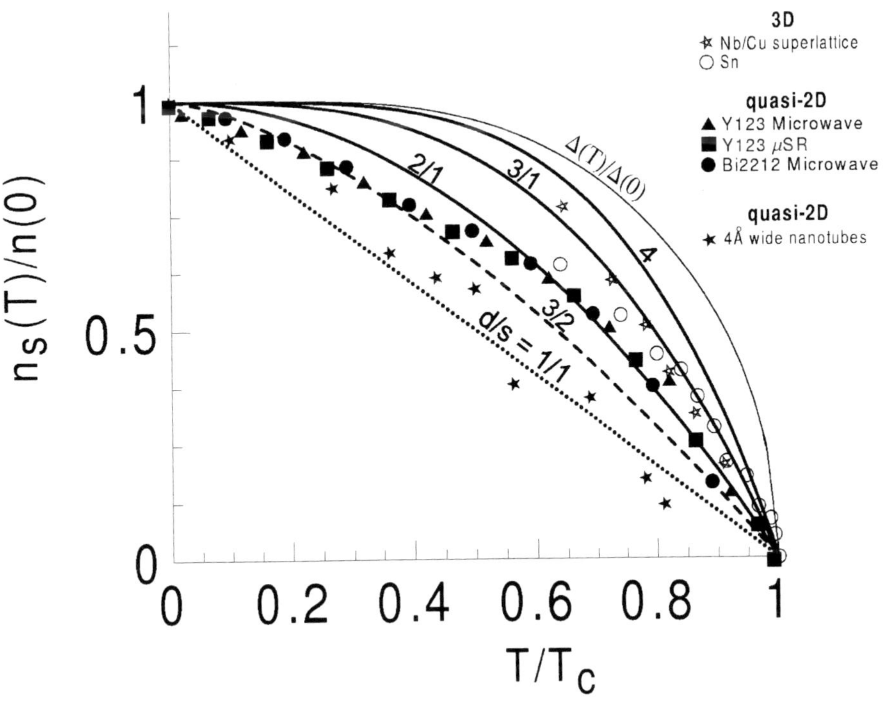

Figure 5: BE condensate-fraction curves $1-(T/T_c)^{d/s}$ for bosons in $d=3$, 2, or 1 with dispersion relation (1) with $s=2$ or 1, for a *pure* phase of either 2e- or 2h-CPs as discussed in text, compared to empirical data for 3D SCs (Nb/Cu and Sn), two quasi-2D SCs ($Y123$ and $Bi2212$) and a quasi-1D SC (4 A-wide nanotubes). Data for the latter are for $\Delta(T)/\Delta(0)$ but are plotted as $[\Delta(T)/\Delta(0)]^2$ so as to reflect 2h-CP condensate fraction $m_0(T)/m_0(0)$ according to (67). The curve marked 1/1 strictly corresponds to $T_c \equiv 0$; however, it serves as a lower bound to all curves with $d/s=(1+\epsilon)/1$ for small but nonzero ϵ for which $T_c>0$. The ordinate axis is labeled with the superelectron number density $n_s(T)$ in units of the normal electron density n. Also shown for reference are the two-fluid model [80] curve $1-(T/T_c)^4$ and the BCS gap $\Delta(T)/\Delta(0)$ order parameter curve [81].

distinct from the better-known one (34) associated with the sound or ABH collective excitation mode whose energy vanishes at $K = 0$. Thus, BF models assuming this CP linearity for the boson component, instead of the quadratic $\hbar^2K^2/2(2m)$ assumed in Refs. [3], [11]-[14], [89]-[92] among many others, can give BEC for all $d > 1$, including exactly 2D. Such BF models can then in principle address not only quasi-2D cuprate but also quasi-1D organo-metallic superconductors.

6 The CBFM Hamiltonian

The CBFM [13, 14] is described (in d dimensions) by the Hamiltonian $H = H_0 + H_{int}$. The unperturbed Hamiltonian H_0 corresponds to a "normal" state which is an *ideal* (i.e., noninteracting) gas mixture of unpaired fermions and both types of CPs, two-electron (2e) and two-hole (2h), and is given by

$$H_0 = \sum_{\mathbf{k}_1,s_1} \epsilon_{\mathbf{k}_1} a^+_{\mathbf{k}_1,s_1} a_{\mathbf{k}_1,s_1} + \sum_{\mathbf{K}} E_+(K) b^+_{\mathbf{K}} b_{\mathbf{K}} - \sum_{\mathbf{K}} E_-(K) c^+_{\mathbf{K}} c_{\mathbf{K}} \qquad (41)$$

where as before $\mathbf{K} \equiv \mathbf{k_1} + \mathbf{k_2}$ is the CP CMM wavevector, $\mathbf{k} \equiv \frac{1}{2}(\mathbf{k_1} - \mathbf{k_2})$ its relative wavevector, while $\epsilon_{\mathbf{k}_1} \equiv \hbar^2 k_1^2/2m$ are the single-electron, and $E_\pm(K)$ the 2e-/2h-CP *phenomenological*, energies. Here $a^+_{\mathbf{k}_1,s_1}$ $(a_{\mathbf{k}_1,s_1})$ are creation (annihilation) operators for fermions and similarly $b^+_{\mathbf{K}}$ $(b_{\mathbf{K}})$ and $c^+_{\mathbf{K}}$ $(c_{\mathbf{K}})$ for 2e- and 2h-CP bosons, respectively. Two-hole CPs are considered *distinct* and *kinematically independent* from 2e-CPs since their Bose commutation relations involve a relative sign change, in sharp contrast with electron or hole fermions whose Fermi anticommutation relations do not. Our present formulation is of course nonrelativistic because of relatively low temperatures.

At the opposite extreme of very high T's (compared with the boson rest-mass energy), however, one has a relativistic regime where pair production takes place and BEC *must* take $\bar{N}$ antibosons of charge, say, $-q$ into account along with the N bosons of charge q. In units such that $\hbar \equiv c \equiv k_B \equiv 1$ the boson energy is $\varepsilon_K = (K^2 + m_B^2)^{1/2}$. Charge conservation requires that not $N \equiv N_0(T) + \sum_{\mathbf{K}\neq\mathbf{0}}[\exp\beta(\varepsilon_K - \mu_B) - 1]^{-1}$ be constant but rather $N - \bar{N}$, where $\bar{N}$ is the same expression as N but with $+\mu_B$ instead of $-\mu_B$. If $\rho \equiv q(N - \bar{N})/L^3 \equiv qn$ is the net conserved charge density, it is shown in Ref. [93] that $T_c = (3|n|/m_B)^{\frac{1}{2}}$ and that the condensate fraction $n_0(T)/n = 1 - (T/T_c)^2$. This is *qualitatively* different from the better-known results assuming only N constant, which are the mass-independent $T_c = [\pi^2 n/\zeta(3)]^{1/3}$, and $n_0(T)/n = 1 - (T/T_c)^3$. This analogy with the CBFM exhibits the strikingly dramatic effect of including or not antiparticles—or, in our nonrelativistic problem, of including or not hole pairs.

The interaction Hamiltonian H_{int} consists of four distinct BF interaction vertices, see Fig. 6, each with two-fermion/one-boson creation or annihilation operators, depicting how unpaired electrons (subindex +) [or holes (subindex −)] combine to form the 2e- (and 2h-CPs) assumed in the d-dimensional system of size L, namely

$$H_{int} = L^{-d/2} \sum_{\mathbf{k},\mathbf{K}} f_+(k)\{a^+_{\mathbf{k}+\frac{1}{2}\mathbf{K},\uparrow} a^+_{-\mathbf{k}+\frac{1}{2}\mathbf{K},\downarrow} b_{\mathbf{K}} + a_{-\mathbf{k}+\frac{1}{2}\mathbf{K},\downarrow} a_{\mathbf{k}+\frac{1}{2}\mathbf{K},\uparrow} b^+_{\mathbf{K}}\}$$

$$+L^{-d/2} \sum_{\mathbf{k},\mathbf{K}} f_-(k)\{a^+_{\mathbf{k}+\frac{1}{2}\mathbf{K},\uparrow} a^+_{-\mathbf{k}+\frac{1}{2}\mathbf{K},\downarrow} c^+_{\mathbf{K}} + a_{-\mathbf{k}+\frac{1}{2}\mathbf{K},\downarrow} a_{\mathbf{k}+\frac{1}{2}\mathbf{K},\uparrow} c_{\mathbf{K}}\}. \qquad (42)$$

Note that the *fermion-pair interaction* H_{int} is reminiscent of the Fröhlich (or Dirac QED) interaction Hamiltonian (Ref. [44], p. 396 ff.) involving two fermion and one boson operators, but with *two* types of CPs instead of phonons (or photons). But in contrast with Fröhlich and Dirac there is no a conservation law for the number of unpaired electrons, i.e., $[H_{int}, \sum_{\mathbf{k}_1,s_1} \varepsilon_{\mathbf{k}_1} a^+_{\mathbf{k}_1,s_1} a_{\mathbf{k}_1,s_1}] \neq 0$. (Note however that $[H_{int}, \sum_{\mathbf{k}_1,s_1} \mathbf{k}_1 a^+_{\mathbf{k}_1,s_1} a_{\mathbf{k}_1,s_1}] = 0$ and $[H_{int}, \sum_{\mathbf{k}_1,s_1} s_1 a^+_{\mathbf{k}_1,s_1} a_{\mathbf{k}_1,s_1}] = 0$.) Just as the Fröhlich (or Dirac) interaction Hamiltonians are the most natural ones to use in a many-electron/phonon (or photon) system, one can conjecture the same of (42) for the BF system under study. Indeed, this H_{int} has *formally* already been employed under various guises by several authors [10]-[12],[84]-[87], but *without* hole pairs. More recently, a similar BF H_{int} has been employed [89]-[92] to study quantum degenerate Fermi gases consisting of neutral ^{40}K atoms and their so-called Feshbach "resonance superfluidity." However, these authors assume quadratically-dispersive CPs, besides also *excluding 2h-CPs* and cannot thus relate their formalism to BCS theory.

The energy form factors $f_\pm(k)$ in (42) are essentially the Fourier transforms of the 2e- and 2h-CP intrinsic wavefunctions, respectively, in the relative coordinate between the paired fermions of the CP. In Refs.[13][14] they are taken simply as

$$f_+(\epsilon) = \begin{cases} f & \text{for } E_f < \epsilon < E_f + \delta\varepsilon, \\ 0 & \text{otherwise,} \end{cases} \qquad (43)$$

$$f_-(\epsilon) = \begin{cases} f & \text{for } E_f - \delta\varepsilon < \epsilon < E_f, \\ 0 & \text{otherwise.} \end{cases} \qquad (44)$$

The quantities E_f and $\delta\varepsilon$ are *new* phenomenological dynamical energy parameters (in addition to the positive BF vertex coupling parameter f) that replace the previous such $E_\pm(0)$, through the relations

$$E_f \equiv \tfrac{1}{4}[E_+(0) + E_-(0)] \quad \text{and} \quad \delta\varepsilon \equiv \tfrac{1}{2}[E_+(0) - E_-(0)], \qquad (45)$$

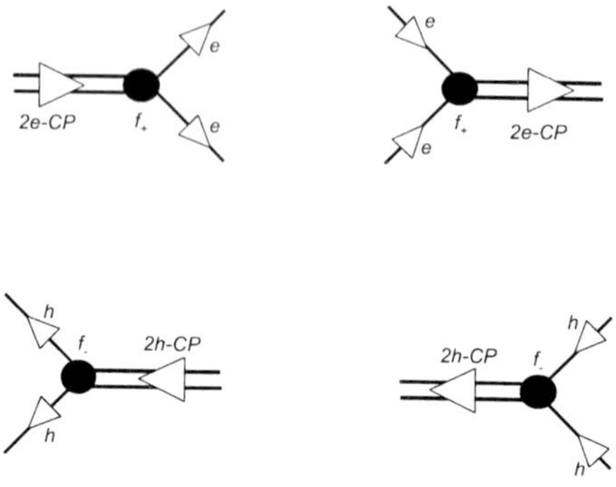

Figure 6: BF vertex diagrams depicting disintegration of 2e-CPs into two unpaired electrons; 2e-CP formation process from the latter; formation of a 2h-CP from two unpaired holes; and the disintegration of a 2h-CP into the latter. All four processes are contained in H_{int} Eq. (42).

where $E_{\pm}(0)$ are the (empirically *un*known) zero-CMM energies of the 2e- and 2h-CPs, respectively. Clearly $E_{\pm}(0) = 2E_f \pm \delta\varepsilon$. The quantity E_f will serve as a convenient energy scale and is not to be confused with the Fermi energy $E_F = \frac{1}{2}mv_F^2 \equiv k_B T_F$ where T_F is the Fermi temperature. The Fermi energy E_F equals $\pi\hbar^2 n/m$ in 2D and $(\hbar^2/2m)(3\pi^2 n)^{2/3}$ in 3D, with n the total number-density of charge-carrier electrons. The quantities E_f and E_F coincide *only* when perfect 2e/2h-CP symmetry holds.

The interaction Hamiltonian (42) can be further simplified by keeping only the $\mathbf{K} = 0$ terms. One can then apply the Bogoliubov "recipe" [68] (see, also e.g., [44] p. 199) of replacing in the full Hamiltonian $H = H_0 + H_{int}$ all zero-CMM 2e- and 2h-CP boson creation and annihilation operators by their respective c-numbers $\sqrt{N_0}$ and $\sqrt{M_0}$, where $N_0(T)$ and $M_0(T)$ are the number of zero-CMM 2e- and 2h-CPs, respectively. One eventually seeks the lowest critical temperature T_c such that, e.g., $N_0(T_c)$ or $M_0(T_c)$ vanish. Note that T_c calculated thusly can, in principle, turn out to be zero, in which case there is no BEC. Now, $H - \mu\hat{N}$ can be diagonalized exactly via a Bogoliubov-Valatin transformation [45] in terms of the thermodynamic potential $\Omega \equiv -PL^d$ for the CBFM, with P its pressure and L^d the system "volume," which is

$$\Omega(T, L^d, \mu, N_0, M_0) = -k_B T \ln \left[\mathrm{Tr} e^{-\beta(H - \mu\hat{N})} \right], \tag{46}$$

where "Tr" stands for "trace." Inserting (41) and (42) into (46) one obtains [13] after some algebra

$$\Omega(T,\, L^d,\, \mu,\, N_0,\, M_0)/L^d =$$

$$\begin{aligned}
&= \int_0^\infty d\epsilon N(\epsilon)\,[\epsilon-\mu-E(\epsilon)] - 2\,k_B T\int_0^\infty d\epsilon\, N(\epsilon)\,\ln\{1+\exp[-\beta\, E(\epsilon)]\} + \\
&\quad +[E_+(0)-2\,\mu]\,n_0 + k_B T\int_{0+}^\infty d\eta\, M(\eta)\,\ln\{1-\exp[-\beta\mathcal{E}_+(\eta)]\} + \\
&\quad +[2\,\mu - E_-(0)]\,m_0 + k_B T\int_{0+}^\infty d\eta\, M(\eta)\,\ln\{1-\exp[-\beta\mathcal{E}_-(\eta)]\}.
\end{aligned} \tag{47}$$

For $d=3$ one has

$$N(\epsilon) \equiv \frac{m^{3/2}}{2^{1/2}\pi^2\hbar^3}\sqrt{\epsilon} \quad \text{and} \quad M(\eta) \equiv \frac{2m^{3/2}}{\pi^2\hbar^3}\sqrt{\eta} \tag{48}$$

for the (one-spin) fermion and boson DOS at energies $\epsilon = \hbar^2k^2/2m$ and $\eta = \hbar^2K^2/2(2m)$, respectively. The latter is an *assumption* to be lifted later so as to include Fermi sea effects which transform the boson dispersion relation from quadratic to linear, as already discussed in Sections 3 to 5. Also, recalling the 2e- and 2h-boson energies $E_\pm(K)$ introduced in (41) the (bosonic) energies $\mathcal{E}_+(\eta)$ and $\mathcal{E}_-(\eta)$ to simplify notation have been defined as

$$E_+(K) - 2\mu = E_+(0) - 2\mu + \eta \equiv \mathcal{E}_+(\eta), \tag{49}$$

$$2\mu - E_-(K) = 2\mu - E_-(0) + \eta \equiv \mathcal{E}_-(\eta). \tag{50}$$

Finally, the relation between the fermion spectrum $E(\epsilon)$ and fermion energy gap $\Delta(\epsilon)$ is of the form

$$E(\epsilon) = \sqrt{(\epsilon-\mu)^2 + \Delta^2(\epsilon)}, \tag{51}$$

$$\Delta(\epsilon) \equiv \sqrt{n_0}f_+(\epsilon) + \sqrt{m_0}f_-(\epsilon). \tag{52}$$

This last expression for the gap $\Delta(\epsilon)$ implies a simple T-dependence rooted in the 2e-CP $n_0(T) \equiv N_0(T)/L^d$ and 2h-CP $m_0(T) \equiv M_0(T)/L^d$ number densities of BE-condensed bosons, i.e.,

$$\Delta(T) = \sqrt{n_0(T)}f_+(\epsilon) + \sqrt{m_0(T)}f_-(\epsilon). \tag{53}$$

A $\Delta(T)^2$ temperature dependence in the order parameter in thin films of the $Tl_2Ba_2CaCu_2O_8$ cuprate suggests itself from thermal difference reflectance spectra [95]. This implies that condensate densities $n_0(T)$ or $m_0(T)$ might be more fundamental as order parameters than $\Delta(T)$, at least for this material.

Minimizing $\Omega(T, L^d, \mu, N_0, M_0)$ with respect to N_0 and M_0, and simultaneously fixing the total number N of electrons by introducing the electron chemical potential μ, one thus specifies an *equilibrium state* of system with volume L^d and temperature T by requiring that

$$\frac{\partial \Omega}{\partial N_0} = 0, \qquad \frac{\partial \Omega}{\partial M_0} = 0, \qquad \text{and} \qquad \frac{\partial \Omega}{\partial \mu} = -N. \tag{54}$$

Here N evidently includes both paired and unpaired CP fermions. Some algebra then leads to the three coupled transcendental Eqs. (7)-(9) of Ref. [13]. These can be rewritten somewhat more transparently as: a) two *"gap-like equations"*

$$2\sqrt{n_0}[E_+(0) - 2\mu] = \int_0^\infty d\epsilon N(\epsilon)\frac{\Delta(\epsilon)f_+(\epsilon)}{E(\epsilon)} \tanh \frac{1}{2}\beta E(\epsilon); \tag{55}$$

$$2\sqrt{m_0}[2\mu - E_-(0)] = \int_0^\infty d\epsilon N(\epsilon)\frac{\Delta(\epsilon)f_-(\epsilon)}{E(\epsilon)} \tanh \frac{1}{2}\beta E(\epsilon), \tag{56}$$

and b) a single *"number equation"* (that ensures charge conservation)

$$2n_B(T) - 2m_B(T) + n_f(T) = n. \tag{57}$$

Here $n \equiv N/L^3$ is the number density of electrons while $n_B(T)$ and $m_B(T)$ are the number densities of 2e- and 2h-CPs in *all* bosonic states, respectively, and are given by

$$n_B(T) \equiv n_0(T) + \int_{0+}^\infty d\eta M(\eta)\frac{1}{e^{\beta\mathcal{E}_+(\eta)} - 1}, \tag{58}$$

$$m_B(T) \equiv m_0(T) + \int_{0+}^\infty d\eta M(\eta)\frac{1}{e^{\beta\mathcal{E}_-(\eta)} - 1}. \tag{59}$$

Clearly,

$$n_f(T) \equiv \int_0^\infty d\epsilon N(\epsilon)[1 - \frac{\epsilon - \mu}{E(\epsilon)} \tanh \frac{1}{2}\beta E(\epsilon)] \tag{60}$$

is the number density of unpaired electrons at any T. Self-consistent (at worst, numerical) solution of the *three coupled equations* (55) to (57) yields the three thermodynamic variables of the CBFM

$$n_0(T, n, \mu), \qquad m_0(T, n, \mu), \qquad \text{and} \qquad \mu(T, n). \tag{61}$$

The pressure P, entropy S and specific heat at constant volume C of an equilibrium state characterized by T and n are then given by

$$P(T,n) = -\Omega/L^d, \quad S(T,n)/L^d = -k_B \frac{\partial}{\partial T}(\Omega/L^d), \tag{62}$$

$$C(T,n)/L^d = T\frac{\partial}{\partial T}\left[S(T,n)/L^d\right], \tag{63}$$

all evaluated at fixed $n_0(T,\mu,n)$, $m_0(T,\mu,n)$ and $\mu(T,n)$. The Helmholtz free energy

$$F(T,L^d,N) \equiv E - TS \equiv \Omega + \mu N \tag{64}$$

where E is the internal energy, then follows from

$$F(T,n)/L^d = -P(T,n) + n\,\mu(T,n). \tag{65}$$

Finally, the critical magnetic field is

$$H_c^2(T,n)/8\pi \equiv F_n(T,n)/L^d - F_s(T,n)/L^d =$$
$$= P_s(T,n) - P_n(T,n) + [\mu_n(T,n) - \mu_s(T,n)]\,n, \tag{66}$$

with subscripts s and n meaning "superconducting" and "normal" states.

7 Main statistical theories as special cases of CBFM

Most significantly, the three CBFM equations just stated contain *five* different theories as special cases, see flow chart in Fig. 7. Perfect 2e/2h CP symmetry $n_B(T) = m_B(T)$ *and* $n_0(T) = m_0(T)$ can be seen from (55) and (56), as well as from $E_{\pm}(0) = 2E_f \pm \delta\varepsilon$, to imply that E_f coincides with μ. The CBFM then reduces to:

i) the gap and number equations of the *BCS-Bose crossover picture* [96] for the BCS model interaction—if the BCS parameters V and Debye energy $\hbar\omega_D$ are identified with the BF interaction Hamiltonian H_{int} parameters $f^2/2\delta\varepsilon$ and $\delta\varepsilon$, respectively. The crossover picture for unknowns $\Delta(T)$ and $\mu(T)$ is now supplemented by the key relation

$$\Delta(T) = f\sqrt{n_0(T)} = f\sqrt{m_0(T)}. \tag{67}$$

The 35-year-old crossover picture is associated with names such as (in chronological order) Friedel and co-workers [97], Eagles [98], Leggett [99], Miyake [100], Nozieres [101], Micnas, Ranninger & Robaszkiewicz [10], Randeria [102], van der Marel [103], Bar-Yam [85], Drechsler & Zwerger [104], Hausmann [105], Pistolesi & Strinati [106], and many others. However, it seems to be a very modest improvement over BCS theory since the unphysically large λ of about 8 is required to bring $\mu(T_c)/E_F$ down from 1.00 to 0.998 [107]. If one imposes that $\mu(T_c) = E_F$ exactly, as follows for weak BF coupling f from the number equation, the crossover picture is well-known to reduce to:

ii) *ordinary BCS theory* which is characterized by a *single* equation, the gap equation for all T. Thus, *the BCS condensate is precisely a BE condensate* whenever both $n_B(T) = m_B(T)$ and $n_0(T) = m_0(T)$ *and* the BF coupling f is small. Indeed, for small coupling λ the CBFM $T = 0$ superconducting state has a *lower* energy than the corresponding BCS state, see Appendix B. The BCS state comes from a variational trial wave function so that its energy expectation value by the Rayleigh-Ritz variational principle is a rigorous upper bound to the exact value. Thus, the CBFM has a somewhat larger condensation energy than that of BCS theory, but both *coincide* in leading order. In addition, at least two universal constants, the gap-to-T_c ratio $2\Delta(0)/k_BT_c$ and the specific heat jump $\Delta C_s(T_c)$ to the normal value $C_n(T_c)$, have been shown [14] to coincide with the BCS values of 3.53 and 1.43 in this limit of the CBFM.

On the other hand, for no 2h-CPs present the CBFM reduces [13] also to:

iii) the *BEC BF model* in 3D of Friedberg and Lee [11, 12] characterized by the relation $\Delta(T) = f\sqrt{n_0(T)}$. With just *one* adjustable parameter (the ratio of perpendicular to planar boson masses) this theory fitted [12] cuprate T_c/T_F data quite well. The ratio turned out to be 66,560—just under the 10^5 anisotropy ratio reported [108] almost contemporaneously for $BSCO$. Finally, when $f = 0$ this model reduces to:

iv) the ideal BF model (IBFM) of Ref. [17, 18] that predicts nonzero BEC T_cs even in 2D. The "gapless" IBFM cannot describe the superconducting phase. But considered as a model for the *normal state* it should provide feasible T_cs as singularities within a BE scenario that are approached from *above* T_c. Figure 8 displays the T_c predictions [18] in 2D for cuprate superconductors with *no* adjustable parameters. Finally, the CBFM reduces to:

v) the familiar T_c-formula of ordinary BEC in 3D, albeit as an *implicit* equation with the boson number-density being T-dependent.

8 Enhanced T_cs from the CBFM

The very general CBFM has been applied and gives sizeable enhancements in T_cs over BCS theory that emerge for moderate departures from perfect 2e/2h-pair symmetry. This is attained for the *same* interaction model (with the same coupling strength λ and cutoff $\hbar\omega_D$ parameters) used in conventional superconductors. The

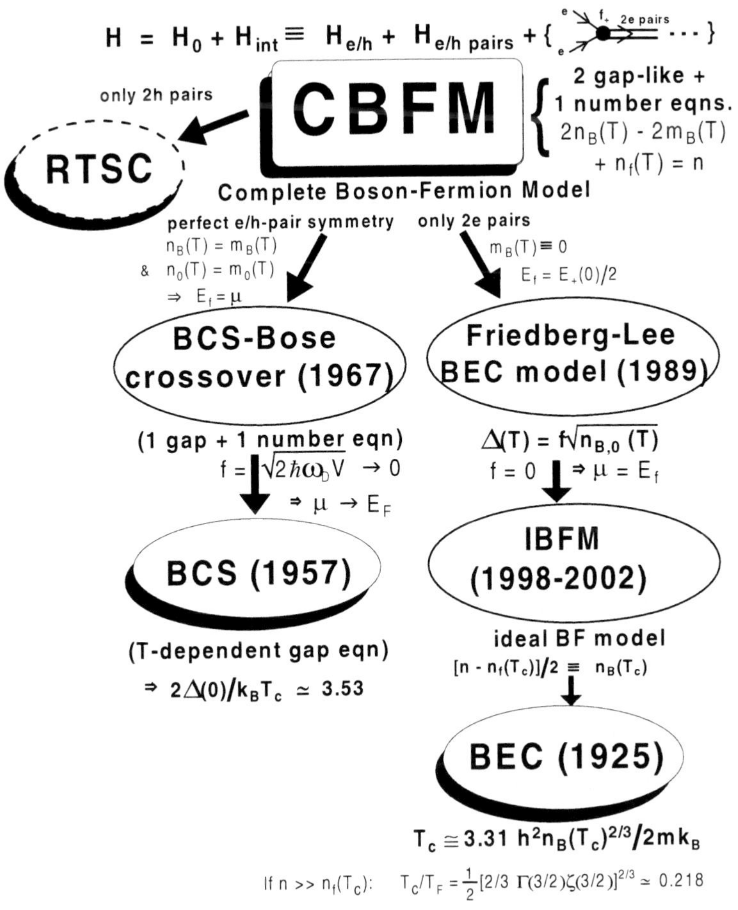

Figure 7: Flow chart of how the CBFM reduces in special cases to the statistical, continuum models of superconductivity discussed in text, thereby displaying how both BCS and BEC theories are unified. The three "legs" refer to: perfect 2e-/2h-CP symmetry (middle leg, giving rise to the BCS-Bose crossover and BCS theories); to no 2h-CPs present (right leg) leading to ordinary BEC as a special case; and to no 2e-CPs present (left leg) predicting room temperature superconductivity (RTSC), see Figs. 10 and 13 below, via a 2h-CP BE condensate.

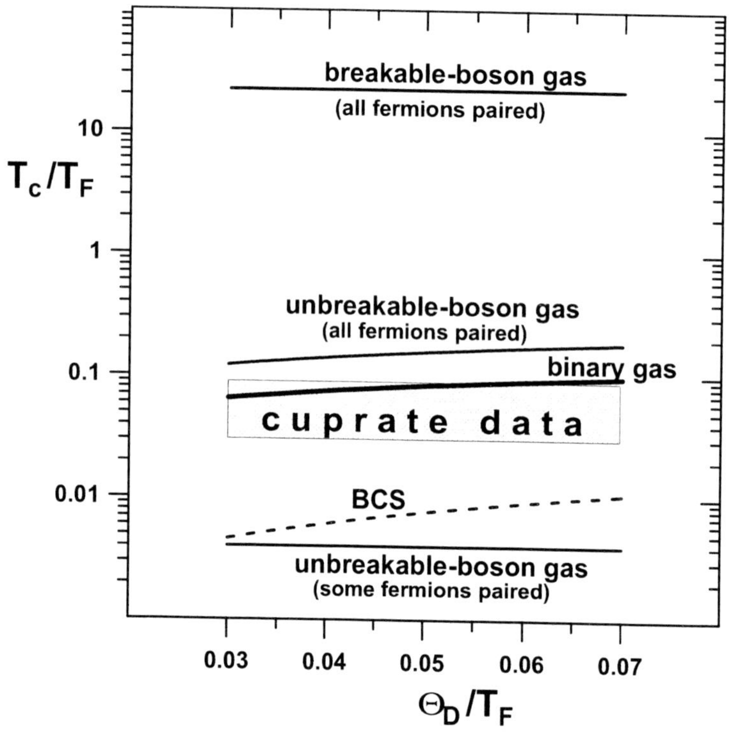

Figure 8: Critical 2D BEC-like temperature (T_c in units of T_F) approached from *above* within the ideal BF model (IBFM) with the BCS model interaction for $\lambda = 1/2$ for varying $\hbar\omega_D/E_F \equiv \Theta_D/T_F$. Results are for: the pure unbreakable-boson gas with *some* and with *all* fermions paired; for the breakable-boson gas; and for the boson-fermion mixture in thermal/chemical equilibrium (thick full curve labeled "binary gas"), all as described in Ref. [18] for original (simple) CPs where $C_1 = (2/\pi)\hbar v_F$ in (1). Dashed curve is the BCS theory T_c, given by (68). Cuprate experimental data are taken from Ref. [116]. The IBFM can be considered a model for the normal state, and its temperature instability a prediction of T_c.

BF (two-fermion) interaction (42) with (43) and (44) bears a one-to-one correspondence with the more familiar "direct" four-fermion electron-phonon interaction, mimicked, e.g., by the BCS model interaction. Its double Fourier transform is a negative constant $-V$, nonzero only within an energy shell $2\hbar\omega_D$ about the Fermi surface, with ω_D the Debye frequency. The correspondence is realized [13, 14] by setting $f^2/2\,\delta\varepsilon \equiv V$ and $\delta\varepsilon \equiv \hbar\,\omega_D$, from which the familiar dimensionless BCS model interaction parameters $\lambda \equiv N(E_F)V$ and $\hbar\,\omega_D/E_F$ are then recovered.

The three coupled equations (55) to (57) of the CBFM that determine the *d*-dimensional BE-condensate number-densities $n_0(T)$ and $m_0(T)$ of 2e- and 2h-CPs, respectively, as well as the fermion chemical potential $\mu(T)$, were solved numerically in 3D for $\lambda = 1/5$ and $\hbar\omega_D/E_F = 0.001$ in Ref. [14] assuming a quadratic boson dispersion relation $\eta = \hbar^2K^2/2(2m)$, i.e., $s = 2$ in (1). For this case Figure 9 maps the phase diagram in the vicinity of the BCS T_c value (marked BCS-B in the figure) at $\Delta n \equiv n/n_f - 1 = 0$ (corresponding to perfect 2e/2h-CP symmetry) where n_f is a very special case of $n_f(T)$ as defined in (60). Namely, n_f can be seen [14] to be the number of unpaired electrons at zero coupling and temperature. Besides the *normal* phase (n) consisting of the ideal BF gas described by H_0, three different stable BEC phases emerged—plus several metastable, i.e., of higher Helmholtz free energy. These are two *pure* phases of *either* 2e-CP ($s+$) *or* 2h-CP ($s-$) BE-condensates, and a lower temperature *mixed* phase (ss) with arbitrary proportions of 2e- *and* 2h-CPs, see Fig. 9. Of greater physical interest are the two higher-T_c *pure* phases so that we focus below only on them. For each pure phase at a critical temperature we have *either* $\Delta(T_{cs+}) = f\sqrt{n_0(T_{cs+})} \equiv 0$ or $\Delta(T_{cs-}) = f\sqrt{m_0(T_{cs-})} \equiv 0$, where $\Delta(T)$ is the electronic (BCS-like) energy gap. Their intersection gives the BCS T_c value of $7.64 \times 10^{-6}T_F$ that also follows from the familiar BCS expression

$$T_c/T_F \simeq 1.134(\hbar\omega_D/E_F)\exp(-1/\lambda). \tag{68}$$

We next focus on $s = 1$ which, as we saw in Sections 3 to 5, occurs in the leading term for "ordinary" CPs in a Fermi sea as well as for "generalized" CPs in a BCS state. For these, the boson energy η in (47) to be used later has leading terms in the many-body Bethe-Salpeter (BS) CP dispersion relation that are

$$\eta \simeq (\lambda/2\pi)\hbar v_F K \qquad \text{2D} \tag{69}$$

[53] and

$$\eta \simeq (\lambda/4)\hbar v_F K \qquad \text{3D} \tag{70}$$

[54]. As before, $\lambda \equiv VN(E_F)$ where $N(E_F)$ is the electron DOS (for one spin) at the Fermi surface. Note that the boson energy η is *not* the quadratic $\hbar^2K^2/2(2m)$

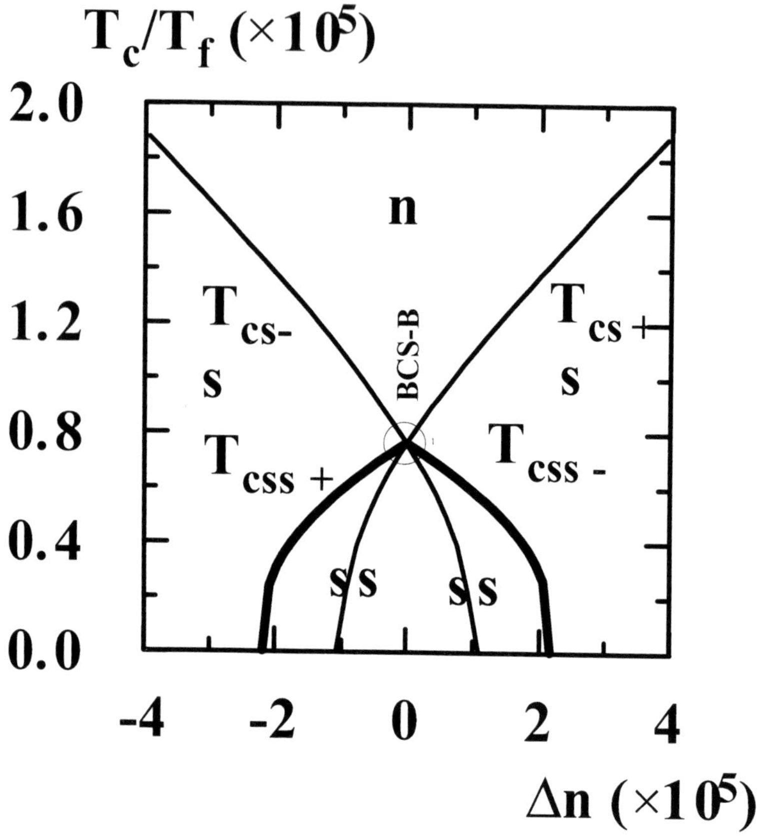

Figure 9: Phase diagram [14] with 3D superconducting critical temperature phase boundaries T_{cs+}, T_{cs-}, T_{css+}, and T_{css-} as functions of $\Delta n \equiv n/n_f - 1$ as defined in text, in the vicinity of the approximate BCS T_c value, assuming the quadratic boson dispersion $\eta = \hbar^2 K^2/2(2m)$, for $\lambda = 1/5$ and $\hbar\omega_D/E_F = 0.001$.

appropriate for a composite boson of mass $2m$ moving not in the Fermi sea but in vacuum [3]-[6], [11]-[14], and assumed in (48). Note also that the BS CP linear dispersion coefficient $\lambda/2\pi$ in 2D (or $\lambda/4$ in 3D) contrasts markedly with the coupling-independent $2/\pi$ coefficient in 2D (or 1/2 in 3D, as apparently first quoted in Ref. [34], p. 33) obtained [43] in the *simple* CP problem [29] which ignores holes. Thus, again with $n_B = n/2$, for $s = 1$ and $C_1 = \lambda b(d)\hbar v_F$ with $b(2) = 1/2\pi$ and $b(3) = 1/4$ according to (69) and (70), (C.1) leads to

$$T_c/T_F = 2\lambda b(d)/\left[d\Gamma(d)\zeta(d)\right]^{1/d}. \tag{71}$$

For $\lambda = 1/2$ this is $\simeq 0.088$ if $d = 2$ since $\zeta(2) = \pi^2/6$, and $\simeq 0.129$ if $d = 3$ since $\zeta(3) \simeq 1.202$. These two values will appear as the black squares in Figs. 10 to 13 (upper ones in Figs. 10 and 11). They mark the BEC limiting values if *all* electrons in our 2D or 3D many-electron system were imagined paired into noninteracting bosons formed with the BCS model interelectron interaction. For $\lambda = 1/4$ the lower black squares in Figs. 10 and 11 apply.

8.1 Two dimensions (2D)

To address cuprates and other copper-plane-free planar superconductors (such as $Sr_2YRu_{1-x}Cu_xO_6$ with $T_c \simeq 49$ K, which is Cu-doped but has no CuO planes) we deal first with the CBFM in 2D. Although it is still controversial [109] as to *which* planes, the CuO or BaO or SrO, etc., the superconductivity resides in, these planes are parallel to each other, say, in the ab directions. Resistivity ρ anisotropies ρ_c/ρ_{ab}, with the c direction perpendicular to the ab denoting the CuO or BaO or SrO planes, can be as high as 10^5 in $Bi_{2+x}Sr_{2-y}CuO_{6+\delta}$ [108], if not higher, even though "only" about 10^2 in $YBa_2Cu_3O_{7-\delta}$ ($YBCO$). From the Drude 1900 resistivity model [110] $\rho = m/ne^2\tau$ for current carriers of charge e, effective mass m, number density n, and τ is some average time between collisions. Thus, if $\rho_c/\rho_{ab} = m_c/m_{ab}$ is ∞ one has a precisely 2D situation; if it is 1 we have the perfectly isotropic 3D case. Hence, the large (10^5) but finite ratio observed implies $(2+\epsilon)D$ or "quasi-2D." For cuprates the value $d \simeq 2.03$ has been extracted independently by two groups [111][112] for $YBCO$ as more realistic than $d = 2$, since that value reflects inter-CuO (or BaO)-layer couplings. Our results in that case would be very close to those for $d = 2$ since, e.g., from Appendix C (C.1), T_c for $s = 1$ (but, perhaps very significantly, *not* for $s = 2$) varies little [113] with d around $d = 2$. This justifies models in exactly 2D, at least as a very good initial approximation.

In 2D the electronic DOS per unit area L^2 is constant, namely $N(\varepsilon) = m/2\pi\hbar^2$. Using the leading term of the BS CP *linear* dispersion relation (69) we get for the

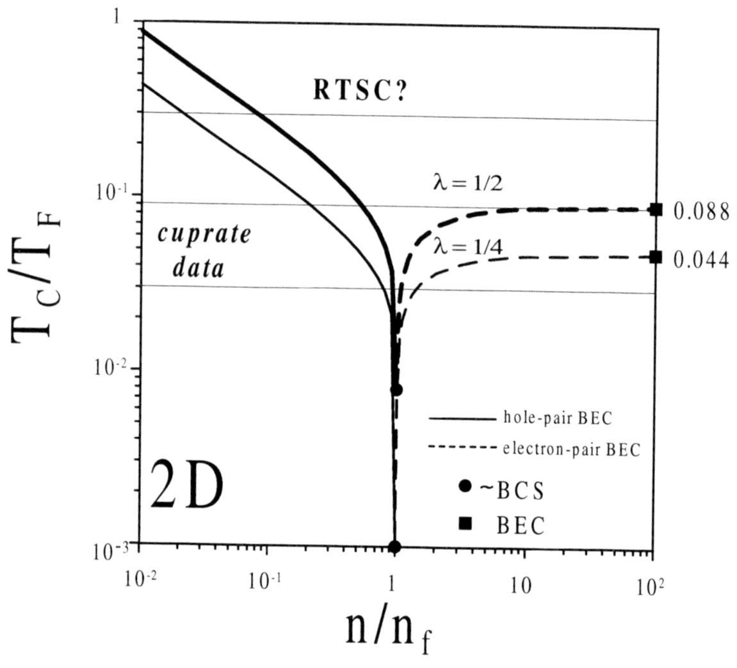

Figure 10: Phase diagram in 2D temperature T (in units of T_F) and electron density n (in units of n_f as defined in text) showing the phase boundaries of T_c's for pure 2e-CP BEC phases (dashed curves) determined by $\Delta(T_c) = f\sqrt{n_0(T_c)} \equiv 0$ and pure 2h-CP BEC phases (full curves) given by $\Delta(T_c) = f\sqrt{m_0(T_c)} \equiv 0$ for $\lambda = 1/4$ and $1/2$ with $\hbar\omega_D/E_F = 0.05$. Intersections corresponding to $n_0(T) = m_0(T)$ approximately reproduce the BCS T_c as given by (67) and are marked by black dots. Black squares mark the BEC limit where all electrons are imagined paired into 2e-CP bosons, as calculated in (71), to which values the dashed curves reach only approximately in the limit $n/n_f \to \infty$.

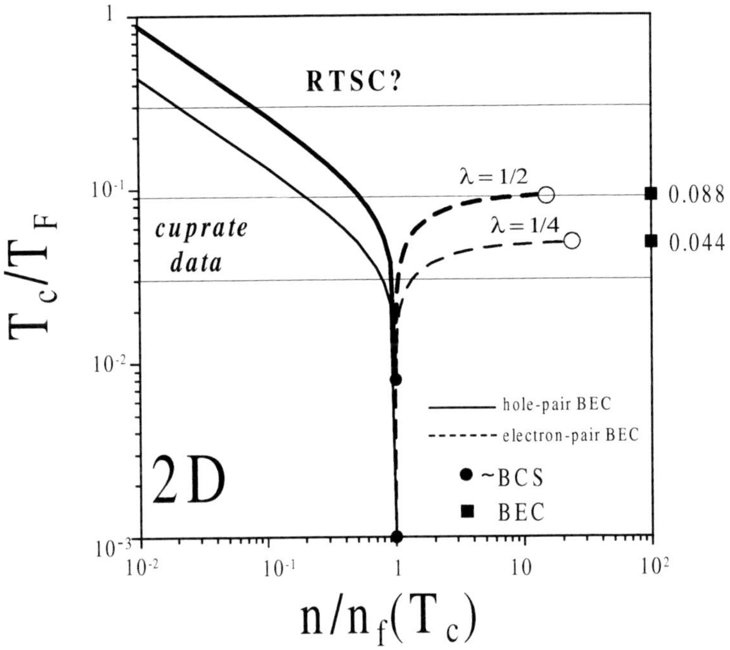

Figure 11: Same as Fig. 10 except that n/n_f is eliminated numerically and abscissa refers to $n/n_f(T_c)$, where $n_f(T_c)$ is the actual number of unpaired electrons at T_c as given by (80). Here, the intersection corresponding to $n_0(T) = m_0(T)$ occurs at $T = 0$ and *not* at the approximate BCS T_c values as in Fig. 10. Open circles mark values of $n/n_f(T_c)$ corresponding to $n/n_f = \infty$.

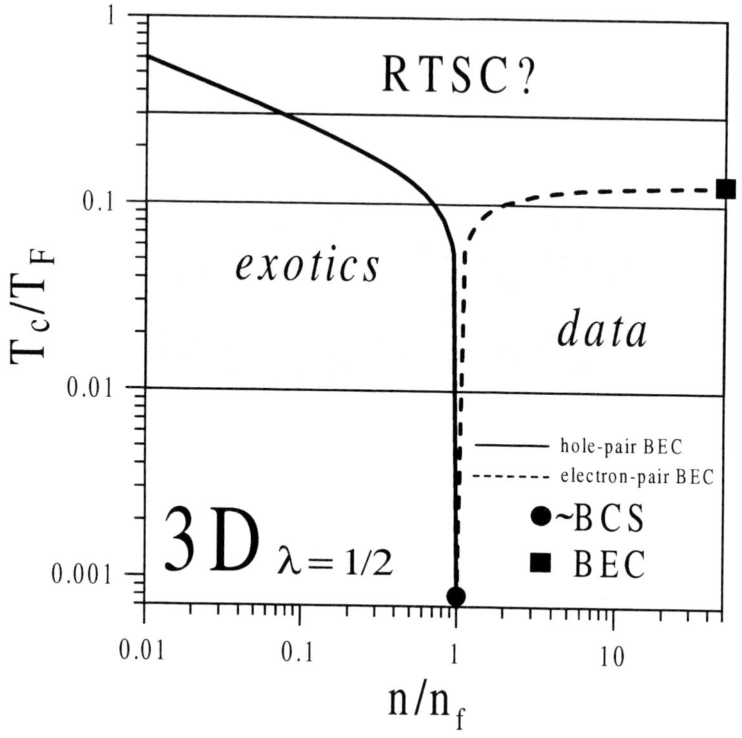

Figure 12: Same as Fig. 10 but in 3D, and only for $\lambda = \frac{1}{2}$.

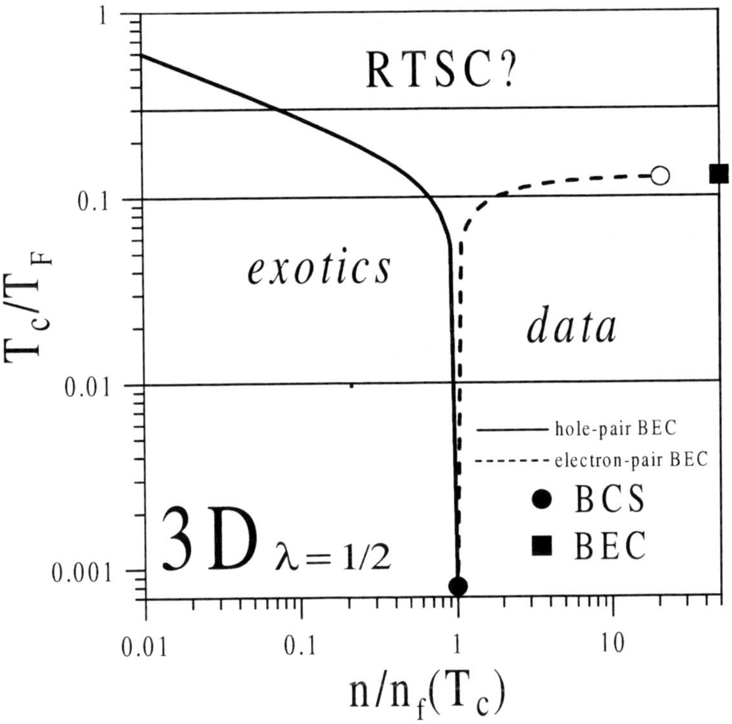

Figure 13: Same as Fig. 11 but in 3D, and only for $\lambda = \frac{1}{2}$.

bosonic DOS

$$M(\eta) \equiv (1/2\pi)K(dK/d\eta) \simeq (2\pi/\lambda^2\hbar^2 v_F^2)\eta \tag{72}$$

instead of the constant that follows in 2D from the quadratic dispersion $\eta = \hbar^2 K^2/2(2m)$. Employing $E_f \equiv \pi\hbar^2 n_f/m = k_B T_f$ as energy/density/temperature scaling factors, and the relation $n/n_f = (E_F/E_f)^{d/2}$ to convert quantities such as T_c/T_f to T_c/T_F, where $E_F \equiv k_B T_F$, the two "working equations" for the *pure 2e-CP phase* [i.e., $m_B(T_c) \equiv 0$] (with all quantities dimensionless, energies in units of E_f and electron particle-densities in units of n_f) become

$$1 + \hbar\omega_D/2 - \mu = \lambda(\hbar\omega_D/2) \int_1^{1+\hbar\omega_D} dx \frac{1}{|x-\mu|} \tanh\frac{|x-\mu|}{2T_c}, \tag{73}$$

$$\frac{1}{2}\int_0^\infty dx[1 - \tanh\frac{x-\mu}{2T_c}] + \frac{\pi^2}{\lambda^2}\frac{1}{n}\int_0^\infty dx x[\coth\frac{x + 2(1+\hbar\omega_D/2-\mu)}{2T_c} - 1] = n. \tag{74}$$

These are just the gap-like equation associated with 2e-CPs and its corresponding number equation. Recall that n_f can be seen [13] to be the number-density of unpaired electrons at zero T and zero λ.

For the *pure 2h-CP phase* (i.e., $n_B \equiv 0$) the two working equations are

$$\mu - 1 + \hbar\omega_D/2 = \lambda(\hbar\omega_D/2) \int_{1-\hbar\omega_D}^{1} dx \frac{1}{|x-\mu|} \tanh\frac{|x-\mu|}{2T_c}, \tag{75}$$

$$\frac{1}{2}\int_0^\infty dx[1 - \tanh\frac{x-\mu}{2T_c}] - \frac{\pi^2}{\lambda^2}\frac{1}{n}\int_0^\infty dx x[\coth\frac{x - 2(1-\hbar\omega_D/2-\mu)}{2T_c} - 1] = n. \tag{76}$$

which are the gap-like equation associated with 2h-CPs and its corresponding number equation. Note that (74) and (76) are quadratic in n. Further, all integrals there are exact, i.e.,

$$\int_0^\infty dx[1 - \tanh\frac{x-\mu}{2T_c}] = \mu + 2T_c \ln[2\cosh(\mu/2T_c)], \tag{77}$$

and

$$\int_0^\infty dx x[\coth\frac{x+\delta}{2T_c} - 1] = 2T_c^2 \mathrm{PolyLog}[2, e^{-\delta/T_c}] \tag{78}$$

where the polylogarithm function as defined in Ref. [114] is

$$PolyLog[\sigma, z] \equiv \sum_{l=1}^{\infty} z^l / l^\sigma. \tag{79}$$

The integrals in (73) and (75), however, were performed numerically. In 2D we use the two extreme values of $\lambda = 1/4$ (lower set of curves in Figs. 10 and 11) and $= 1/2$ (upper set of curves), and $\hbar\omega_D/E_F = 0.05$ (a typical value for cuprates). If $\lambda > 1/2$ the ionic lattice in 3D becomes unstable, [115] and Ref. [3] p. 204. Equations (73) to (76) lead to the T_c/T_F *vs.* n/n_f phase diagram which is graphed in Figs. 10 and 11 for both 2e-CP (dashed curve) and 2h-CP (full curve) pure, stable BEC-like phases. The value $n/n_f = 1$ corresponds to perfect 2e/2h-CP symmetry for the lower-T_c mixed phase (not shown), while $n/n_f > 1$ (and < 1) signifies more (less) 2e-CPs than 2h-CPs in the mixed phase. The T_c value where both phase-boundary curves $n_0(T_c) = m_0(T_c) = 0$ intersect is marked by the large dots in the figure. The values are consistent with those gotten from (68) which gives $\simeq 0.001$ for $\lambda = 1/4$ and $\simeq 0.008$ for $\lambda = 1/2$, for $\hbar\omega_D/E_F = 0.05$. [The values from (68) hardly differ from those from the exact BCS (implicit) T_c-formula (Ref. [44], p. 447) $1 = \lambda \int_0^{\hbar\omega_D/2k_BT_c} dx x^{-1} \tanh x$.] Cuprate data empirically [116] show T_c's and T_F's falling within the range $T_c/T_F \simeq 0.03 - 0.09$. Thus, moderate departures from perfect 2e/2h-CP symmetry enable the CBFM to predict quasi-2D cuprate empirical T_c values, *without abandoning electron-phonon dynamics*—contrary to popular belief.

As the variable n_f used to scale the electron number density n in Fig. 10 does not appear at all in the number equation (57), we also scaled n with the variable $n_f(T)$ evaluated at $T = T_c$ which does appear in (57) and which has a clear-cut physical meaning. Since $\Delta(T_c) = 0$, from (51) and (52), (60) reduces in 2D to the analytic expression

$$n_f(T_c)/n \equiv (T_c/T_F) \ln[1 + \exp\{\mu(T_c)/k_BT_c\}]. \tag{80}$$

For the pure 2e-CP condensate case, i.e., $m_B(T) \equiv 0$, we must have $n/n_f(T_c) \geq 1$ from (57), where in general $n_f(T_c) \neq n_f$. Here $n_f(T_c)$ is the actual number density of unpaired electrons at $T = T_c$ since the number equation (57) for $m_B(T) = 0$ then becomes just

$$n_f(T_c) + 2n_{B+}(T_c) = n. \tag{81}$$

Here $n_{B+}(T_c)$ is the total number density of all *excited* (or $K > 0$) 2e-CPs, also commonly known as "preformed CPs." It is defined in (58) at any T as

$$n_{B+}(T) \equiv \int_{0+}^{\infty} d\eta M(\eta) \frac{1}{e^{\beta \mathcal{E}_+(\eta)} - 1}. \tag{82}$$

Preformed CPs seem to be the main conjecture to explain a "pseudogap" [117] observed above T_c in many underdoped cuprates.

The complete number equation (57) then explicitly reads

$$2n_0(T) + 2n_{B+}(T) - 2m_0(T) - 2m_{B+}(T) + n_f(T) = n \tag{83}$$

with $m_{B+}(T)$ being the number of preformed 2h-CPs, defined as the integral term in (59). Using $n_f(T_c)$ instead of n_f to scale electron densities n in (73) to (76) which are solved numerically, scaling all energies with E_F instead of E_f as before, and on eliminating n_f, gives the results in Fig. 11. Curiously, these curves are hard to distinguish from those of Fig. 10. In Fig. 11 the BCS values (black dots in figure) are *not* associated as before with the intersection of the 2e- and 2h-CP condensation curves, but are merely values calculated with the BCS T_c formula (68). On the other hand, the T_c values from the CBFM equations scaled with the previous (and somewhat opaque) variable n_f, match only *approximately* in the limit $n/n_f \to \infty$ with the analytical BEC limits of (71). It has been verified numerically that coincidence in the BEC limit is perfect only in the trivial limit of zero coupling, as expected.

In view of Figs. 10 and 11 we note that *room temperature superconductivity* (RTSC in figures) is possible, e.g., in Fig. 11, for $n/n_f(T_c)$ sufficiently less than unity. From (83) with $n_B(T) \equiv n_0(T) + n_{B+}(T) \equiv 0$ this translates into this recipe: $2m_{B+}(T_c)$ must be sufficiently larger than $n_f(T_c)$. Specifically, from Fig. 11 RTSC occurs for $\lambda = \frac{1}{2}$ if $n/n_f(T_c) \lesssim 0.1$, which from (57) means $2m_{B+}(T_c) \gtrsim 0.9 n_f(T_c)$ or that the total number of individual holes bound into *preformed* 2h-CPs at T_c must somehow be larger than about 90% of the number of unpaired electrons at T_c.

8.2 Three dimensions (3D)

In 3D the electronic DOS if $\epsilon \equiv \hbar^2 k^2/2m$ is the familiar expression

$$N(\epsilon) \equiv (1/2\pi^2) k^2 (dk/d\epsilon) = (m^{\frac{3}{2}}/2^{\frac{1}{2}}\pi^2\hbar^3)\sqrt{\epsilon} \tag{84}$$

which coincides with (48). Analogously as before, $E_f = (\hbar^2/2m)(3\pi^2 n_f)^{2/3} \equiv k_B T_f$ again differs from $E_F = (\hbar^2/2m)(3\pi^2 n)^{2/3} \equiv k_B T_F$ unless perfect 2e/2h-CP symmetry holds in which case they coincide. On the other hand, the leading term in the BS CP boson dispersion energy is now the linear expression (70) so that

$$M(\eta) \equiv (1/2\pi^2)K^2(dK/d\eta) \simeq (32/\pi^2\lambda^3\hbar^3 v_F^3)\eta^2. \tag{85}$$

The above working equations for the *pure 2e-CP phase* in 3D (all quantities dimensionless as before in terms of E_f and n_f) are

$$1 + \hbar\omega_D/2 - \mu = \lambda(\hbar\omega_D/2)\frac{1}{n^{1/3}} \int_1^{1+\hbar\omega_D} dx\sqrt{x}\frac{1}{|x-\mu|}\tanh\frac{|x-\mu|}{2T_c}, \tag{86}$$

$$\frac{3}{4}\int_0^\infty dx\sqrt{x}[1-\tanh\frac{x-\mu}{2T_c}] + \frac{12}{\lambda^3}\frac{1}{n}\int_0^\infty dx x^2[\coth\frac{x+2(1+\hbar\omega_D/2-\mu)}{2T_c}-1] = n, \tag{87}$$

while for the *pure 2h-CP phase* they are

$$\mu - 1 + \hbar\omega_D/2 = \lambda(\hbar\omega_D/2)\frac{1}{n^{1/3}} \int_{1-\hbar\omega_D}^{1} dx\sqrt{x}\frac{1}{|x-\mu|}\tanh\frac{|x-\mu|}{2T_c}, \tag{88}$$

$$\frac{3}{4}\int_0^\infty dx\sqrt{x}[1-\tanh\frac{x-\mu}{2T_c}] - \frac{12}{\lambda^3}\frac{1}{n}\int_0^\infty dx x^2[\coth\frac{x-2(1-\hbar\omega_D/2-\mu)}{2T_c}-1] = n. \tag{89}$$

Results in 3D are reported only for $\lambda = 1/2$, and $\hbar\omega_D/E_F = 0.005$ was used here. In Figs. 12 and 13 the full curves are again the 2h-CP BEC phase boundaries while the dashed curves are the 2e-CP BEC ones. The large dot again marks the BCS T_c/T_F values obtainable from (68) of 0.0001 for $\lambda = 1/4$ and of 0.0008 for $\lambda = 1/2$. Besides Ref. [116], mpirical data for both exotic and conventional, elemental superconductors in 3D are also graphed in Ref. [118]. We see that whereas BCS theory roughly reproduces T_c/T_F values well for the latter SCs, it takes moderate departures from perfect 2e/2h-CP symmetry to access 3D exotic SC T_c/T_F values, which empirically fall within the range $0.01-0.1$. This is much larger than the range $\lesssim 0.001$ for conventional (elemental) superconductors, also shaded in the figure.

9 Hole superconductivity

Finally, we address the unique but mysterious role played by *hole* charge carriers [46] in the normal state of superconductors in general. For example: a) of the cuprates, those that are hole-doped have transition temperatures T_c about *six* times higher than electron-doped ones; and even in conventional superconductors [47] b) over 80% of all superconducting elements have positive Hall coefficients (meaning hole charge carriers); while c) over 90% of non-superconducting metallic, non-magnetic elements have electron charge carriers. This greater "efficiency" of individual, unpaired hole carriers in producing higher T_cs is clearly reflected in Figs. 10 and 11 for both 2D and 3D superconductors, at least insofar as pure 2h-CP BE condensates exhibiting higher T_cs than those associated with pure 2e-CP BE condensates.

10 Conclusions

This review began with a survey of "ordinary" and "generalized" Cooper pairing, and stressed that if hole pairing is treated on an equal footing with electron pairing the original "ordinary" Cooper problem (based on the pure-kinetic-energy unperturbed Hamiltonian) is meaningless. However, "generalized" Cooper pairs defined in terms of the Bethe-Salpeter equation including both electron and hole pairs, in the ladder approximation, but based on the BCS ground state as unperturbed Hamiltonian instead of on the ideal Fermi gas sea, gives rise to physically meaningful positive-energy resonances with a finite lifetime for CMM $K > 0$ and infinite lifetime for $K = 0$.

It was then sketched how five statistical continuum theories of superconductivity—including both the BCS and BEC theories—are contained as special limiting cases within a single theory, the "complete boson-fermion model" (CBFM). This model includes, for the first time, both two-electron and two-hole pairs in freely variable proportions, along with unpaired electrons. Thus, the BCS and BEC theories are fully *unified* within the CBFM. The BCS condensate [specified by a single equation, namely the T-dependent gap equation for $\Delta(T)$] follows directly from the CBFM *as a BE condensate* through the condition for phase equilibria when both total 2e- and 2h-pair number, as well as their condensate, densities are *equal* at a given temperature and coupling—provided the coupling is weak enough so that the electron chemical potential μ roughly equals the Fermi energy E_F. Ordinary BEC theory, on the other hand, is recovered from the CBFM when hole pairs are completely neglected, the BF coupling f is made to vanish, and the limit of zero unpaired electrons is taken.

Lastly, the practical outcome of the BCS-BEC unification via the CBFM is fourfold: a) *enhancements* in T_c, by more than an order-of-magnitude in 2D, and more than two orders-of-magnitude in 3D, are obtained with pure electron-pair, and even more so with pure hole-pair, BE condensates for the same electron-phonon dynamics mimicked by the BCS model interaction; b) these enhancements in T_c fall within empirical ranges for 2D and 3D "exotic" SCs, whereas BCS T_c values remain low and within the empirical ranges for conventional, elemental SCs using standard interaction-parameter values; c) hole-doped SCs are predicted in both 2D and 3D to have higher T_c's than electron-doped ones, in agreement with observation; and finally that d) room temperature superconductivity is possible, with the *same* interaction parameters used in BCS theory for conventional SCs, but only via hole-pair BE condensates.

Acknowledgements I thank V.C. Aguilera-Navarro, J. Batle, M. Casas, J.R. Clem, M. Fortes, F.J. Sevilla, M.A. Solís, S. Tapia, V.V. Tolmachev, O. Rojo, J.J. Valencia, A.A. Valladares and H. Vucetich for discussions and/or for providing material prior to its publication. MdeLl acknowledges UNAM-DGAPA-PAPIIT (Mexico) grant # IN106401, and CONACyT (Mexico) grant # 41302, for partial support.

References

[1] R.A. Ogg, Jr., *Phys. Rev.* **69**, 243 (1946).

[2] V.L. Ginzburg, *Usp. Fiz. Nauk.* **48**, 25 (1952); *Fortschr. Phys.* **1**, 101 (1953).

[3] J.M. Blatt, *Theory of Superconductivity* (Academic, New York, 1964).

[4] M.R. Schafroth, *Phys. Rev.* **96**, 1442 (1954).

[5] M.R. Schafroth, S.T. Butler, and J.M. Blatt, *Helv. Phys. Acta* **30**, 93 (1957).

[6] M.R. Schafroth, *Sol. State Phys.* **10**, 293 (1960).

[7] J. Bardeen, L.N. Cooper and J.R. Schrieffer, *Phys. Rev.* **108**, 1175 (1957).

[8] N.N. Bogoliubov, *JETP* **34**, 41 (1958).

[9] N.N. Bogoliubov, V.V. Tolmachev and D.V. Shirkov, *Fortschr. Phys.* **6**, 605 (1958); and also in *A New Method in the Theory of Superconductivity* (Consultants Bureau, NY, 1959).

[10] J. Ranninger and S. Robaszkiewicz, *Physica B* **135**, 468 (1985).

[11] R. Friedberg and T.D. Lee, *Phys. Rev. B* **40**, 6745 (1989).

[12] R. Friedberg, T.D. Lee, and H.-C. Ren, *Phys. Lett. A* **152**, 417 and 423 (1991).

[13] V.V. Tolmachev, *Phys. Lett. A* **266**, 400 (2000).

[14] M. de Llano and V.V. Tolmachev, *Physica A* **317**, 546 (2003).

[15] J. Batle, M. Casas, M. Fortes, M. de Llano, F.J. Sevilla, M.A. Solís, V.V. Tolmachev, *Cond. Matter Theories* **18** (11) (2003); BCS and BEC Finally Unified: A brief review. Cond-mat/0211456.

[16] M. Casas, A. Rigo, M. de Llano, O. Rojo, and M.A. Solís, *Phys. Lett. A* **245**, 5 (1998).

[17] M. Casas, N.J. Davidson, M. de Llano, T.A. Mamedov, A. Puente, R.M. Quick, A. Rigo, and M.A. Solís, *Physica A* **295**, 146 (2001).

[18] M. Casas, M. de Llano, A. Puente, A. Rigo, and M.A. Solís, *Sol. State Comm.* **123**, 101 (2002).

[19] B.S. Deaver, Jr. and W.M. Fairbank, *Phys. Rev. Lett.* **7**, 43 (1961).

[20] R. Doll and M. Näbauer, *Phys. Rev. Lett.* **7**, 51 (1961).

[21] C.E. Gough, M.S Colclough, E.M. Forgan, R.G. Jordan, M. Keene, C.M. Muirhead, I.M. Rae, N. Thomas, J.S. Abell, and S. Sutton, *Nature* **326,** 855 (1987).

[22] J.G. Bednorz and K.A. Müller, *Z. Phys.* **64**, 189 (1986).

[23] L. Gao, Y.Y. Xue, F. Chen, Q. Xiong, R.L. Meng, D. Ramírez, C.W. Chu, J.H. Eggert and H.K. Mao, *Phys. Rev. B* **50**, 4260 (1994).

[24] J.E. Hirsch, *Science* **295**, 2226 (2002).

[25] J. Bardeen, *Physics Today* (Jan. 1963) p. 25.

[26] A.A. Abrikosov (2002) semi-priv. comm.

[27] A.S. Alexandrov (2003) unpublished.

[28] L.N. Cooper, *Am. J. Phys.* **28**, 91 (1960).

[29] L.N. Cooper, *Phys. Rev.* **104**, 1189 (1956).

[30] Anonymous Phys. Rev. Lett. reviewer (2001).

[31] M. Randeria (1996) semi-priv. comm.

[32] J.R. Schrieffer, *Nobel Lecture,* Dec. *1972.*

[33] J.R. Clem (2003) priv. comm.

[34] J.R. Schrieffer, *Theory of Superconductivity* (Benjamin, New York, 1964).

[35] C.N. Lau, N. Markovic, M. Bockrath, A. Bezryadin, and M. Tinkham, *Phys. Rev. Lett.* **87**, 217003 (2001).

[36] A. Bezryadin, C.N. Lau, and M. Tinkham, *Nature* **404**, 971 (2000).

[37] M. Casas, C. Esebbag, A. Extremera, J.M. Getino, M. de Llano, A. Plastino and H. Rubio, *Phys. Rev. A* **44**, 4915 (1991).

[38] A. Salazar, M. de Llano and M.A. Solís, *Am. J. Phys.* (submitted) Two-dimensional delta potential well and condensed-matter physics.

[39] P. Gosdzinsky and R. Tarrach, *Am. J. Phys.* **59**, 70 (1991).

[40] S.K. Adhikari, M. Casas, A. Puente, A. Rigo, M. Fortes, M.A. Solís, M. de Llano, A.A. Valladares & O. Rojo, *Phys. Rev. B* **62**, 8671 (2000).

[41] S.K. Adhikari, M. Casas, A. Puente, A. Rigo, M. Fortes, M. de Llano, M.A. Solís, A. A. Valladares & O. Rojo, *Physica C* **351**, 341 (2001).

[42] L. Van Hove, *Physica* **25**, 849 (1959).

[43] M. Casas, S. Fujita, M. de Llano, A. Puente, A. Rigo, M.A. Solís, *Physica C* **295**, 93 (1998).

[44] A.L. Fetter and J.D. Walecka, *Quantum Theory of Many-Particle Systems* (McGraw-Hill, New York, 1971).

[45] N.N. Bogoliubov, *N. Cim.* **7**, 794 (1958).

[46] I.M. Chapnik, *Phys. Status Solidi B* **123**, K1L3 (1984) and refs. therein.

[47] J. Hirsch, *Physica C* **341-348**, 213 (2000) and also www.iitap.iastate.edu/htcu/forum.html#Q3.

[48] A. Lanzara, P.V. Bogdanov, X.J. Zhou, S.A. Kellar, D.L. Feng, E.D. Lu, T. Yoshida, H. Eisaki, A. Fujimori, K. Kishio, J.-I. Shimoyama, T. Noda, S. Uchida, Z. Hussain, and Z.-X. Shen, *Nature* **412**, 510 (2001).

[49] P.W. Anderson, *Phys. Rev.* **112**, 1900 (1958).

[50] P.W. Higgs, *Phys. Lett.* **12**, 132 (1964).

[51] S.V. Traven, *Phys. Rev. Lett.* **73**, 3451 (1994).

[52] S.V. Traven, *Phys. Rev.* **51**, 3242 (1995).

[53] V.C. Aguilera-Navarro, M. Fortes, and M. de Llano, *Sol. St. Comm.* **129**, 577 (2004). cond-mat/0306726.

[54] M. Fortes, M.A. Solís, M. de Llano, and V.V. Tolmachev, *Physica C* **364-365**, 95 (2001).

[55] S. Schmitt-Rink, C.M. Varma, and A.E. Ruckenstein, *Phys. Rev. Lett.* **63**, 445 (1989).

[56] S. Sachdev and Z. Wang, *Phys. Rev.* **B 43**, 10229 (1991).

[57] B.D. Brandow, *Phys. Repts.* **296**, 1 (1998).

[58] V.L. Berezinskii, *Sov. Phys. JETP* **34,** 610 (1972).

[59] J.M. Kosterlitz and D.J. Thouless, *J. Phys.* **C6**, 1181 (1973).

[60] D. Jérome, *Science* **252**, 1509 (1991).

[61] J.M. Williams, A.J. Schultz, U. Geiser, K.D. Carlson, A.M. Kini, H.H. Wang, W.K. Kwok, M.H. Whangbo, and J.E. Schirber, *Science* **252**, 1501 (1991).

[62] H. Hori, *Int. J. Mod Phys. B* **8,** 1 (1994).

[63] D. Vollkardt and P. Wölfle, *The Superfluid Phases of Helium 3*, (Taylor & Francis, London, 1990).

[64] M.J. Holland, B. DeMarco, and D.S. Jin, *Phys. Rev. A* **61**, 053610 (2000), and refs. therein.

[65] K.M. O'Hara, S.L. Hemmer, M.E. Gehm, S.R. Granade, and J.E. Thomas, *Science* **298**, 2179 (2002).

[66] A.A. Abrikosov, L.P. Gorkov, and I.E. Dzyaloshinskii, *Methods of Quantum Field in Statistical Physics* (Dover, NY, 1975) §33.

[67] L. Belkhir and M. Randeria, *Phys. Rev. B* **49**, 6829 (1994).

[68] N.N. Bogoliubov, *J. Phys. (USSR)* **11**, 23 (1947).

[69] H. Matsui, T. Sato, T. Tkahashi, S.-C. Wang, H.-B. Yang, H. Ding, T. Fujii, T. Watanabe, and A. Matsuda, *Phys. Rev. Lett.* **90**, 217002 (2003), see esp. Fig. 3.

[70] J.A. Wilson, *Phil. Mag* (in press). Cond-mat/0304661, see esp. Fig. 2.

[71] J.E. Hoffman, K. McElroy, D.-H. Lee, K.M. Lang, H. Eisaki, S. Uchida, and J.C. Davis, *Science* **297**, 1148 (2002).

[72] K. McElroy, R.W. Simmonds, J.E. Hoffman, D.-H. Lee, J. Orenstein, H. Eisaki, S. Uchida, and J.C. Davis, *Nature* **422**, 592 (2003); see also feature article there by J. Zaanen, p. 569.

[73] M. de Llano and J.J. Valencia, to be published.

[74] J. Guimpel, F. de la Cruz, J. Murduck, and I.K. Schuller, *Phys. Rev. B* **35**, 3655 (1987).

[75] A.H. Harker, *Superconductivity II* (2002) www.cmmp.ucl.ac.uk/~ahh/ teaching/3C25/Lecture31p.pdf

[76] T. Jacobs, S. Sridhar, Q. Li, G.D. Gu, and N. Koshizuka, *Phys. Rev. Lett.* **75,** 4516 (1995).

[77] J.E. Sonier, J.H. Brewer, R.F. Kiefl, G.D. Morris, R.I. Miller, D.A. Bonn, J. Cakhalian, R.H. Heffner, W.N. Hardy, and R. Liang, *Phys. Rev. Lett.* **83,** 4156 (1999).

[78] D.A. Bonn, S. Kamal, K. Zhang, R. Liang, D.J. Baar, E. Klein, W.N. Hardy, *Phys. Rev. B* **50,** 4051 (1994).

[79] Z.K. Tang, Lingyun Zhang, N. Wang, X.X. Zhang, G.H. Wen, G.D. Li, J.N. Wang, C.T. Chan, and Ping Sheng, *Science* **292**, 2462 (2001).

[80] C.J. Gorter and H.B.G. Casimir, *Physica* **1**, 306 (1934).

[81] B. Mühlschlegel, *Z. Phys.* **155**, 313 (1959).

[82] M. de Llano, F.J. Sevilla, S. Tapia, and J.R. Clem, *Cooper pairs as bosons* (to be published).

[83] P. Samuelsson and M. Büttiker, *Phys. Rev. Lett.* **89**, 046601 (2002).

[84] J. Ranninger, R. Micnas, and S. Robaszkiewicz, *Ann. Phys.* (Paris) **13**, 455 (1988).

[85] Y. Bar-Yam, *Phys. Rev. B* **43**, 359 and 2601 (1991).

[86] V.B. Geshkenbein, L.B. Ioffe, and A.I. Larkin, *Phys. Rev. B* **55**, 3173 (1997).

[87] Y. Domanski and J. Ranninger, *Phys. Rev. B* **63**, 134505 (2001).

[88] K.E. Strecker, G.B. Partridge, and R.G. Hulet, *Phys. Rev. Lett.* **91**, 080406 (2003).

[89] M.J. Holland, S.J.J.M.F. Kokkelmans, M.L. Chiofalo, and R. Walser, *Phys. Rev. Lett.* **87**, 1204061 (2001).

[90] E. Timmermans, K. Furuya, P.W. Milonni, and A.K. Kerman, *Phys. Lett. A* **285**, 228 (2001).

[91] M.L. Chiofalo, S.J.J.M.F. Kokkelmans, J.N. Milstein, and M.J. Holland,*Phys. Rev. Lett.* **88**, 090402 (2002).

[92] Y. Ohashi and A. Griffin, *Phys. Rev. Lett.* **89**, 130402 (2002).

[93] H.E. Haber and H.A. Weldon, *Phys. Rev. Lett.* **46**, 1497 (1981).

[94] L. Pitaevskii and S. Stringari, *Science* **298**, 2144 (2002).

[95] W.A. Little, K. Collins, and M.J. Holcomb, *J. Supercond.* **12**, 89 (1999).

[96] For a review, see M. Randeria, in: *Bose-Einstein Condensation*, ed. A. Griffin *et al.* (Cambridge University, Cambridge, 1995) p. 355.

[97] J. Labbé, S. Barisic, and J. Friedel, *Phys. Rev. Lett.* **19**, 1039 (1967).

[98] D.M. Eagles, *Phys. Rev.* **186**, 456 (1969).

[99] A.J. Leggett, *J. Phys. (Paris) Colloq.* **41**, C7-19 (1980).

[100] K. Miyake, *Prog. Theor. Phys.* **69**, 1794 (1983).

[101] P. Nozières, S. Schmitt-Rink, *J. Low. Temp. Phys.* **59**, 195 (1985).

[102] M. Randeria *et al.*, *Phys. Rev. Lett.* **62**, 981 (1989) and *Phys. Rev. B* **41**, 327 (1990).

[103] D. van der Marel, *Physica C* **165**, 35 (1990).

[104] M. Drechsler and W. Zwerger, *Ann. der Physik* **1**, 15 (1992).

[105] R. Haussmann, *Z. Phys. B* **91**, 291 (1993) and *Phys. Rev. B* **49**, 12975 (1994).

[106] F. Pistolesi and G.C. Strinati, *Phys. Rev. B* **49**, 6356 (1994).

[107] F.J. Sevilla, priv. comm.

[108] A.T. Fiory, S. Martin, R.M. Fleming, L.F. Schneemeyer, J.V. Waszczak, A.F. Hebard, and S.A. Sunshine, *Physica* **C 162-164**, 1195 (1989).

[109] J.D. Dow and D.R. Harshman, *J. Supercond.* **15**, 455 (2002) and refs. therein.

[110] N.W. Ashcroft and N.D. Mermin, *Solid State Physics* (Saunders, Philadelphia, PA, 1976) p. 7.

[111] X.-G. Wen and R. Kan, *Phys. Rev. B* **37**, 595 (1988).

[112] R.K. Pathak and P.V. Panat, *Phys. Rev. B* **41**, 4749 (1990).

[113] F.J. Sevilla, M. Grether, M. Fortes, M. de Llano, O. Rojo, M.A. Solís, and A.A. Valladares, *J. Low Temp. Phys.* **121**, 281 (2000) see esp. Fig. 1.

[114] S. Wolfram, *The MATHEMATICA Book*, 3rd ed. (Wolfram Media, IL, 1996) p. 743.

[115] A.B. Migdal, *JETP***7**, 996 (1958).

[116] D.R. Harshman and A.P. Mills, *Jr., Phys. Rev.* **B 45**, 10684 (1992). See esp. Table IV.

[117] T. Timusk and B. Statt, *Rep. Prog. Phys.* **62**, 61 (1999).

[118] Y.J. Uemura, *Physica B* **282**, 194 (1997). Also cond-mat/0212643.

[119] A. Jeffrey, *Handbook of Mathematical Formulas and Integrals*, (Academic Press, Newcastle, UK, 1995).

[120] R.K. Pathria, *Statistical Mechanics*, 2nd Ed. (Pergamon, Oxford, 1996), App. D.

Appendix A. Why CPs are bosons while BCS pairs are not.

This assertion is simply visualized *qualitatively* with the aid of Fig. 2 for the BCS model interaction (15). The vector $\mathbf{k}$ ends in all points of a simple-cubic lattice in k-space with lattice spacing $2\pi/L$ with L the system size. In 3D these points are within the overlap volume (shaded in the figure) where the interaction is nonzero. But, in the thermodynamic limit there are infinitely many acceptable

$\mathbf{k}$ values allowed for the energy $\mathcal{E}_K$ of the CP state, whether for ordinary CPs (7), (16) or for Bethe-Salpeter CPs (37). This implies BE statistics for either ordinary or BS CPs as each CP energy $\mathcal{E}_K$ level has no occupation limit. Not so for BCS pairs as we now show.

More *quantitatively*, consider fermion creation $a^\dagger_{\mathbf{k}_1 s}$ and annihilation $a_{\mathbf{k}_1 s}$ operators that satisfy the anti-commutation relations.

$$\begin{aligned} \{a^\dagger_{\mathbf{k}_1 s}, a^\dagger_{\mathbf{k}'_1 s'}\} &= \{a_{\mathbf{k}_1 s}, a_{\mathbf{k}'_1 s'}\} = 0 \\ \{a_{\mathbf{k}_1 s}, a^\dagger_{\mathbf{k}'_1 s'}\} &= \delta_{\mathbf{k}_1 \mathbf{k}'_1} \delta_{ss'}. \end{aligned} \tag{A.1}$$

The BCS pair annihilation and creation operators, respectively, are then

$$b_{\mathbf{kK}} \equiv a_{\mathbf{k}_2\downarrow} a_{\mathbf{k}_1\uparrow} \qquad \text{and} \qquad b^\dagger_{\mathbf{kK}} \equiv a^\dagger_{\mathbf{k}_1\uparrow} a^\dagger_{\mathbf{k}_2\downarrow}. \tag{A.2}$$

Here

$$\mathbf{k} \equiv \frac{1}{2}(\mathbf{k_1} - \mathbf{k_2}) \qquad \text{and} \qquad \mathbf{K} \equiv \mathbf{k_1} + \mathbf{k_2} \tag{A.3}$$

are the relative and total (or center-of-mass) momenta wavevectors, respectively, associated with two fermions with wavevectors

$$\mathbf{k}_1 = \mathbf{K}/2 + \mathbf{k} \qquad \text{and} \qquad \mathbf{k}_2 = \mathbf{K}/2 - \mathbf{k}. \tag{A.4}$$

We show below that $b_{\mathbf{kK}}$ and $b^\dagger_{\mathbf{kK}}$ satisfy: a) the sometimes called "pseudo-boson" commutation relations

$$[b_{\mathbf{kK}}, b^\dagger_{\mathbf{k'K}}] = (1 - n_{\mathbf{K}/2-\mathbf{k}\downarrow} - n_{\mathbf{K}/2+\mathbf{k}\uparrow})\delta_{\mathbf{kk'}}, \tag{A.5}$$

$$[b^\dagger_{\mathbf{kK}}, b^\dagger_{\mathbf{k'K}}] = [b_{\mathbf{kK}}, b_{\mathbf{k'K}}] = 0, \tag{A.6}$$

where

$$n_{\mathbf{K}/2\pm\mathbf{k}\downarrow} \equiv a^\dagger_{\mathbf{K}/2\pm\mathbf{k}\downarrow} a_{\mathbf{K}/2\pm\mathbf{k}\downarrow} \tag{A.7}$$

are fermion number operators; as well as b) a "pseudo-fermion" anti-commutation relation

$$\{b_{\mathbf{kK}}, b_{\mathbf{k'K}}\} = 2b_{\mathbf{kK}} b_{\mathbf{k'K}}(1 - \delta_{\mathbf{kk'}}). \tag{A.8}$$

Our only restriction is that $\mathbf{K} \equiv \mathbf{k}_1 + \mathbf{k}_2 = \mathbf{k}'_1 + \mathbf{k}'_2$. Clearly, BCS pairs are *not* bosons as they do *not* satisfy (Ref. [34] p. 38) the ordinary boson commutation relations

$$[b_{\mathbf{kK}}, b^\dagger_{\mathbf{k'K}}] = \delta_{\mathbf{kk'}} \qquad \text{and} \qquad [b^\dagger_{\mathbf{kK}}, b^\dagger_{\mathbf{k'K}}] = [b_{\mathbf{kK}}, b_{\mathbf{k'K}}] = 0. \tag{A.9}$$

If $\mathbf{K}=0$ (so that $\mathbf{k}_1=-\mathbf{k}_2=\mathbf{k}$), and calling $b_{\mathbf{kK=0}}\equiv b_{\mathbf{k}}$, etc., (A.5) and (A.6) become Eqs. (2.11) and (2.12) of Ref. [7], and (A.8) becomes Eq. (2.13) thereof.

To prove (A.5) to (A.8) write

$$[b_{\mathbf{kK}},b^{\dagger}_{\mathbf{k'K}}]\equiv b_{\mathbf{kK}}b^{\dagger}_{\mathbf{k'K}}-b^{\dagger}_{\mathbf{k'K}}b_{\mathbf{kK}}\equiv a_{\mathbf{k}_2\downarrow}a_{\mathbf{k}_1\uparrow}a^{\dagger}_{\mathbf{k}'_1\uparrow}a^{\dagger}_{\mathbf{k}'_2\downarrow}-a^{\dagger}_{\mathbf{k}'_1\uparrow}a^{\dagger}_{\mathbf{k}'_2\downarrow}a_{\mathbf{k}_2\downarrow}a_{\mathbf{k}_1\uparrow}\quad\text{(A.10)}$$

using (A.2). This can alternately be rewritten, using (A.4), as

$$[b_{\mathbf{kK}},b^{\dagger}_{\mathbf{k'K}}]=a_{\mathbf{K}/2-\mathbf{k}\downarrow}a_{\mathbf{K}/2+\mathbf{k}\uparrow}a^{\dagger}_{\mathbf{K}/2+\mathbf{k}'\uparrow}a^{\dagger}_{\mathbf{K}/2-\mathbf{k}'\downarrow}-a^{\dagger}_{\mathbf{K}/2+\mathbf{k}'\uparrow}a^{\dagger}_{\mathbf{K}/2-\mathbf{k}'\downarrow}a_{\mathbf{K}/2-\mathbf{k}\downarrow}a_{\mathbf{K}/2+\mathbf{k}\uparrow}.\quad\text{(A.11)}$$

The pair of Fermi operators $a_{\mathbf{K}/2+\mathbf{k}\uparrow}a^{\dagger}_{\mathbf{K}/2+\mathbf{k}'\uparrow}$ in the first term gives, using (A.1),

$$\begin{aligned}&a_{\mathbf{K}/2-\mathbf{k}\downarrow}(\delta_{\mathbf{kk}'}-a^{\dagger}_{\mathbf{K}/2+\mathbf{k}'\uparrow}a_{\mathbf{K}/2+\mathbf{k}\uparrow})a^{\dagger}_{\mathbf{K}/2-\mathbf{k}'\downarrow}\\&=a_{\mathbf{K}/2-\mathbf{k}\downarrow}a^{\dagger}_{\mathbf{K}/2-\mathbf{k}'\downarrow}\delta_{\mathbf{kk}'}-a_{\mathbf{K}/2-\mathbf{k}\downarrow}a^{\dagger}_{\mathbf{K}/2+\mathbf{k}'\uparrow}a_{\mathbf{K}/2+\mathbf{k}\uparrow}a^{\dagger}_{\mathbf{K}/2-\mathbf{k}'\downarrow}.\end{aligned}\quad\text{(A.12)}$$

Using (A.1) again the first term becomes $\delta_{\mathbf{kk}'}(1-a^{\dagger}_{\mathbf{K}/2-\mathbf{k}'\downarrow}a_{\mathbf{K}/2-\mathbf{k}\downarrow})$. The last term of (A.12), after anticommuting all creation operators to the left and recalling that$\delta_{\uparrow\downarrow}\equiv 0$, etc., gives $-\delta_{\mathbf{kk}'}a^{\dagger}_{\mathbf{K}/2+\mathbf{k}'\uparrow}a_{\mathbf{K}/2+\mathbf{k}\uparrow}+a^{\dagger}_{\mathbf{K}/2+\mathbf{k}'\uparrow}a^{\dagger}_{\mathbf{K}/2-\mathbf{k}'\downarrow}a_{\mathbf{K}/2-\mathbf{k}\downarrow}a_{\mathbf{K}/2+\mathbf{k}\uparrow}$. Inserting this in (A.11) leaves precisely (A.5) if we recall the number operators (A.7). To prove (A.6) write

$$[b_{\mathbf{kK}},b_{\mathbf{k'K}}]\equiv b_{\mathbf{kK}}b_{\mathbf{k'K}}-b_{\mathbf{k'K}}b_{\mathbf{kK}}\equiv a_{\mathbf{k}_2\downarrow}a_{\mathbf{k}_1\uparrow}a_{\mathbf{k}'_2\downarrow}a_{\mathbf{k}'_1\uparrow}-a_{\mathbf{k}'_2\downarrow}a_{\mathbf{k}'_1\uparrow}a_{\mathbf{k}_2\downarrow}a_{\mathbf{k}_1\uparrow}\quad\text{(A.13)}$$

using (A.2); or equivalently

$$[b_{\mathbf{kK}},b_{\mathbf{k'K}}]\equiv a_{\mathbf{K}/2-\mathbf{k}\downarrow}a_{\mathbf{K}/2+\mathbf{k}\uparrow}a_{\mathbf{K}/2-\mathbf{k}'\downarrow}a_{\mathbf{K}/2+\mathbf{k}'\uparrow}-a_{\mathbf{K}/2-\mathbf{k}'\downarrow}a_{\mathbf{K}/2+\mathbf{k}'\uparrow}a_{\mathbf{K}/2-\mathbf{k}\downarrow}a_{\mathbf{K}/2+\mathbf{k}\uparrow}.\quad\text{(A.14)}$$

The first term is easily brought into a form cancelling the last term by simply anti-commuting operators with primed subindices to the left, thus proving (A.6). Finally to prove (A.8) write

$$\begin{aligned}\{b_{\mathbf{kK}},b_{\mathbf{k'K}}\}&\equiv b_{\mathbf{kK}}b_{\mathbf{k'K}}+b_{\mathbf{k'K}}b_{\mathbf{kK}}\equiv a_{\mathbf{k}_2\downarrow}a_{\mathbf{k}_1\uparrow}a_{\mathbf{k}'_2\downarrow}a_{\mathbf{k}'_1\uparrow}+a_{\mathbf{k}'_2\downarrow}a_{\mathbf{k}'_1\uparrow}a_{\mathbf{k}_2\downarrow}a_{\mathbf{k}_1\uparrow} &\text{(A.15)}\\&\equiv a_{\mathbf{K}/2-\mathbf{k}\downarrow}a_{\mathbf{K}/2+\mathbf{k}\uparrow}a_{\mathbf{K}/2-\mathbf{k}'\downarrow}a_{\mathbf{K}/2+\mathbf{k}'\uparrow}+a_{\mathbf{K}/2-\mathbf{k}'\downarrow}a_{\mathbf{K}/2+\mathbf{k}'\uparrow}a_{\mathbf{K}/2-\mathbf{k}\downarrow}a_{\mathbf{K}/2+\mathbf{k}\uparrow}, &\text{(A.16)}\\&=2a_{\mathbf{K}/2-\mathbf{k}\downarrow}a_{\mathbf{K}/2+\mathbf{k}\uparrow}a_{\mathbf{K}/2-\mathbf{k}'\downarrow}a_{\mathbf{K}/2+\mathbf{k}'\uparrow}\equiv 2b_{\mathbf{kK}}b_{\mathbf{k'K}}\qquad\text{if}\quad \mathbf{k}\neq\mathbf{k}'. &\text{(A.17)}\end{aligned}$$

However, if $\mathbf{k}=\mathbf{k}'$ then

$$\{b_{\mathbf{kK}},b_{\mathbf{kK}}\}=2a_{\mathbf{K}/2-\mathbf{k}\downarrow}a_{\mathbf{K}/2+\mathbf{k}\uparrow}a_{\mathbf{K}/2-\mathbf{k}\downarrow}a_{\mathbf{K}/2+\mathbf{k}\uparrow}=0\quad\text{(A.18)}$$

since $(a_{\mathbf{K}/2\pm\mathbf{k}\downarrow})^2\equiv 0$. Hence (A.8) is true.

The main point here is simply this: *any* number of CPs with a definite $\mathbf{K}$ but *different* values of $\mathbf{k}$ can occupy a state of CP energy $\mathcal{E}_K$ and thus not only obey BE statistics but (as this in turn demands) also obey the boson commutation relations (A.5) for $\mathbf{k} \neq \mathbf{k}'$. Hence, CPs can suffer a BEC as a given CP state involves no two BCS pairs with the same $\mathbf{k}$.

Appendix B. CBFM and BCS condensation energies compared.

Using (47) for $T = 0$ when $n_0(T) = m_0(T)$ and $n_B(T) = m_B(T)$ we obtain for the superconducting state, calling $\Delta(T = 0) \equiv \Delta$,

$$\frac{\Omega_s(T=0)}{L^d} = 2\hbar\omega_D n_0(0) + \int_{-\mu}^{\infty} d\xi N(\xi)[\xi - \sqrt{\xi^2 + \Delta^2}]$$

where $\xi \equiv \varepsilon - \mu$. Recalling the expression (52) for Δ, using (43) and (44), and since $\mu = E_f$, gives

$$\frac{\Omega_s(T=0)}{L^d} = 2\hbar\omega_D n_0(0) + 2\int_{-\mu}^{-\hbar\omega_D} d\xi N(\xi)\xi + N(E_F)\int_{-\hbar\omega_D}^{\hbar\omega_D} d\xi[\xi - \sqrt{\xi^2 + \Delta^2}]. \tag{B.1}$$

The first and second members of the last term have respectively odd and even integrands, so that this term becomes

$$-2N(E_F)\int_0^{\hbar\omega_D} d\xi[\sqrt{\xi^2 + \Delta^2}].$$

On the other hand, for the normal state $n_0 = 0$ and $m_0 = 0$, so that from (52) $\Delta(T) = 0$. Hence, from (64) the CBFM condensation energy $E_s - E_n$ per unit volume is just

$$\frac{E_s - E_n}{L^d} = 2\hbar\omega_D n_0(0) + 2N(E_F)\int_0^{\hbar\omega_D} d\xi(\xi - \sqrt{\xi^2 + \Delta^2}) \qquad \text{(CBFM)}. \tag{B.2}$$

From Eq. (2), Sec. 4.3.3.1, Ref. [119] the integral evaluates to

$$\begin{aligned} & -\frac{1}{2}\hbar\omega_D\sqrt{(\hbar\omega_D)^2 + \Delta^2} + \frac{(\hbar\omega_D)^2}{2} + \frac{1}{2}\Delta^2 \ln\frac{\Delta}{\hbar\omega_D + \sqrt{(\hbar\omega_D)^2 + \Delta^2}} \\ = \; & \frac{1}{2}\Delta^2\ln(\Delta/2\hbar\omega_D) - \frac{1}{4}\Delta^2 - \frac{1}{16}[\Delta^4/(\hbar\omega_D)^2] + O\left[\Delta^6/(\hbar\omega_D)^4\right]. \end{aligned}$$

Thus, since $n_0 = \Delta^2/f^2$, (B.2) for weak coupling $\Delta = f\sqrt{n_0} \to 0$ becomes

$$\frac{E_s - E_n}{L^d} \xrightarrow[\lambda \to 0]{} -\frac{1}{2}N(E_F)\Delta^2\left[1 + \frac{1}{4}(\Delta/\hbar\omega_D)^2 + O(\Delta/\hbar\omega_D)^4\right] \qquad \text{(CBFM)}. \tag{B.3}$$

By contrast, the original expressions (2.41) and (2.43) in Ref. [7] give

$$\frac{E_s - E_n}{L^d} = 2N(E_F)\int_0^{\hbar\omega_D} d\xi \left(\xi - \frac{\xi^2}{\sqrt{\xi^2+\Delta^2}}\right) - \frac{\Delta^2}{V} \qquad \text{(BCS)} \qquad \text{(B.4)}$$

where V is defined in (15). Multiplying (32) by $\Delta^2/2$ is equivalent to

$$2N(E_F)\int_0^{\hbar\omega_D} d\xi \frac{\Delta^2}{2\sqrt{\xi^2+\Delta^2}} = \frac{\Delta^2}{V}$$

which when combined with (B.4) gives

$$\frac{E_s - E_n}{L^d} = 2N(E_{\mathrm{F}})\int_0^{\hbar\omega_{\mathrm{D}}} d\xi \left[\xi - \frac{1}{2}\frac{2\xi^2+\Delta^2}{\sqrt{\xi^2+\Delta^2}}\right].$$

Using Eqs. (3) and (10), Sec. 4.3.3.1, of Ref. [119] finally gives

$$\frac{E_s - E_n}{L^d} = N(E_F)(\hbar\omega_D)^2\left[1 - \sqrt{1+(\Delta/\hbar\omega_D)^2}\right] \qquad \text{(B.5)}$$

which on expansion leads to

$$\frac{E_s - E_n}{L^d} \xrightarrow[\lambda\to 0]{} -\frac{1}{2}N(E_F)\Delta^2\left[1 - \frac{1}{4}(\Delta/\hbar\omega_D)^2 + O(\Delta/\hbar\omega_D)^4\right] \qquad \text{(BCS)}. \quad \text{(B.6)}$$

Thus, the CBFM condensation energy (B.3) is *larger* than that of BCS, but only the latter is a rigorous upper bound to the exact condensation energy since it follows [7] from a variational trial wavefunction.

Appendix C. BEC as limit of all electrons paired.

Here we discuss generalizations of the well-known result that the BEC transition temperature T_c of a d-dimensional N-fermion gas of Fermi temperature T_F in which *all* fermions are imagined paired into bosons, is just $0.218T_F$. (See dashed line in "Uemura plot" of Ref. [118], Fig. 2). These results will provide a convenient pure BEC limit which in effect turn out to be an *upper limit* for the pure 2e-CP phase separation boundary T_c values deduced in Sec. 8.

The general BEC T_c-formula for identical noninteracting bosons in d-dimensions of energy $\eta = C_s K^s$, $s > 0$, where as before K is the boson CMM, is [16]

$$T_c = \frac{C_s}{k_B}\left[\frac{s\Gamma(d/2)(2\pi)^d}{2\pi^{d/2}\Gamma(d/s)g_{d/s}(1)}n_B\right]^{s/d} \qquad \text{(C.1)}$$

where n_B is the boson number-density and $g_\sigma(z)$ the Bose integral [120], $z \equiv e^{\mu_B/k_BT}$ is the "*fugacity*" and μ_B the boson chemical potential. For $z = 1$, $g_\sigma(1) \equiv \zeta(\sigma)$, the Riemann Zeta-function, if $\sigma > 1$, while for $0 < \sigma \leq 1$ the infinite series $g_\sigma(1)$ diverges. Eq. (C.1) is formally valid for all $d > 0$ and $s > 0$. Hence, for $0 < d \leq s$, $T_c = 0$ since $g_{d/s}(1) = \infty$ for $d/s \leq 1$ but T_c is otherwise finite. We stress that as a consequence of the former *all* 2D T_c predictions in Fig. 7 (except the BCS one that survives for all $d > 0$, including $d = 1$) would collapse to *zero* had $s = 2$ been used in 2D instead of the correct $s = 1$ arising from the Fermi sea. For $s = 2$, $C_2 = \hbar^2/2m_B$ (C.1) leads to the familiar 3D result

$$T_c \simeq 3.31\hbar^2 n_B^{2/3}/m_B k_B \tag{C.2}$$

since $\zeta(3/2) \simeq 2.612$. Recalling that $k_BT_F = \hbar^2k_F^2/2m$ with $k_F = [2^{d-2}\pi^{d/2}d\Gamma(d/2)n]^{1/d}$ from (36), then if $m_B = 2m$ and $n_B = n/2$ (all electrons paired) for $s = 2$ (C.1) implies that

$$T_c/T_F = \tfrac{1}{2}[2/d\Gamma(d/2)g_{d/2}(1)]^{2/d} = 0 \quad \text{for} \quad d \leq 2 \tag{C.3}$$

since $g_{d/2}(1) = \infty$ for $d/2 \leq 1$. When $d > 2$ then T_c is nonzero. For $d = 3$ we get the familiar limit mentioned before

$$T_c/T_F = \tfrac{1}{2}\,[2/3\Gamma(3/2)\zeta(3/2)]^{2/3} \simeq 0.218, \tag{C.4}$$

(see also dashed line Fig. 2 of Ref. [118]).

Equilibrium and Dynamic Properties of d-wave Ceramic Superconductors

D. Dominguez[1], H. Kawamura[2] and Mai Suan Li[31]

[11] *Centro Atómico Bariloche, 8400 S. C. de Bariloche, Rio Negro, Argentina*
[2] *Department of of Earth and Space Science, Faculty of Science, Osaka University, Toyonaka 560-0031, Japan*
[3] *Institute of Physics, Polish Academy of Sciences, Al. Lotnikow 32/46, 02-668 Warsaw, Poland*

We present a review of the results of our simulations on equilibrium and dynamic properties of the d-wave ceramic high-T_c superconductors. We represent disordered superconductors by a three-dimensional lattice model of randomly distributed π Josephson junctions with finite self-inductance. The paramagnetic Meissner effect observed experimentally in ceramic high-T_c superconductors is well reproduced by this model. In equilibrium, one can show that there is a low temperature chiral glass phase, which is characterized by chiralities frozen in time and in space. Experimental attempts on the search for the chiral glass phase are discussed. Dynamical phenomena such as anomalous microwave absorption, AC resistivity and enhancement of critical current by external electric fields are also considered by Langevin dynamics simulations. A satisfactory agreement of the simulations with several experiments in ceramic high T_c superconductors was obtained.

INTRODUCTION

It is well established that the phonon mediated electron-electron interaction gives rise to spin-singlet pairing with s-wave symmetry [1] in conventional low-T_c superconductors. The situation may become different in the case of high-T_c ceramic superconductors with the critical temperature T_c ranging from 7 K to 100 K. The materials of this family which have been studied most throughly, namely $La_{2-x}Sr_xCuO_4$ and $YBa_2Cu_3O_{7-x}$, have crystal lattices of tetragonal symmetry, i.e. $G = D_{4h} = D \times I$. The accumulated data obtained by phase-insensitive experiments (the low-temperature behaviour of thermodynamic properties [2, 3], the angle-resolved photoemission measurements [4]) and phase-sensitive ones [5, 6] have led researchers to the conclusion that the superconducting state in these compounds is described by a one-component non-trivial order parameter corresponding to singlet pairing and transforming according to the B_{1g} representation, that is [7] $\Delta(\vec{k}) \sim k_x^2 - k_y^2$, where $\vec{k}$ is a wave vector. This type of pairing is called 'd-wave pairing'.

As shown by Sigrist and Rice [8], the critical current of the Josephson junctions between d-wave superconductors may become negative, i.e. the phase across such π-junctions is shifted by π, and thus they are called π-junctions (note that π-junctions may also occur in the s-wave case due to the effect of magnetic impurities present in the thin insulator layer [9, 10]). On the other hand a ceramic superconductor may be modeled as a system consisting of superconducting grains embedded in a nonsuperconducting host [11, 12]. Assuming that grains are linked by Josephson junctions and each of them may be characterized by a phase of the superconducting order parameter one can write the Hamiltonian of a d-wave ceramic superconductor in the following form [13]

$$\mathcal{H} = -\sum_{<ij>} J_{ij}\cos(\theta_i - \theta_j - A_{ij}) + \frac{1}{2\mathcal{L}}\sum_p (\Phi_p - \Phi_p^{ext})^2,$$

$$\Phi_p = \frac{\phi_0}{2\pi}\sum_{<ij>}^{p} A_{ij},\ A_{ij} = \frac{2\pi}{\phi_0}\int_i^j \vec{A}(\vec{r})d\vec{r},$$

$$\Phi_p^{ext} = \begin{cases} HS & \text{if } p \text{ is on the } <xy> \text{ plane} \\ 0 & \text{otherwise} \end{cases}, \qquad (1)$$

Here θ_i ($0 \leq \theta < 2\pi$) represents the phase of the condensate at a grain on the i-th site of the lattice, J_{ij} the Josephson coupling, $\vec{A}$ being the fluctuating gauge potential, ϕ_0 the flux quantum, $\mathcal{L}$ the self-inductance of a loop (an elementary plaquette). Φ_p is the total magnetic flux threading through the p-th plaquette, Φ_p^{ext} is the flux due to an external magnetic field H applied along the z-direction and S denotes the area of an elementary plaquette. The first sum in Eq.(1) is taken over all nearest-neighbor bonds on the lattice whereas the second sum is over all elementary plaquettes on the lattice. The lattice is a simple-cubic lattice with $N = L^3$ sites. Quenched randomness occurs only in the distribution of the critical current J_{ij}, which is assumed to be an independent random variable taking the values $-J$ and J with probabilities c and $1-c$, respectively, each representing π and 0 junctions. Typically the case of $c = 0.5$ ($\pm J$ distribution) is considered.

The aim of this review is to discuss main physical phenomena which may be captured by the Hamiltonian (1). We show that the existence of frustrated loops in the Josephson network of d-wave superconductors leads to rich physics which was not known for conventional materials. Concerning the nature of ordering in superconductors described by the Hamiltonian (1), it has been predicted by Monte Carlo simulations that the so called chiral glass phase may occur at nonzero temperatures even in the presence of screening currents ($\mathcal{L} > 0$) [14]. In this phase the "chiralities" or the spontaneous fluxes, similar to the spin glass, are frozen in time but randomly distributed in space. The chiral glass phase may be detected, say, by the divergence of the nonlinear susceptibility. Below we will discuss in detail experimental attempts to search for this phase. Although many experimental facts favor the existence of the chiral glass phase, this question remains unsettled.

One of the most interesing findings in the condensed matter physics in recent years is the paramagnetic Meissner effect (PME). Contrary to the standard diamagnetic response to the external field, a paramagnetic signal was observed in certain ceramic superconductors upon cooling in low enough fields [15, 16]. In other words, the field cooled (FC) susceptibility becomes positive whereas the zero field cool (ZFC) magnetization remains negative. The PME can be explained by the Hamiltonian (1) in the following way. Due to frustration arising from negative and positive J_{ij} the spontaneous supercurrents circulating around π loops become nonzero. The system, therefore, behaves like a paramagnet and should have the paramagnetic response to the external magnetic field.

It should be noted that the PME may be understood without the notion of the d-wave pairing because the paramagnetic signal is also possible due to the flux compression inside of a sample [17]. Therefore it can not serve as an indicator for the existence of the d-wave superconductivity. In this review we consider two dynamical phenomena which allow us to distinguish between the s- and d-wave symmetry of the order parameter. The first one is the microwave absorption (MWA) [16] and the second one is the enhancement of the critical current by the electric field [18]. For s-wave superconductors the MWA has minimum at zero magnetic field whereas a maximum was observed for d-wave ones. This interesting effect is fully reproduced by the Hamiltonian (1). As shown by Dominguez, Wiecko and Jose [19], the anomalous enhancement of the critical current by electric fields may be explained assuming the existence of d-wave pairing. We will also discuss the effect of pairing symmetry on the AC resistivity of ceramic superconductors.

EQUILIBRIUM PROPERTIES

In this section, we analyze equilibrium thermodynamic properties of ceramic high-T_c superconductors on the basis of the lattice model introduced in the previous section. Our main interest here is the ordering behavior of ceramic high-T_c superconductors. Particular attention is paid to the peculiar paramagnetic response of the system, called the paramagnetic Meissner effect (PME)[15, 16], as well as to the possible novel thermodynamic phase of ceramic high-T_c superconductors, called the chiral-glass phase[20, 21]. The former (PME) is basically a non-cooperative effect, whereas the latter (chiral-glass phase) is essentially a cooperative phenomenon.

As argued in the previous section, due to the *d*-wave nature of the paring symmetry, ceramic high-T_c superconductors possess π-junctions where the Cooper pair acquires a phase shift of π[8]. When a loop contains odd number of π-junctions, it is called a π-loop. The π-loop is frustrated due to the phase mismatch, and the phases of the condensate wave functions in the grains tend to be canted with each other in order to minimize its frustration. This phase canting necessarily gives rise to a finite loop-supercurrent flowing along the π-loop. Loop-supercurrent also generates a magnetic flux threading the π-loop [8, 22]. The two "chiral" states with the loop-supercurrents flowing either in clockwise or counter-clockwise directions are energetically degenerate in zero external field. One may call these two chiral states a state with + or − "chirality"[20]. In ceramic superconductors, the sense of such loop-supercurrents, *i.e.* the chirality, is expected to appear in a spatially random manner.

In the circumstance where each loop can be regarded as thermodynamically independent, as occurs at high enough temperatures or in the type of ceramic samples where the loops are mutually disconnected, the sense of loop-supercurrents will fluctuate also in time. Fluctuating sense of loop-supercurrents means fluctuating direction of the induced flux, which causes the paramagnetic response in the system. If this paramagnetic response overcomes the diamagnetic response intrinsic to the superconductivity, there occurs the PME[8, 22, 23].

In the circumstance where each loop can be regarded as strongly correlated, by contrast, some sort of cooperative phenomenon could occur among the loop-supercurrents induced at the frustrated π-loops. Indeed, based on an analogy to the ordering of the XY spin glass[24], one of the present authors (H.K.) proposed some time ago that a novel thermodynamic phase, 'chiral-glass phase', might occur *in zero external field* in certain ceramic high-T_c superconductors [20]. This phase is characterized by a spontaneously broken Z_2 time-reversal symmetry with keeping a $U(1)$ gauge symmetry. The order parameter is then the chirality introduced above, *i.e.*, the sense of the local loop-supercurrent circulating over grains. The chiral-glass phase should not be confused with the well-known vortex-glass phase, the latter being the in-field phase with a broken $U(1)$ gauge symmetry[25–27]. In the chiral-glass phase, chiralities are frozen in time in a spatially random manner. It is also characterized by frozen-in random fluxes which are generated by the frozen-in chiralities. In Ref.[20], it was predicted that the random freezing of fluxes leads to the negative divergence of the nonlinear magnetic susceptibility at the chiral-glass transition. Subsequent numerical studies by two of the present authors (H.K. and M.S.L.) showed that this chiral-glass phase is stable against finite screening effect[14, 28].

In the remainder of this section, we review the results of recent numerical simulations performed to investigate the ordering properties of ceramic high-T_c superconductors. We then briefly review the recent experimental situation concerning the detection of the possible chiral-glass state in ceramic high-T_c superconductors.

Numerical simulations

We focus on the model (1) with the bimodal distribution of couplings J_{ij}. While previous simulations were performed for this particular distribution of J_{ij}, the results are expected to be rather insensitive to the details of the distribution, *e.g.*, a slight asymmetry between $\pm J$ or the detailed form of the distribution.

The dimensionless inductance, defined by $\tilde{\mathcal{L}} = (2\pi/\phi_0)^2 J\mathcal{L}$, is related to the bare Josephson penetration depth in units of lattice spacing via

$$\lambda_0 = 1/\sqrt{\tilde{\mathcal{L}}}. \tag{2}$$

Larger inductance corresponds to smaller penetration depth with enhanced effects of screening. In the limit $\tilde{\mathcal{L}} \to 0$, or $\lambda_0 \to \infty$, the screening effect becomes negligible and one recovers the XY spin-glass Hamiltonian[29]. In the opposite limit $\tilde{\mathcal{L}} \to \infty$, on the other hand, it can be shown that the model reduces to the noninteracting one[29] Hence, in the $\tilde{\mathcal{L}} \to \infty$ limit, the system remains in the disordered state even at $T = 0$.

The local chirality may be defined at each plaquette by the gauge-invariant quantity[20, 29],

$$\kappa_p = 2^{-3/2} \sum_{<ij>}^{p} (J_{ij}/J) \sin(\theta_i - \theta_j - A_{ij}), \tag{3}$$

where the sum runs over a directed contour along the sides of the plaquette p.

The model Hamiltonian of Eq.(1) was first introduced by Domínguez, Jagla and Balseiro [13]. These authors studied the magnetic properties of the model by means of dynamical Langevin simulation, with particular interest in the PME (see next section on dynamical properties). Subsequently, the ordering behavior of this model was studied by means of extensive Monte Carlo simulations in a series of numerical works of Refs.[14, 28–30] focusing on the chirality.

Because of the intrinsic effects of both frustration and randomness, the model (1) exhibits a glassy behavior with an extremely slow dynamics. Hence, in order to obtain truly equilibrium properties, special care has to be taken in simulations to fully thermalize the system. This has been achieved in Ref.[14, 28] by making use of the temperature-exchange (or parallel tempering) method[31]. Below, we show some of the numerical data from Refs.[14, 28] concerning the equilibrium properties of the model.

A convenient quantity to probe the spatially random freezing of the chirality may be the chiral overlap q and the associated chiral Binder ratio. The chiral overlap is defined by

$$q = N_p^{-1} \sum_p \kappa_p^{(1)} \kappa_p^{(2)}, \tag{4}$$

where N_p is the total number of plaquettes on the lattice, while (1) and (2) denote the two independent configuration generated by the two independent simulations for the same bond realization. In terms of this chiral overlap q, the Binder ratio of the chirality is defined by

$$g_{\mathrm{CG}} = \frac{1}{3}(3 - \frac{[< q^4 >]}{[< q^2 >]^2}), \tag{5}$$

where $< \cdots >$ represents the thermal average and $[\cdots]$ represents the average over bond disorder. At the chiral-glass transition point, curves of g_{CG} against T for different sizes should intersect or merge, which may be used to identify the chiral-glass transition point.

Fig.1a displays the size and temperature dependence of g_{CG} calculated for the range of sizes $L = 3, 4, 6, 8$ and 10. The inductance is chosen here to be $\tilde{\mathcal{L}} = 1$, which corresponds to the bare penetration depth λ_0 equal to one lattice spacing. As can be seen from Fig.1(a), the data of g_{CG} for $L = 3, 4, 6, 8$ all cross at almost the same temperature $T \sim 0.28 - 0.29$, suggesting the occurrence of a finite-temperature chiral-glass transition at $T_g = 0.286 \pm 0.01$ (T is measured in units of J).

One can also estimate the critical exponent characterizing the chiral-glass transition by applying the finite-size scaling analysis to the data. From the finite-size scaling plot of the Binder ratio shown in Fig.1(b), one can estimate the chiral-glass correlation-length exponent to be $\nu = 1.3 \pm 0.2$. A similar finite-size scaling analysis has also been made for the chiral-glass susceptibility $\chi_{CG} = N[< q^2 >]$, yielding the chiral-glass critical-point-decay exponent $\eta = -0.2 \pm 0.2$[14, 28]. From the standard scaling relation for the exponents, one gets the chiral-glass order parameter exponent $\beta \simeq 0.5$ and the chiral-glass susceptibility exponent $\gamma \simeq 2.9$. The dynamical critical exponent at the chiral-glass transition z was also estimated by means of dynamical Monte Carlo simulation of Ref.[30] to be $z \simeq 6.3$.

Figs.2(a) and (b) exhibit the the temperature and size dependences of the zero-field linear and nonlinear susceptibilities, χ and χ_2 defined by $\chi \equiv \mathrm{d}m/\mathrm{d}H$ and $\chi_2 \equiv (1/6)\mathrm{d}^3m/\mathrm{d}H^3$ (H is the external field). The inductance is again set to $\tilde{\mathcal{L}} = 1$. As can be seen from Fig.2a, the linear susceptibility χ of the model turns out to be positive over an entire temperature range studied, including in the disordered phase $T > T_g$, without a clear anomaly at T_g. This indicates that the magnetic response of the model is indeed paramagnetic (PME). The result also indicates that the sign of the susceptibility has no direct correlation with the chiral-glass transition itself: Note that no sign change nor any detectable anomaly occurs at $T = T_g$. As stated above, the PME is essentially a single-loop effect.

It should be noted that the effect of intragranular supercurrents is not taken into account in the present model, which is certainly present in real samples and is expected to give a diamagnetic contribution to the total susceptibility. Thus, the susceptibility of real samples would be either paramagnetic or diamagnetic, depending on the details of the sample.

By contrast, on general theoretical grounds, the nonlinear susceptibility χ_2 is expected to show a negative divergence at the chiral-glass transition point[20]. Indeed, as shown in Fig.2b, the data of χ_2 exhibit a behavior fully consistent with this expectation. The exponent associated with this negative divergence is estimated as $\gamma_2 \sim 4.4$[14, 28].

Next, let us turn to the $\mathcal{L}$-dependence of the chiral-glass ordering. The inductance $\mathcal{L}$ is a highly sample-dependent quantity: If one models a loop as a cylinder of radius r and height h, its inductance is given by $\mathcal{L} = 4\pi^2r^2/h$. Thus, $\tilde{\mathcal{L}} = (2\pi/\phi_0)^2J\mathcal{L}$ sensitively depends not only on the size of the grain, but also on the way of the contact between the grains.

As mentioned above, screening becomes negligible in the $\tilde{\mathcal{L}} \to 0$ limit, and the model reduces to the XY spin glass. Recent simulation of Ref.[32] strongly suggests that the 3D XY spin glass with the $\pm J$ coupling also exhibits an equilibrium chiral-glass transition at a finite temperature $T_g = 0.39 \pm 0.03$, although the nature of the chiral-glass ordered state and the universality class of the transition might differ from the ones with finite screening. The estimated chiral-glass transition temperature in the $\tilde{\mathcal{L}} \to 0$ limit is considerably higher than that for $\tilde{\mathcal{L}} = 1$, indicating that the screening suppresses the chiral-glass ordering. Meanwhile, in the $\tilde{\mathcal{L}} \to \infty$ limit, the model reduces to the noninteracting system exhibiting no chiral-glass transition at any temperature.

How the chiral-glass transition is suppressed as $\tilde{\mathcal{L}}$ is increased toward $\tilde{\mathcal{L}} = \infty$ was also examined in Ref.[28]. In Fig.3(a) and (b), the temperature dependence of the chiral Binder ratio g_{CG}, defined by eq.(1), is shown for larger inductances $\tilde{\mathcal{L}} = 3$ and 5. For $\tilde{\mathcal{L}} = 3$,

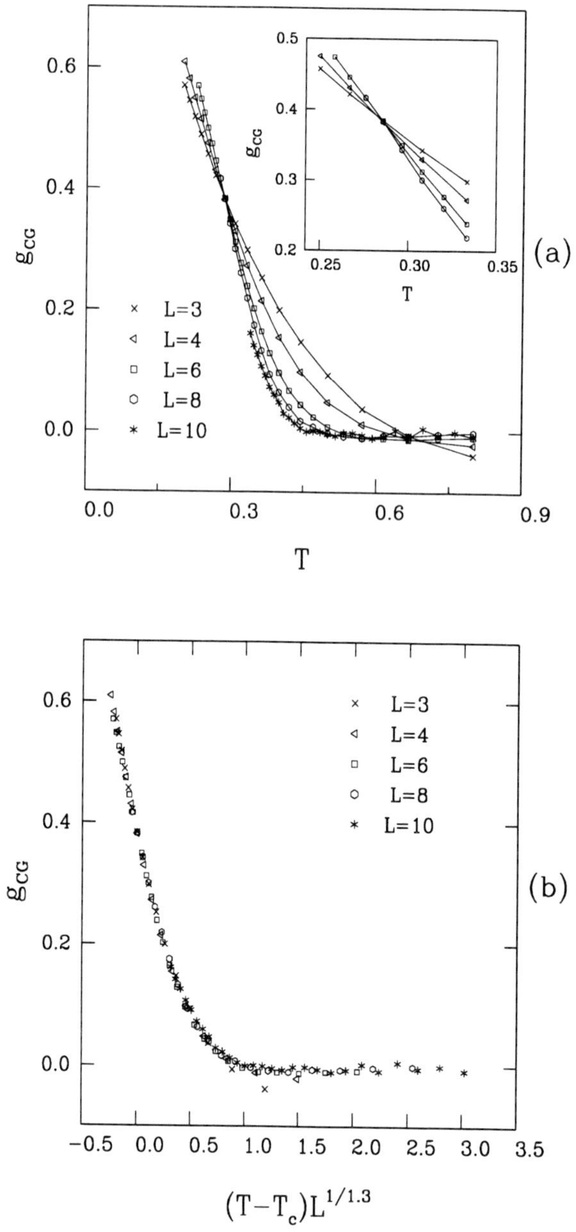

FIG. 1: (a) The temperature and size dependence of the Binder ratio of the chirality, g_{CG}, for $\tilde{\mathcal{L}} = 1$. Inset is a magnified view around the transition temperature $T_{CG} \simeq 0.286$. (b) Finite-size scaling plot of g_{CG} with $T_{CG} = 0.286$ and $\nu_{CG} = 1.3$.

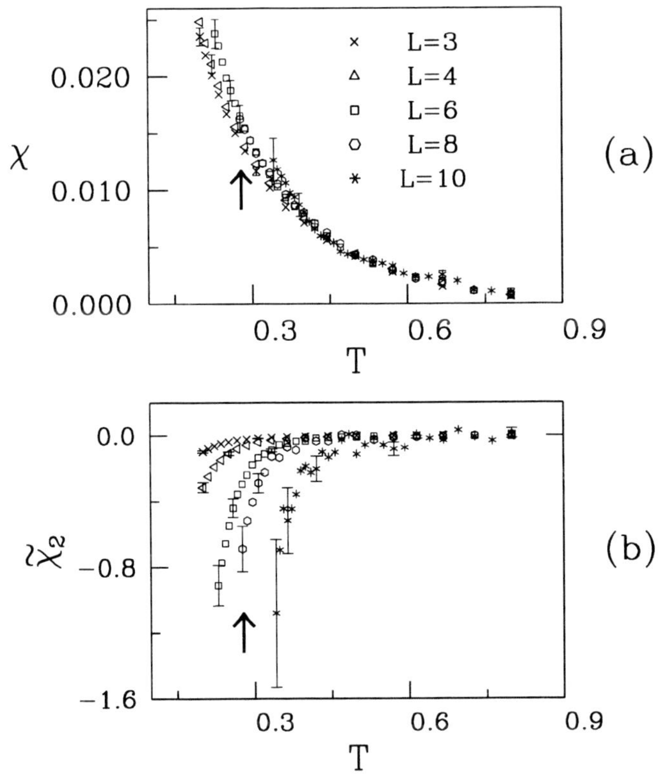

FIG. 2: (a) The temperature and size dependence of the zero-field linear susceptibility, χ, for $\tilde{\mathcal{L}} = 1$. An arrow in the figure represents the location of the chiral-glass transition point. (b) The temperature and size dependence of the zero-field nonlinear susceptibility, $\tilde{\chi}_2$, for $\tilde{\mathcal{L}} = 1$. $\tilde{\chi}_2$ is a dimensionless quantity given in units of $(4\pi S/\phi_0)^2$ where S is the area of a plaqutte. An arrow in the figure represents the location of the chiral-glass transition point.

the curves of g_{CG} for different L appear to cross at a finite temperature. As expected, the chiral-glass transition temperature monotonically decreases as $\tilde{\mathcal{L}}$ increases. For $\tilde{\mathcal{L}} = 5$, no crossing of g_{CG} is observed in the temperature range $T \geq 0.1$, suggesting that the chiral-glass transition is highly suppressed at this inductance. Numerical studies located a critical value of the inductance $\tilde{\mathcal{L}}_c$ above which there is no equilibrium chiral-glass transition to be $5 \lesssim \tilde{\mathcal{L}}_c \lesssim 7$[28].

The existence of a critical value of $\tilde{\mathcal{L}}$ means that, if the sample has too large grain size or too strong Josephson coupling, an equilibrium chiral-glass phase may not be realized at all in such samples. A rough estimate of typical value of $\tilde{\mathcal{L}}$ in the type of granular sample used in Ref.[21] was made in Ref.[14, 28] to yield $\tilde{\mathcal{L}} \sim 10^{-2}$, by putting $r \sim 1\mu$m, $h/r \sim 0.01$ and $J \sim 20$K. Since this value is considerably smaller than the $\tilde{\mathcal{L}}_c$ value quoted above, an equilibrium chiral-glass phase may well be realized in such samples. In fact, the precise value of the inductance of the real sample, which might depend sensitively on the details of sample preparation, remains largely unknown.

In contrast to the chiral-glass ordering tendency, the paramagnetic tendency tends to be rather enhanced on increasing $\tilde{\mathcal{L}}$. This is evident from Fig.4 in which the temperature and

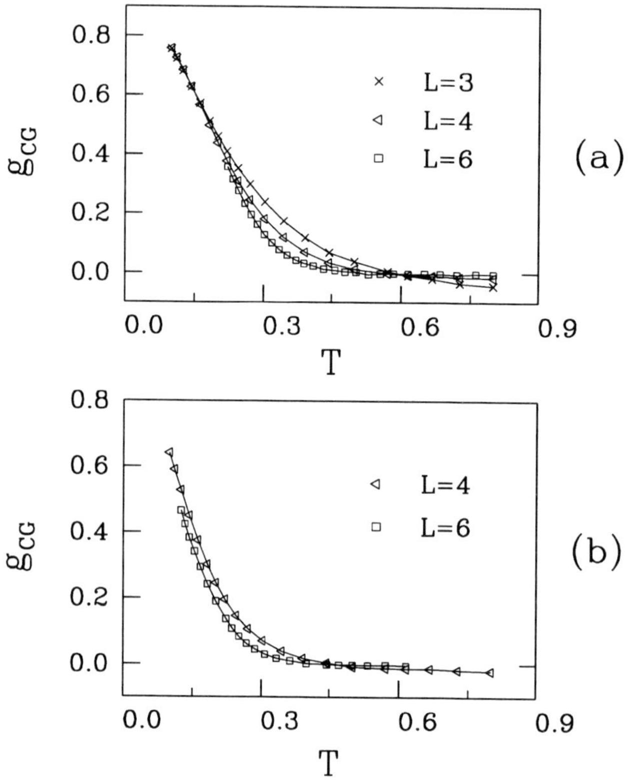

FIG. 3: The temperature and size dependence of the Binder ratio of the chirality, g_{CG}, for (a) $\tilde{\mathcal{L}} = 3$ and (b) $\tilde{\mathcal{L}} = 5$.

inductance dependence of the linear susceptibility, χ, is shown for a fixed lattice size $L = 6$. This tendency is another manifestation of the fact that the PME is a non-cooperative effect. As the inductance becomes larger, the magnitude of the flux induced by the circulating current tends to get larger.

Experiments

We now review the current experimental situation concerning the detection of the possible chiral-glass state in ceramic high-T_c superconductors. Several types of ceramic high-T_c samples, including $La_{1.8}Sr_{0.2}CuO_4$ (LSCO)[33], $Bi_2Sr_2CaCu_2O_8$ (Bi2212 or BSCCO)[36–38], $YBa_2Cu_4O_8$ and $YBa_2Cu_3O_{7-\delta}$ (YBCO-124 and YBCO-123) [21, 34, 35].

One experimental signature of the chiral-glass transition is a negatively divergent anomaly in the nonlinear susceptibility χ_2. A sharp negatively-divergent anomaly of χ_2 was indeed reported in $YB_2C_4O_8$ ceramic samples by the ac method by Matsuura and collaborators [21], and was interpreted as a signal of the chiral-glass transition. In the sample used in Ref.[21], the intergranular transition takes place at a temperature much lower than the intragranular superconducting transition, which enables one to regard the Josephson coupling as temperature independent as implicitly assumed in the present theoretical model. By contrast, in some ceramic samples, the intragranular superconducting transition and the intergranular transition take place at mutually close temperatures. In such samples, since

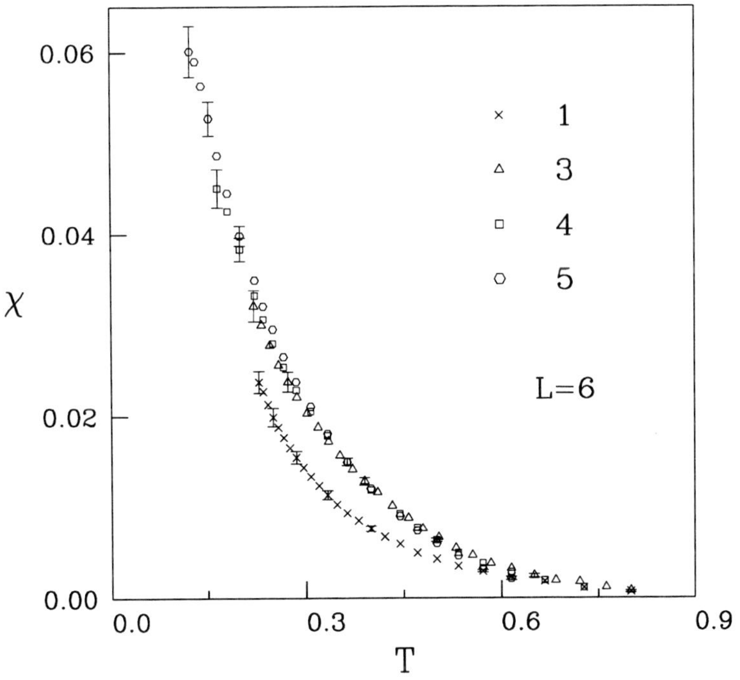

FIG. 4: The temperature and inductance dependence of the zero-field linear susceptibility, χ, for various values of inductance (shown next to symbols) and for a fixed lattice size $L = 6$.

the Josephson coupling J would actually be strongly temperature-dependent around the intergranular transition point, care has to be taken in analyzing the experimental data.

Since the chiral-glass transition is a thermodynamic second-order transition, the linear and nonlinear susceptibilities should obey the standard scaling relations near the chiral-glass transition point. For example, the out-of-phase component of the linear susceptibility, $\chi''(\omega)$, is expected to satisfy the dynamic scaling relation of the form[28],

$$\chi''(\omega, T) \approx \omega^{\frac{\beta}{z\nu}} \bar{\chi}''(\frac{\omega}{t^{z\nu}}). \tag{6}$$

Such dynamic scaling analyses were made by several groups, *i.e.*, by Leylekian, Ocio and Hammann for $La_{1.8}Sr_{0.2}CuO_4$ (LSCO) ceramic samples[33], by Deguchi *et al* for $YBa_2Cu_3O_{7-\delta}$ (YBCO-123) ceramic samples[34], and by Papadopoulou *et al* for $Bi_2Si_2CaCu_2O_8$ (Bi2212 or BSCCO) samples[36]. Leylekian *et al* performed both the ac susceptibility and the noise measurements, and observed an intergranular transition in zero field fairly close to the intragranular superconducting transition, at a temperature about 10% below the superconducting transition temperature. By taking into account the temperature dependence of the Josephson coupling, these authors estimated the exponent $z\nu$ to be $z\nu \simeq 10 - 15$. Deguchi *et al* performed the dynamical scaling analysis of the ac susceptibility for YBCO-123, to obtain $z\nu \simeq 8$ and $\beta \simeq 0.5$, which seem reasonably close to the Monte Carlo estimates, $\beta \simeq 0.5$ and $z\nu \simeq 8.2$[28, 30]. Papadopoulou, Svedlindh and Nordblad also performed a dynamical scaling analysis of the out-of-phase ac susceptibility for BSCCO, to obtain $z\nu \simeq 11$.

Other notable signature of the chiral-glass state might be its glassy slow dynamics similar to the one observed in spin glasses[39]. In particular, characteristic glassy phenomena such as aging, memory and rejuvenation are expected to occur. Indeed, clear aging phenomenon was observed by Papadopoulou *et al* in melt-cast BSCCO samples exhibiting the PME[37]. This is in sharp contrast to sintered samples, which do not exhibit aging although it still exhibits the PME. Such difference in the aging behavior between the melt-cast and sintered samples can naturally understood if one notes that the grains are connected in melt-cast samples while they are disconnected in sintered samples. Recall that aging is a collective phenomenon in nature, while the PME is not. The aging behaviors similar to those observed experimentally were also reproduced in a dynamical simulation of the model (1) by Li, Nordblad and Kawamura[40]. More recently, strong memory and rejuvenation effects as observed in canonical spin glasses were observed in the melt-cast BSCCO samples by Gardchareon *et al*[38]. These characteristic off-equilibrium phenomena quite similar to those observed in spin glasses strongly suggest that the system indeed forms a glassy ordered state at low temperatures.

Theory also gives predictions on the transport properties at the chiral-glass transition, particularly, on the behavior of the linear and nonlinear resistivities[27]. According to Ref.[27], the nonlinear resistivity should exhibit a strong anomaly while the linear resistivity stays nonzero at the transition point. These predictions were examined by Yamao *et al* for YBCO-124 samples[35], and the experimental result appears to be in favor of the chiral-glass picture.

Hence, it appears that considerable amount of experimental evidence is now accumulating for the occurrence of a new glassy zero-field state in ceramic high-T_c superconductors, the chiral-glass state.

DYNAMICAL PROPERTIES

Dynamical model

In order to study the dynamical response and transport properties, we model the current I_{ij} flowing between two grains i, j with the resistively shunted junction model (RSJ) [41–43], which gives:

$$I_{ij} = \frac{2e}{\hbar} J_{ij} \sin\theta_{ij} + \frac{\hbar}{2eR}\frac{d\theta_{ij}}{dt} + \eta_{ij}(t) \tag{7}$$

Here the first term is the Josephson current $I^J_{ij}\sin\theta_{ij}$ ($I^J_{ij} = \frac{2e}{\hbar}J_{ij}$), the second term is the contribution of a dissipative ohmic current due to an intergrain resistance R and the last term is the Langevin noise current $\eta_{ij}(t)$ which has correlations

$$\langle \eta_{ij}(t)\eta_{i'j'}(t')\rangle = \frac{2kT}{R}\delta_{i,i'}\delta_{j,j'}\delta(t-t') \tag{8}$$

The dynamical variable in this case is the gauge invariant phase difference $\theta_{ij} = \theta_i - \theta_j - A_{ij}$. The total flux through each plaquette p depends on the mesh current C_p [43]:

$$\Phi_p = (\vec{\nabla} \times \vec{A})_p = \Phi^{ext}_p + \mathcal{L}C_p \tag{9}$$

The mesh currents C_p, the link currents I_{ij} and the external current I_{ext} are related through current conservation. At this point, it is better to redefine notation: the site of each grain is at position $\mathbf{n} = (n_x, n_y, n_z)$ (i.e. $i \equiv \mathbf{n}$); the lattice directions are $\mu = \hat{\mathbf{x}}, \hat{\mathbf{y}}, \hat{\mathbf{z}}$; the link variables are between sites $\mathbf{n}$ and $\mathbf{n} + \mu$ (i.e. link $ij \equiv$ link $\mathbf{n}, \mu$); and the plaquettes p ara defined by the site $\mathbf{n}$ and the normal direction μ (i.e plaquette $p \equiv$ plaquette $\mathbf{n}, \mu$, for example the plaquette $\mathbf{n}, \hat{\mathbf{z}}$ is centered at position $\mathbf{n} + (\hat{\mathbf{x}} + \hat{\mathbf{y}})/2$). The current $I_\mu(\mathbf{n})$ is related to the mesh currents $C_\nu(\mathbf{n})$ and the external current in the y-direction as

$$I_\lambda(\mathbf{n}) = \varepsilon_{\lambda\mu\nu} \Delta_\mu^- C_\nu(\mathbf{n}) + \delta_{\lambda,y} I_{ext} \tag{10}$$

where $\varepsilon_{\lambda\mu\nu}$ is the Levi-Civita tensor, Δ_μ^- is the backward difference operator, $\Delta_\mu^- C_\nu(\mathbf{n}) = C_\nu(\mathbf{n}) - C_\nu(\mathbf{n} - \mu)$, and repeated indices are summed. The magnetic flux $\Phi_\lambda(\mathbf{n})$ and the gauge invariant phases $\theta_\nu(\mathbf{n}) = \Delta_\nu^+ \theta(\mathbf{n}) - A_\nu(\mathbf{n})$ are related as

$$\Phi_\lambda(\mathbf{n}) = -\frac{\Phi_0}{2\pi} \varepsilon_{\lambda\mu\nu} \Delta_\mu^+ \theta_\nu(\mathbf{n}) \tag{11}$$

with the forward difference operator $\Delta_\mu^+ \theta_\nu(\mathbf{n}) = \theta_\nu(\mathbf{n} + \mu) - \theta_\nu(\mathbf{n})$. We therefore obtain the Langevin dynamical equations:

$$\begin{aligned} \frac{\hbar}{2eR} \frac{d\theta_\mu(\mathbf{n})}{dt} &= -\frac{2e}{\hbar} J_\mu(\mathbf{n}) \sin\theta_\mu(\mathbf{n}) - \delta_{\mu,y} I_{ext} \\ &\quad -\frac{\hbar}{2e\mathcal{L}} \Delta_\nu^- \left[\Delta_\nu^+ \theta_\mu(\mathbf{n}) - \Delta_\mu^+ \theta_\nu(\mathbf{n})\right] \\ &\quad -\eta_\mu(\mathbf{n}, t)\,. \end{aligned} \tag{12}$$

We can also obtain these equations in another way, after adding to the Hamiltonian $\mathcal{H}$ the external current term $\sum_\mathbf{n} \frac{\hbar}{2e} I_{ext} \theta_y(\mathbf{n})$,

$$\frac{\hbar}{2eR} \frac{d\theta_\mu(\mathbf{n})}{dt} = -\frac{2e}{\hbar} \frac{\delta \mathcal{H}}{\delta \theta_\mu(\mathbf{n})} - \eta_\mu(\mathbf{n}, t) \tag{13}$$

The system of equations (12) describes the dynamics in the case of finite λ_0 and have been introduced for d-wave granular systems in [13]. When $\lambda_0 = \infty$ (*i.e.*, $\tilde{\mathcal{L}} = 0$) we have that $\Phi_p = \Phi_p^{ext}$ and thus the vector potential is fully determined by the external magnetic field, $A_{ij} = A_{ij}^{ext}$. In this case the dynamical variables are the on-site phases θ_i and the dynamical equations are obtained considering the RSJ model of Eq. (7) together with current conservation condition in each node, $\sum_j I_{ij} = I_i^{ext}$, see for example [41, 42].

In what follows we will consider currents normalized by $I_J = 2eJ/\hbar$, time by $\tau = \phi_0/2\pi I_J R$, voltages by RI_J, inductance by $\phi_0/2\pi I_J$ and temperature by J/k_B. The system of differential equations is typically integrated with a second order stochastic Runge-Kutta algorithm [44].

Paramagnetic Meissner effect

The paramagnetic Meissner effect (PME) has been measured in [15, 16] at very low magnetic fields (~ 0.1 Oe) in ceramic $BiSrCaCuO$ samples. It was found that, while a zero-field cooling (ZFC) measurement shows full flux expulsion, a field cooling (FC) measurement shows a paramagnetic response In many samples the FC low-temperature susceptibility at very low fields is paramagnetic and large and, as the field increases, the susceptibility decreases and becomes diamagnetic for larger fields.

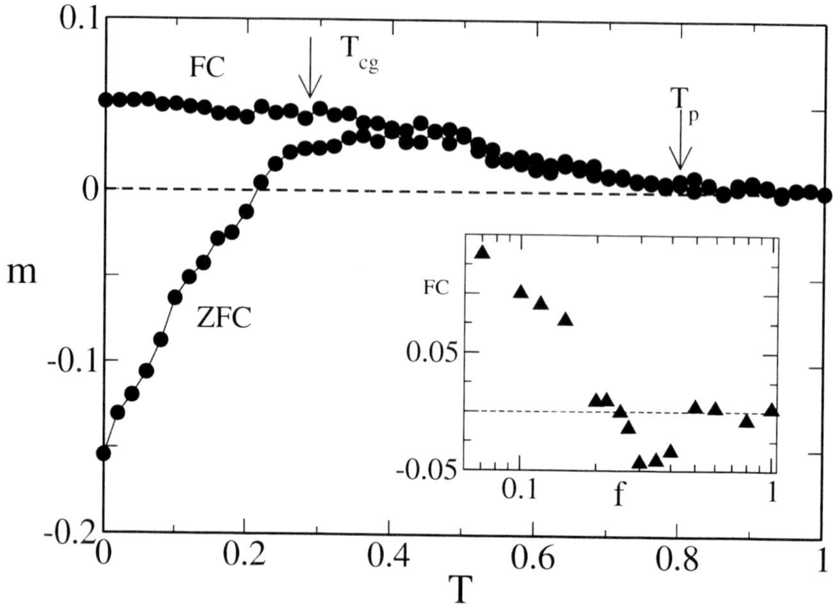

FIG. 5: Temperature dependence of the magnetization m (normalized by $\frac{\Phi_0}{4\pi S}$ for a $8\times8\times8$ network with a concentration of $c = 0.5$ π-junctions and $\tilde{\mathcal{L}} = 1$, averaged over 20 samples. ZFC: zero field cooled curve; FC: field cooled curve. Inset: field cooled dc susceptibility, $\tilde{\chi}_{FC} = m/f = 4\pi\chi$, as a function of magnetic field, $f = HS/\phi_0$, for a $8 \times 8 \times 8$ network with a concentration of $c = 0.3$ π-junctions and $\tilde{\mathcal{L}} = 8$, averaged over 40 samples.

Domínguez, Jagla and Balseiro [13], have been able to reproduce the paramagnetic Meissner effect with the model with π-junctions by means of dynamic simulations using Eq.(12). To simulate a ZFC measurement, the system is started at $T = 0$ in the absence of external field, this state is used as the initial condition to determine the stable state after turning on the external field and then the temperature is increased by steps of δT to high temperatures. To simulate a FC process, the system is started at a high temperature with the magnetic field on and then the temperature is decreased with steps of $-\delta T$ with the field still on. At each temperature the magnetization $M(T, H, c)$ along the z direction is calculated as

$$m = \frac{4\pi MS}{\Phi_0} = \left\langle \frac{1}{N_t} \sum_{\vec{R}} \frac{\Phi_{\hat{z}}(\vec{R},t)}{\Phi_0} \right\rangle - f \ , \qquad (14)$$

where $f = HS/\Phi_0$ is the normalized external field, the network has $N \times N \times N$ grains and $N_t = N(N-1)^2$. We show in Fig. 5 the magnetization obtained in this way at a finite magnetic field $f = HS/\phi_0 = 0.1$ and for $\tilde{\mathcal{L}} = 1$. We show both the zero-field cooling (ZFC) and field cooling (FC) curves. We observe that at a temperature T_p there is an onset of positive magnetization in the FC curve, i.e. the paramagnetic Meissner effect starts to be observed. It should also be noted that above T_p the real part of the linear magnetic susceptibility, obtained in equilibrium MC simulations, also vanishes (see Fig. 18 from [29]).

In [13] it was also found that the FC susceptibility ($\tilde{\chi}_{FC} = m/f = 4\pi\chi$, with $\chi = M/H$) is positive for small fields, it decreases as the field increases, it goes through a diamagnetic minimum and tends to zero at large fields. This behavior is shown in the inset of Fig. 5. This same type of field dependence of χ_{FC} has been observed experimentally (see for example Fig.14 of [16]).

We see in Fig. 5 that the temperature T_p for the onset of the PME is clearly larger than the temperature T_g for the chiral glass transition. The irreversibility point, where the FC and ZFC curves start to differ, is found in the simulations to be dependent on the heating or cooling rate and typically occurs at a temperature T_i such that $T_g \lesssim T_i \ll T_p$. Moreover, the PME is also observed in simulations of two dimensional systems or in three dimensional systems with large inductances ($\tilde{\mathcal{L}} > \tilde{\mathcal{L}}_c$) [13], which are cases where $T_g = 0$.

In principle, one can identify the temperature T_p to correspond to the onset of local chiral short-range order, where there are local magnetic moments in the individual plaquettes that can be polarized by the external magnetic field. In this sense, T_p is the temperature that separates the normal state phase (without local magnetic moments) from a "chiral paramagnet". At lower temperatures collective interactions among the chiral moments will start to be important, leading to the transition to the chiral glass phase at T_g. Even when several dynamical phenomena start to be observable at T_p, as we will see below, it is more likely that T_p corresponds to a temperature for a dynamical crossover rather than a phase transition. Indeed, the paramagnetic Meissner effect can also be obtained with a model consisting on non-interacting loops with π-junctions [23, 45].

Anomalous microwave absorption

The mechanism of the PME based on the presence of π-junctions, due to the *d*-wave symmetry of the order parameter, remains ambiguous, since the paramagnetic response has been seen even in the conventional Nb [46–48], Al [49] superconductors and in arrays of Nb-AlO_x-Nb tunnel junctions [50]. In these cases of conventional superconductivity, the PME can be explained with the idea of the flux compression inside of a sample. Such phenomenon becomes possible either due to inhomogeneities[17] or due to the sample boundary[51]. Thus, the intrinsic mechanisms that can lead to a PME do not restrict to the *d*-wave superconductivity.

In this regard, as mentioned in Introduction, one of the most valuable tools to distinguish between the $s-$ and *d*-wave symmetry of the ceramic samples is the study of the microwave absorption [52]. In fact, Braunisch *et al.* [16] have found a nontrivial field dependence of the MWA in the high-T_c ceramic samples that display the PME. The MWA has a maximum at $H = 0$, when plotted against H, whereas for conventional *s*-wave superconductors it should have a minimum.

In order to study the MWA one has to calculate the linear response to an external electromagnetic field. Using the relation between the MWA and the conductivity (as given by the Kubo formula [53]) one can show that this response is proportional to a voltage – voltage correlation function. Integrating over all of frequencies of the electromagnetic field the following expression for the MWA can be obtained

$$\Omega = \frac{4\pi}{cnRT} \sum_i < V_i^2 > , \qquad (15)$$

where $< V_i^2 >$ is a mean value of the square of the voltage induced by the thermal noise on each junction, n is the light refraction coefficient and R is the normal resistance of the links.

To calculate V_i, one can use the dynamics based on the resistively shunted junction (RSJ) model as given by Eq.(12). In this way, Domínguez, Jagla and Balseiro [54] have qualitatively

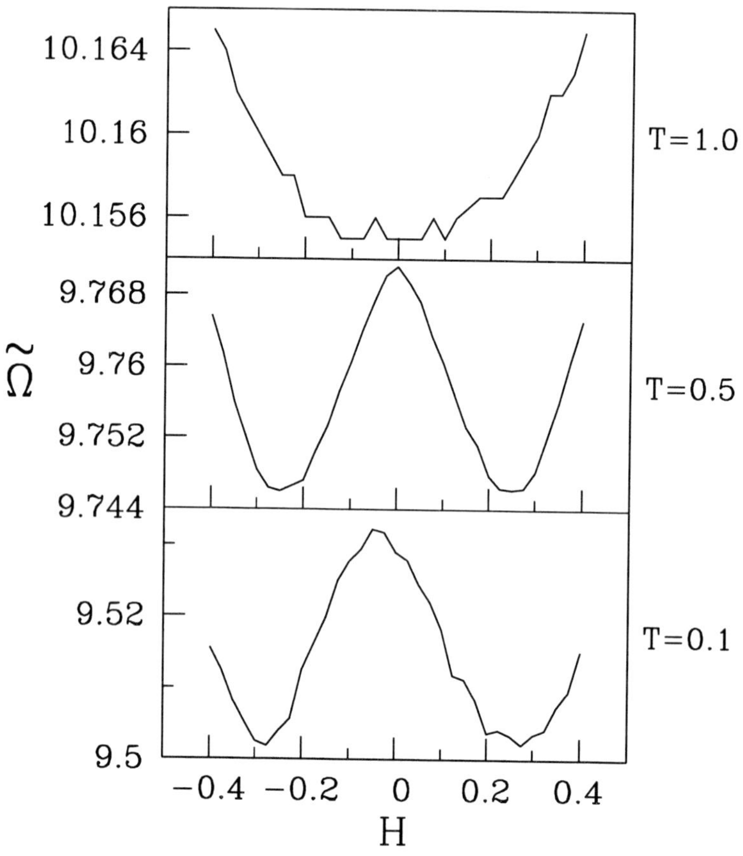

FIG. 6: Magnetic field dependence of the microwave absorption $\tilde{\Omega}$ for the $8 \times 8\times$ networks with $c = 0.5$ π-junctions and $\tilde{\mathcal{L}} = 1$. Temperatures $T = 0.1, 0.5$ and 1. The results are averaged over 10 -20 samples.

reproduced the experimental findings for the MWA, simulating two-dimensional samples. More recently, Li [55] has calculated the MWA in the more realistic case of three dimensional samples and the dependence with temperature and inductance was studied in detail.

In conventional granular superconductors, the microwave absorption as a function of magnetic field H has a minimum at $H = 0$ and grows as H^2. For example, Li in [55] has reproduced this conventional behavior in a model for s-wave granular superconductors consisting on a network of Josephson junctions with random, but all positive, critical currents and dynamics as given by Eq.(12). When a concentration of π junctions with negative critical currents is allowed in the model, an anomalous dependence of the MWA with H is observed. These results of [55] are shown in Fig. 6 where the field dependence of the MWA for $\tilde{\mathcal{L}} = 1$ and various values of temperature T is plotted. At low temperatures there is a maximum in the MWA at $H = 0$. This maximum *disappears at high temperatures*. Qualitatively, above some characteristic temperature, T^*, the extra dissipation effect of the local magnetic moments becomes less important and the d-wave system behaves like the conventional s-wave one. In [55], it has found that this temperature coincides with the onset of the paramagnetic Meissner effect, *i.e.* $T^* = T_p$. Therefore, the anomalous field dependence of the MWA is directly correlated with the occurrence of the PME in *d*-wave granular superconductors. Another observation found in [55] is that the MWA decreases with screening not monotonically but it has a minimum at $\tilde{\mathcal{L}} \approx 1$. Such a behavior was related to a change in time and length scales when one goes from the weak to the strong screening limit.

Linear and nonlinear ac resistance

Yamao *et al.*[35] have measured the ac linear resistivity ρ_0 and the nonlinear resistivity ρ_2 of ceramic superconductor $YBa_2Cu_4O_8$. ρ_2 is defined as the third coefficient of the expansion of the voltage $V(t)$ in terms of the external current I_{ext} as $V = \rho_0 I_{ext} + \rho_2 I_{ext}^3 + \ldots$. When the sample is driven by an ac current $I_{ext}(t) = I_0 \sin(\omega t)$, one can obtain ρ_2 from

$$\rho_2 = -\frac{4V'_{3\omega}}{I_0^3}\ , \quad V'_{3\omega} = \frac{1}{2\pi}\int_{-\pi}^{\pi} V(t)\sin(3\omega t) d(\omega t)\ . \tag{16}$$

Yamao *et al.* have found that ρ_0 is finite for any temperature and decreases monotonically with T, while ρ_2 has a maximum value at a temperature T^* near the intergrain ordering temperature of their sample. They also observed that the maximum of $\rho_2(T)$ depends with the ac amplitude I_0 as $\rho_2(T_p) \sim I_0^{-\alpha}$, with $\alpha \approx 1.1$.

Recently, Li and Domínguez [56] and Li, Zung and Domínguez [57] have calculated the linear and nonlinear ac resistivity using the model dynamics of Eq.(12) with finite screening ($\tilde{\mathcal{L}} > 0$). It was found in [56] that the linear resistivity $\rho_0 = V'_\omega / I_0$, for small enough I_0, is nonzero for all temperatures $T > 0$. This in agreement with the result that the breaking of U(1) symmetry is not correlated with the chiral glass transition [14, 28, 29], and therefore there is no need of superconductivity for any finite T. However, we note that Granato [58] has found a transition to a low temperature phase with zero linear resistivity, but in the dynamical model without screening ($\tilde{\mathcal{L}} = 0$) in three dimensions (see, however, also Ref. [32]). This may not be in contradiction with the results of [56] since a similar situation is observed in the gauge glass model where a superconducting transition is found in the model without screening, but it disappears when the magnetic screening is taken into account [59].

The temperature dependence of the *nonlinear* resistivity ρ_2 for different values of I_0 was studied in [56, 57]. In Fig. 7 the results for $\tilde{\mathcal{L}} = 1$ and $\omega = 0.001$ are shown. We see that $\rho_2(T)$ has a peak at a finite temperature. In [56] it was found that the position of the peak coincides with the temperature T_p for the onset of the PME. The maximum value of ρ_2 at T_p tends to diverge when I_0 decreases. The dependence of $\rho_2(T_p)$ with I_0 has been studied in [56, 57] for different values of $\tilde{\mathcal{L}}$, and it is shown in Fig. 7(b). Two different regimes of power law behavior for small and large currents [57] have been found. In the weak current regime (WCR), for $I_0 \leq 0.1$, it is possible to fit a dependence $\rho_2(T_p) \sim I_0^{-\alpha}$. A value of $\alpha = 0.5 \pm 0.1$ is obtained independently of the value of $\tilde{\mathcal{L}}$. In the strong current regime (SCR) one can also try to fit an exponent α_{SCR}. However, the value of α in this regime depends strongly on $\tilde{\mathcal{L}}$. For $1 < \tilde{\mathcal{L}} < 5$ one obtains $\alpha_{SCR} \approx 1$ in coincidence with the experiment of Yamao *et al.*. Since real current is $I = \frac{2eJ}{\hbar} I_0$, and $J \sim 10^2$ K, then for $I_0 \sim 0.1$ we have $I \sim 10^{-2}$ mA. The experiments of [35] used a current $I \sim 10$ mA. This suggests that they were performed in the SCR. This interval of inductance is realistic for some ceramics [60] where typical values of $\tilde{\mathcal{L}}$ are bigger than 3. An accurate comparison between theory and experiments requires, however, the knowledge of $\tilde{\mathcal{L}}$ which is not known for the compound of $YBa_2Cu_4O_8$ studied in [35].

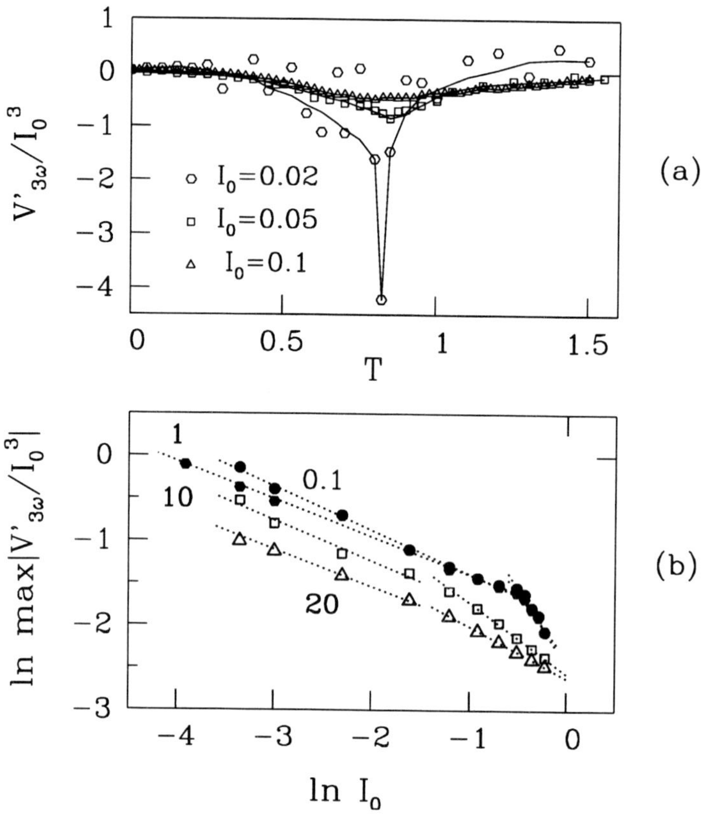

FIG. 7: (a) Temperature dependence of the nonlinear resistivity $\rho_2 \propto V'_{3\omega}/I_0^3$ for $\tilde{\mathcal{L}} = 1$, $\omega = 0.001$ and $8 \times 8 \times 8$ samples. (b) The current dependence of $max|V'_{3\omega}/I_0^3|$ for system sizes $8 \times 8 \times 8$, $\omega = 0.001$ and $\tilde{\mathcal{L}}$= 0.1, 1, 10 and 20 (the values of $\tilde{\mathcal{L}}$ are shown next to the curves).

It is tempting to interpret the two regimes for α as the WCR corresponding to the critical regime for $\rho_2(T_c, I_0)$ (since $I_0 \to 0$) and the SCR corresponding to a mean-field regime (away from criticality). If there is a continuous phase transition at a critical temperature $T_c = T_p$, then current-voltage scaling [26] predicts that $V \sim I^{\frac{z+1}{d-1}}$ at T_c, with z the dynamical exponent. Therefore, the non-linear resistivity should be $\rho_2(T_c) \sim I_0^{\frac{z+1}{d-1}-3}$, and thus the expected WCR value is $\alpha = (5-z)/2$ in $d = 3$. This predicts that a peak in $\rho_2(T)$ at T_c is possible if $z < 5$ (i.e. $\alpha > 0$). However, in the simulations of [56] T_p is the temperature where there is an onset of positive magnetization, i.e. the paramagnetic Meissner effect starts to be observed, but it does not seem to correspond to a phase transition. The chiral glass phase transition temperature T_{cg} is at a lower temperature, $T_{cg} < T_p$. Kawamura [30] has found $z = 6.3 \pm 1.7$ for the chiral-glass transition based on the Metropolis dynamics in the phase representation. Since this value of z is likely to exceed 5, no divergent peak in $\rho_2(T)$ might be expected at the chiral-glass transition according to the scaling argument, although in view of the quoted error bar and also of the fact that the dynamical universality class often depends on the details of the dynamics, it should be taken with some care. Therefore, the peak measured by Yamao *et. al.* may not correspond to the chiral glass transition, but to the crossover found at the temperature for the onset of the paramagnetic Meissner effect.

Electric field effect

Several experiments in ceramic high-T_c superconductors find an *enhancement* in the critical current when applying an electric field E through an insulating layer [18, 61–63]. Studies of the electric field effects (EFE) in superconducting films also find changes in the critical current, which are attributed to variations in the charge density or to a redistribution of carriers. In this case, this affects the surface layer with depths of the order of the electrostatic screening length d_E (in HTCS, $d_E \approx 5\,\AA$) [64]. For example, experiments in ultrathin $YBa_2Cu_3O_{7-x}$ films ($5 - 10$ nm thick) have found that E can affect T_c and the IV characteristics [65], in good agreement with this picture [64]. In this case, there is either an enhancement or a depletion of the critical current depending on the polarity of E [65]. However, in *bulk* ceramic HTCS (1.5 mm thick) the strong EFE observed in [18, 61–63] can not be explained by a surface phenomenon. Moreover, for high enough electric fields, the critical current *always increases* regardless of the polarity of the field [62].

Dominguez, Wiecko and Jose [19] have shown that the presence of π-junctions in ceramic samples can explain these unusual electric field effects observed in [18, 61–63]. They have considered the resistively shunted junction model given by Eq.(7), in the case $\lambda_0 = \infty$ (*i.e.*, $\tilde{\mathcal{L}} = 0$), with a random concentration $c = 0.5$ of π-junctions. An external electric field $\mathbf{E}$ is applied in the $\hat{z}$ direction, and therefore the z component of the vector potential is given by:

$$A_z(\mathbf{n}, t) = A_z(\mathbf{n}, 0) - \frac{2\pi c d}{\Phi_0} E t, \tag{17}$$

with d the intergrain distance or junction thickness. This results in a high-frequency alternating supercurrent in the z-direction due to the ac Josephson effect [66]. In addition, the sample is driven by an external current density I_{ext} along the $\hat{y}$ direction.

The applied electric field is assumed to be screened inside the grains and acting only in the insulating intergrain region of the junctions, of typical thickness $d \sim 10 - 20\AA$. The effects of intergrain capacitance C_i and intragrain capacitance C_g were neglected. In general, the effect of the capacitances is to screen the applied field E_{ext} inside the sample within an overall screening length $\lambda_E \sim (C_i/C_g)^{1/2}$. Since $C_g \ll C_i$, λ_E is very large, one can consider that the internal field acting in the intergrain junctions is $E_{in} = E \approx \alpha_p E_{ext}$ with the polarizability $\alpha_p \lesssim 1$.

After all these physical approximations, the dynamical model considered in [19] focus on the *collective* aspects of the ac Josephson effect induced by the electric field. In this case, the electric field scale is given by $E_0 = RI_0(T = 0)/d = \pi\Delta_s(0)/2ed$, with $\Delta_s(0)$ the superconducting energy gap; for the YBaCu0 ceramics one has $\Delta_s(0) \approx 20meV$, which gives $E_0 \sim 30MV/m$, i.e. in the same range as the fields used in [18, 61–63].

In the absence of disorder, the IV curves are unaffected by the electric field. In a perfect cubic network, a finite electric field induces an ac supercurrent $I_0 \sin(\omega_E t)$ along the z axis only, and therefore the IV curves in the xy plane are not affected by the value of E. Dominguez, Wiecko and Jose considered first the case of s-wave granular superconductors, with random and positive values of the Josephson critical currents. In this case, when there is small disorder, the amplitude of the ac supercurrents in the z direction is random and, due to current conservation in each node of the network, this induces small ac-currents in the xy planes with random amplitudes $\sim \Delta_c I_0 \sin(\omega_E t)$. Adding a small ac current to a Josephson

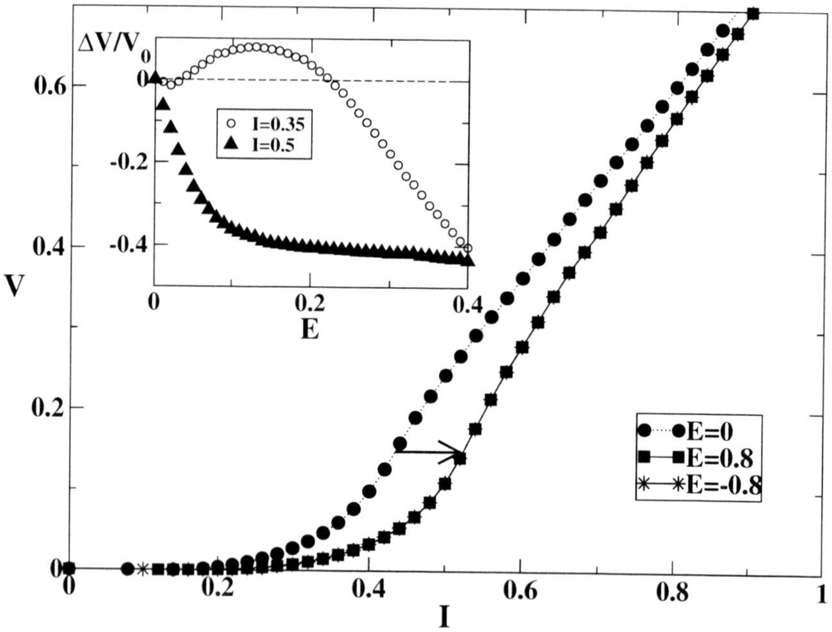

FIG. 8: Current-voltage characteristics before and after applying an electric field $E = \pm 0.8$, for a granular d-wave superconductor with concentration $c = 0.5$ of π-junctions. Voltages are normalized by NRI_J and currents by $N^2 I_J$ and lattice sizes are $16 \times 16 \times 16$ ($N = 16$). Inset:Change in voltage, $\Delta V/V_0 = (V(E) - V(0))/V(0)$, as a function of E for different driving currents.

junction *reduces* its effective dc critical current [66]. In fact, a decrease of the critical current with the electric field was observed in [19] in the case of random s-wave networks. However, this is in the opposite direction of the experimental results of [18, 61–63], where an *increase* in the critical current was observed.

The case of a granular d-wave superconductor turns out to be different. The presence of randomly distributed negative and positive critical currents changes the previous simplistic picture, since now frustration is introduced in each loop containing an odd number of π-junctions [8, 13]. For example, Marconi *et al.* [67] have found recently that Josephson junction arrays with frustration can show an increase in their critical currents when a transverse ac current is applied. In Fig. 8 we show the IV curve obtained in [19] when there is a concentration $c = 0.5$ of π-junctions. We note that after applying the electric field the IV curve is shifted towards higher currents, i.e. the "apparent" critical current *increases.* If one changes $E \to -E$ the IV curves overlap showing that the effect is independent of the polarity of the electric field. A similar effect was seen in the experiments of [62]: the IV curves shift upwards for large E and almost overlap when changing the polarity of the field. This result is surprising since in the usual electric field effect observed in films a change in the polarity of the field drastically changes the sign of the shift of the IV curves [65].

In the inset of Fig. 8 the relative change in voltage $\Delta V/V(0)$ for a fixed bias current (above the critical current) as a function of E is shown. One can see that for a large bias current, there is a decrease in the voltage, i.e. $\Delta V < 0$, which is a consequence of the increase in the critical current. There are other interesting aspects that are similar to the experimental results. In the experiments, a typical measurement shows that, when applying a current near the critical current, $\Delta V/V_0$ increases as a function of E and, after reaching a maximum, it falls and then becomes negative for large enough fields. The simulations of [19] also reproduce this effect for intermediate currents, in good agreement with experiment, as it is shown in the inset of Fig. 8. This later result is shown in [19] to correspond to the fact that for low electric fields E there is a crossing of the IV curves.

The work of [19] have qualitatively explained all the experimental features of the electric field effect observed in [18, 61–63] with a model of a granular superconductor, which includes: (a) the collective frustration effects due to π-junctions and (b) the ac Josephson effect induced by the electric field. However, it remains open the question if the electric field effect exists for the same temperatures and inductance values of the paramagnetic Meissner effect and its relationship with the chiral glass phase.

CONCLUSIONS

From the Monte Carlo simulations one can expect the existence of the chiral glass phase in the *d*-wave superconductors. Contrary to the vortex glass, this phase occurs at zero external magnetic field and it is stable against the screening. One should emphasize that the nature of the strongly disordered chiral glass is very different from the Bragg glass which is observable only in a system with slightly distorted periodicity [68]. Since the existing experiments do not give an unambiguous evidence for existence of the chiral glass phase in high-T_c materials, much more work in this direction is left for future studies. In frustrated magnets with the chiral degrees of freedom, there are several recent attempts and proposals to directly probe the chirality [69, 70]. In superconductors, the chirality is directly observable by detecting the spontaneous loop-supercurrent or the associated spontaneous flux in zero external field. This might be achieved by means of, *e.g.*, polarized neutrons.

We have explored the role of the pairing symmetry on dynamical phenomena such as the PME, MWA, the enhancement of critical current by the external electric field and the ac resistivity in ceramic materials. All of these effects are adequately described by the XY-like Hamiltonian (1). From both the theoretical and experimental points of views it would be interesting to see if the flux compression mechanism can give rise to the anomalous MWA and the enhancement of critical current by an electric field.

ACKNOWLEDGEMENTS

We acknowledge E. Jagla, C. Balseiro, J. V. José, C. Wiecko and H. Zung for very fruitful collaborations in this subject. This work has been supported by Conicet, CNEA, Fundacion Antorchas and ANPCYT and the NATO grant PST.CLG.979446.

[1] J. Bardeen, L. N. Cooper and J. R. Schrieffer, Theory of superconductivity, *Phys. Rev.* 108 (1957) 1175-1204

[2] W. H. Hardy, D. A. Bonn, D. C. Morgan, R. Liang, and K. Zhang, *Phys. Rev. Lett.* **70**, 3999 (1993).

[3] K. Moler, D. J. Baar, J. S. Urbach, R. Liang, W. N. Hardy, and A. Kapitulnik, *Phys. Rev. Lett.* **73**, 2744 (1994)
[4] Z.-X. Shen *et al*, *Phys. Rev. Lett.* **70**, 1553 (1993).
[5] D. J. Van Harlingen, *Rev. Mod. Phys.* **67**, 515 (1995).
[6] C. C. Tsuei and J. R. Kirtley, *Rev. Mod. Phys.* **72**, 969 (2000).
[7] J. F. Annett, *Adv. Phys.* **39**, 83 (1991).
[8] M. Sigrist and T.M. Rice, *J. Phys. Soc. Jpn.* **61** (1992) 4283; *Rev. Mod. Phys.* **67** (1995) 503.
[9] I. O. Kulik, *Zh. Eksp. Teor. Fiz.* 65 (1965) 1211-1214.
[10] L. N. Bulaevskii, V. V. Kuzii and A. A. Sobyanin, *Pis'ma Eksp. Theor. Fiz.* 25 (1977) 314-318 (*JETP lett.* 25 (1977) 290).
[11] C. Ebner and D. Stroud, *Phys. Rev. B* 31 (1995) 165-171.
[12] S. John and T. C. Lubensky, *Phys. Rev. B* 34 (1986) 4815-4825.
[13] D. Domínguez, E.A. Jagla and C.A. Balseiro, *Phys. Rev. Lett.* **72** (1994) 2773.
[14] H. Kawamura and M.S. Li, *Phys. Rev. Lett.* **78**, 1556 (1997).
[15] P. Svedlindh, K. Niskanen, P. Nordblad, L. Lundgren, B. Lönnberg and T. Lundström, *Physica* **C162-164** (1989) 1365.
[16] W. Braunisch, N. Knauf, V. Kataev, S. Neuhausen, A. Grütz, A. Kock, B. Boden, D. Khomskii, and D. Wohlleben, *Phys. Rev. Lett.* **68**, 1908 (1992); W. Braunisch, N. Knauf, G. Bauer, A. Kock, A. Becker, B. Freitag, A. Grütz, V. Kataev, S. Neuhausen, B. Boden, D. Khomskii, D. Wohlleben, J. Bock and E. Preisler, *Phys. Rev.* **B48** (1993) 4030.
[17] A. E. Koshelev and A. I. Larkin, Phys. Rev. B **52**, 13559 (1995); A. E. Khalil, *Phys. Rev. B* **55**, 6625 (1997).
[18] B.I. Smirnov, S.V. Krishtopov and T.S. Orlova, *Phys. Solid State* **34**, 1331 (1992).
[19] D. Domínguez, C. Wiecko and J. V. José, *Phys. Rev. Lett.* **83**, 4164 (1999).
[20] H. Kawamura, *J. Phys. Soc. Jpn.* **64** (1995) 711.
[21] M. Matsuura, M. Kawachi, K. Miyoshi, M. Hagiwara and K. Koyama, *J. Phys. Soc. Jpn.* **64** (1995) 4540.
[22] F.V. Kusmartsev, *Phys. Rev. Lett.* **69** (1992) 2268; *J. of Superconductivity* **5** (1992) 463.
[23] J. Magnusson, J.-O. Andersson, M. Björnander, P. Nordblad and P. Svedlindh, *Phys. Rev.* **B51** (1995) 12776; J. Magnusson, M. Björnander, L. Pust, P. Svedlindh, P. Nordblad and T. Lundström, *Phys. Rev.* **B52** (1995) 7675.
[24] H. Kawamura and M. Tanemura: *J. Phys. Soc. Jpn.* **60**, 608 (1991); H. Kawamura, *Phys. Rev. Lett.* **62**, 3785 (1992); H. Kawamura, *Phys. Rev. B* **51**, 12398 (1995).
[25] M.P.A. Fisher, *Phys. Rev. Lett.* **62**, 1415 (1989)
[26] D.S. Fisher, M.P.A. Fisher and D.A. Huse, *Phys. Rev. B* **43**, 130 (1991).
[27] H. Kawamura, *J. Phys. Soc. Jpn.* **69**, 29 (2000).
[28] H. Kawamura and M.S. Li, *J. Phys. Soc. Jpn.* **66**, 2110 (1997).
[29] H. Kawamura and M.S. Li, *Phys. Rev.* **B54** (1996) 619.
[30] H. Kawamura, *J. Phys. Soc. Jpn. Suppl. A* **69**, 281 (2000).
[31] K. Hukushima and K. Nemoto, *J. Phys. Soc. Jpn.* **65** 1604 (1995).
[32] H. Kawamura and M. S. *Li, Phys. Rev. Lett.* **87**, 187204 (2001).
[33] L. Leylekian, M. Ocio and J. Hammann, *Physica C* **185-189** (1991) 2243; *Physica B* **194-196** (1991) 1865.
[34] H. Deguchi, M. Yasunaka, R. Oniki, S. Takagi and K. Koyama, *Physica C* **388-389**, 269 (2003).
[35] T. Yamao, M. Hagiwara, K. Koyama and M. Matsuura, *J. Phys. Soc. Jpn.* **68**, 871 (1999).
[36] E.L. Papadopoulou P. Svedlindh and P. Nordblad, *Phys. Rev. B* **65**, 144524 (2002); *Physica C* **341-348**, 1379 (2000).
[37] E.L. Papadopoulou, P. Nordblad, P. Svedlindh, R. Schöneberger and R, Gross, *Phys. Rev. Lett.* **82**, 173 (1999);
[38] A. Gardchareon, R. Mathieu, P.E. Jönsson and P. Nordblad, *Phys. Rev. B* **67**, 052505 (2003); E.L. Papadopoulou and P. Nordblad, *Eur. Phys. J. B* **22**, 187 (2001).
[39] For reviews, see, *e.g.*, E. Vincent, J. Hammann, M. Ocio, J-P. Bouchaud and L.F. Cugliandolo, Sitges Conference on Glassy Systems, 1996 (Springer) cond-mat/9607224; J.-P. Bouchaud, L.F. Cugliandolo, J. Kurchan and M. Mezard, in *Spin Glasses and Random Fields* ed. by A.P. Young, 1998 (World Scientific), p.161; P. Nordblad and P. Svedlindh, *ibid*, p.1.

[40] M.S. Li, P. Nordblad and H. Kawamura, *Phys. Rev. Lett.* **86**, 1339 (2001).
[41] J. S. Chung, K. H. Lee, and D. Stroud, *Phys. Rev. B* **40**, 6570 (1989)
[42] D. Domínguez, J. V. José, A. Karma and C. Wiecko, *Phys. Rev. Lett.* (1991) **67**, 2367; D. Domínguez, *Phys. Rev. Lett.* **82**, 181 (1999); V. I. Marconi and D. Domínguez, *Phys. Rev. B* **63**, 174509 (2001).
[43] D. Domínguez and J. V. José, *Phys. Rev. Lett.* **69**, 514 (1992); D. Domínguez and J. V. José, *Phys. Rev. B.* **53**, 11692 (1996).
[44] H. S. Greenside and E. Helfand, *Bell. Syst. Tech. J.* **60**, 1927 (1981).
[45] M. Sigrist and T.M. Rice, *J. Low Temp. Phys.* **40**, 389 (1994).
[46] D. J. Thompson, M. S. M. Minhaj, L. E. Wegner, and J. T. Chen, *Phys. Rev. Lett.* **75**, 529 (1995).
[47] P. Kostic, B. Veal, A. P. Paulikas, U. Welp, V. R. Todt, C. Gu, U. Geiser, J. M. Williams, K. D. Carlson, and R. A. Klemm, *Phys. Rev. B* **53**, 791 (1996); **55**, 14649 (1997).
[48] L. Pust, L. E. Wegner, and M. R. Koblischka, *Phys. Rev. B* **58**, 14191 (1998).
[49] A. K. Geim, S. V. Dubonos, J. G. S. Lok, M. Henini, and J. C. Maan, *Nature* **396**, 144 (1998).
[50] F. M. Araujo-Moreira, P. Barbara, A. B. Cawthorne, and C. J. Lobb, *Phys. Rev. Lett.* **78**, 4625 (1997); P. Barbara, F. M. Araujo-Moreira, A. B. Cawthorne, and C. J. Lobb, *Phys. Rev. B* **60**, 7489 (1999).
[51] V. V. Moshchalkov, X. G. Qui, and V. Bruyndoncz, *Phys. Rev. B* **55**, 11793 (1997).
[52] M. Sigrist, *Nature* **396**, 110 (1998).
[53] R. Kubo, M. Toda, and N. Hashitsume, *Statistical Physics II, Springer Series in Solid-State Sciences*, Eds: M. Cardona, P. Fulde and H.-J. Queisser, Springer-Verlag Berlin Heidelberg (1985).
[54] D. Domínguez, E. A. Jagla, and C. A. Balseiro, *Physica* (Amsterdam) **235C - 240C**, 3283 (1994).
[55] M. S. Li, *Phys. Rev. B* **64**, 144501 (2001).
[56] M. S. Li and D. Dominguez, *Phys. Rev. B* **62**, 14554 (2000).
[57] M. S. Li, H. Zung and D. Dominguez, *Phys. Rev. Lett.* **88**, 257004 (2002).
[58] E. Granato, *Phys. Rev. B* **58**, 11161(1998); E. Granato *J. Magn. Magn. Matter.* **226**, 366 (2001) and cond-mat/0012238.
[59] H. S. Bokil and A. P. Young, *Phys. Rev. Lett.* **74**, 3021 (1995).
[60] R. Marcon, R. Fastampa, M. Giura, and C. Matacotta, *Phys. Rev.* **39**, 2796 (1989).
[61] B.I. Smirnov, T.S.Orlova and S.V. Krishtopov, *Phys. Solid State* **35**, 1118 (1993).
[62] T.S. Orlova and B.I. Smirnov, *Supercond. Sci. Techn.* **7**, 899 (1994); B. I. Smirnov, T. S. Orlova and N. Kudymov, *Phys. Solid State* **36**, 837 (1994).
[63] B. I. Smirnov and T. S. Orlova, *Phys. Solid State* **36**, 1883 (1994); T.S. Orlova *et al*, *Physica C* **253**, 194 (1995); B. I. Smirnov *et al.*, *Phys. Solid State* **37**, 977 (1995); **38**, 1603 (1996); **39**, 1759 (1997); T. S. Orlova, B. I. Smirnov and J. Y. Laval, *Phys. Solid State* **40**, 1088 (1998); T. S. Orlova *et al.*, *Supercond. Sci. Techn.* **12**, 356 (1999).
[64] J. Mannhart, *Mod. Phys. Lett.* **6**, 555 (1992) and *Supercond. Sci. Techn.* **9**, 49 (1996); V. V. Lemanov and A. L. Kholkin, *Phys. Solid State* **36**, 841 (1994).
[65] J. Mannhart et al., *Phys. Rev. Lett.* **67**, 2099 (1991); X. X. Xi et al. *ibid* **68**, 1240 (1992).
[66] A. Barone and G. Paterno, *Physics and Applications of the Josephson Effect* (Wiley, New York, 1982).
[67] V. I. Marconi, A. B. Kolton, D. Domínguez, N. Grønbech-Jensen, *Phys. Rev. B* **68**, 104521 (2003).
[68] T. Nattermann and S. Scheidl, *Adv. Phys.* **49**, 607 (2000).
[69] V.P. Plakhty, J. Kulda, D. Visser, E.V. Moskvin and J. Wosnitza, *Phys. Rev. Lett.* 85, 3942 (2000).
[70] H. Kawamura, *Phys. Rev. Lett.* 90, 047202 (2003).

Pairing Symmetry of the Superconducting Gap Analyzed by Means of Measurement for Inhomogeneous High-T_c Superconductors

Hyun-Tak Kim*
Telecom. Basic Research Lab., ETRI, Taejon 305-350, Korea

Abstract

In order to analyze pairing symmetry of an intrinsic superconducting true gap for inhomogeneous high-T_c superconductors, we explain the intrinsic inhomogeneity of high-T_c superconductors on the basis of the metal-insulator instability and the extended Brinkman-Rice picture explaining the first-order metal-insulator transition, and justify a relation between a fractional effective charge and band filling ($e' = \rho e$; $0< \rho \leq 1$ is band filling) by means of measurement. An observed superconducting gap is given as a function of band-filling and intrinsic true gap ($\triangle_{obs}=\frac{\triangle_i}{\rho}$) and is the effect of measurement when $0< \rho <1$. The true gap is observed only when $\rho=1$. The peak width of conductance curve as the density of states determines pairing symmetry. The identity of the observed superconducting gap anisotropy for $Bi_2Sr_2CaCu_2O_8+x$ (Bi-2212)is also revealed that the gap anisotropy is attributed to inhomogeneity of a d-wave insulating phase and a metal phase in the measurement region and is not evidence of the d-wave symmetry. The Ambegaokar-Baratoff (AB) theory based on the BCS theory is extended. Small I_cR_n values observed by experiments are explained by the extended AB theory. The magnitude of the true gap deduced from I_cR_n values for Bi-2212 is $8.5< \triangle_i <17$ meV. In addition, the half-flux quantum ($\Phi_0/2$) as evidence of the d-wave symmetry observed by the triple-π-junction experiments, is caused by flux trap. Comments on a flux trap of the magnetic modulation experiment using Pb-YBCO dc SQUIDs are also given on the ground of experimental results for the observation of paramagnetic Meissner effect of $Ba_{0.6}K_{0.4}BiO_3$. Recent researches on tunnel effect as well as proximity effect are discussed by means of measurement. Finally, it is concluded that an analyzed pairing symmetry is s-wave.

1 Introduction

Since the discovery of cuprate high-T_c superconductors, pairing symmetry of superconducting gaps has been controversial for the mechanism of high-T_c supercon-

*htkim@etri.re.kr, kimht45@hotmail.com

ductivity, until recently. Many experimental data have been obtained for the problem. Many researchers have believed that pairing symmetry of high-T_c superconductors is $d_{x^2-y^2}$-wave, which is based on following observations of anisotropic superconducting gaps [1−5] by angle resolved photoemission spectroscopy (ARPES), the half-flux quantum as evidence of Josephson-π junction [6] by using Pb-$YBa_2Cu_3O_7$(YBCO) dc SQUID [7, 8] and frustrated YBCO films deposited on tricrystal substrates [9−11], the zero-bias conductance peak [12, 13], the B_{1g} peak in Raman scattering [14], the V shape near zero-bias voltage of the tunnelling conductance [15], the angle dependence of the Josephson current [16], and the linear temperature dependence of the penetration depth [17]. These have been observed in underdoped crystals and frustrated films.

However, some researchers have also suggested evidence of the s-wave symmetry in high quality crystals and overdoped crystals. The evidences are U-type tunnelling conductances observed by atomic site tunnelling spectroscopy for YBCO and $Bi_2Sr_2CaCu_2O_{8+x}$ (Bi-2212) single crystals [18], the absence of angle dependence of the Josephson current [19], observations of flux trap for s-wave superconductors [20 − 23], the absence of the zero-bias conductance peak in overdoped crystals [24, 25], the independent temperature dependence of the penetration depth at low temperatures [26, 27], integer Sapiro-steps [28], small I_cR_n values [29, 30]. Two opposite results arise from a quality of crystals.

Generally, it has been known that high-T_c superconductors are intrinsically inhomogeneous. The fact that the homogeneous superconducting region is within 14$\mathring{A}$ [31] or 30$\mathring{A}$ [32 − 34] was revealed by scanning tunnelling microscopy (STM). In particular, Lang *et al.* [34] showed that underdoped crystals are much more inhomogeneous than overdoped crystals and have multi-phases greater than two phases. Kim *et al.* [35] observed satellite peaks for a $Ba_{0.6}K_{0.4}BiO_3$ (BKBO) superconductor, using neutron powder diffraction. The temperature dependence of the peaks follows that of $BaBiO_3$ which is the parent material of BKBO superconductors. Chainani *et al.* [36] also found a suppression in intensity up to 70 meV binding energy which corresponds to the highest phonon energy and is associated with the breathing mode phonon energy (570cm^{-1} ≈70meV) of $BaBiO_3$, using angle-resolved photoemission spectroscopy. Kim *et al.* [37] also measured the temperature dependence of Bi-O bond lengths in a high quality $Ba_{0.6}K_{0.4}BiO_3$ single crystal. The magnitude of the bond length is the same as that of $BaBiO_3$ and independent of temperature. The observations for BKBO indicate that the BKBO crystals are inhomogeneous without the proximity effect. Krasnov *et al.* [38] and Miyakawa *et al.* [39] revealed coexistence of the superconducting gap and the pseudo-gap for high-T_c superconductors. Bozovic *et al.* [40] asserted that superconductivity and anti-ferromagnetism do not mix on the basis of observations of the resistibility and the Meissner effect for stacking layers of $La_{1.85}Sr_{0.15}CuO_4$ and La_2CuO_4 superlattices. Thus, we indicate that there is no the proximity effect for inhomogeneous high-T_c superconductors, although a research [41] suggested anti-ferromagnetic and superconducting proximity effects in YBCO/PBCO superlattices.

For the intrinsic inhomogeneity, the cause of multi-phases can be theoretically explained by the metal-insulator instability [42] of the charge-density-wave potential energy and the divergence [43, 44] near the Mott metal-insulator transition. Furthermore, for the inhomogeneous superconductors, the band filling dependence of both the 2-dimensional density of states [44] and a superconducting gap [45] were revealed by introducing the fractional charge justified by means of measurement.

Even though many experimental data have explained and shown pairing symmetry on the mechanism of high-T_c superconductivity, many researchers have believed that the pairing symmetry is not clear. The unclear reason is due to the absence of understanding of the inhomogeneous system.

In this paper, we justify inhomogeneity and analyze pairing symmetry of superconducting gaps for inhomogeneous high-T_c superconductors, using means of measurement. In particular, gap-anisotropy data observed by ARPES and flux trap to observations of half-flux quantum are deeply analyzed, and the BCS density of states (DOS) and the Ambegaokar-Baratoff theory are extended. Small I_cR_n values observed by experiments are explained. Justification of the s-wave symmetry is naturally deduced from analysis of experimental data. An experimental evidence of the Mott transition is also shown. Moreover, recent researches are also analyzed by means of measurement.

2 Inhomogeneity

2.1 Metal-insulator instability

In order to justify the microscopic inhomogeneity [31 − 34] for high-T$_c$ superconductors, the metal-insulator instability [42] and the divergence [43, 44] near on-site Coulomb energy U/U_c=1 need to be introduced. First, we start from the charge-density-wave (CDW) theory of $BaBiO_3$, which is known as a charge-density-wave insulator and a parent material of a superconductor $Ba_{0.6}K_{0.4}BiO_3$. Band structure calculations of $BaBiO_3$ have indicated that $BaBiO_3$ is a metal with a half-filled band, but it is in fact a semiconductor with a CDW energy gap of 2 eV. The CDW theories have proposed that $Bi^3(6s^2)$ and $Bi^5(6s^0)$ valences occupy alternative sites due to the breathing-mode distortion.

We introduce a CDW theory in which $Bi^{3+\alpha'}$ and $Bi^{5-\beta'}$ valences are placed on alternate nearest-neighbor sites in $BaBiO_3$, where the $\alpha'(=2\alpha)$ and $\beta'(-2\beta)$ are called hole and electron doping factors (i.e., band-filling factors), respectively [42]. We assume that the carriers in the half-filled band revealed by the band calculation are bound by a local CDW potential energy. The difference in charge between the set $Bi^{3+\alpha'}$ and $Bi^{5-\beta'}$ and the set Bi^3 and Bi^5 results in the production of carriers. Further, the difference in electron or hole charge between $Bi^{3+\alpha'}$ and $Bi^{5-\beta'}$ is associated with charge disproportionation, producing the CDW gap. The

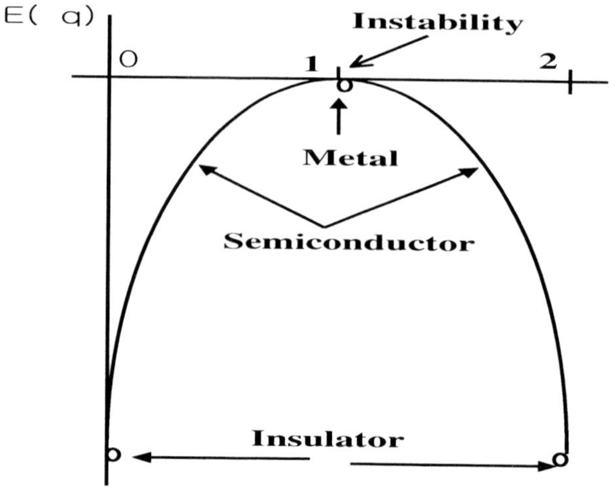

Figure 1: Relation of the CDW-potential energy $E(\delta q)$ vs band filling ρ=α+β.

CDW-potential energy can be obtained from the attractive potential energy of Rice and Sneddon [46] and Kim [42]:

$$
\begin{aligned}
E(\delta q) &= -(g^2/2c)(q_i - q_j)^2, && (1)\\
&= -(2(eg)^2/c)[1-(\alpha+\beta)]^2, && (2)\\
&= -(2(eg)^2/c)[1-\rho]^2, && (3)
\end{aligned}
$$

where c and g are constants used in the Rice-Sneddon theory, q_i=e[1-(1-α)($n_{\uparrow_i}$+$n_{\downarrow_i}$)] and q_j=e[1-β($n_{\uparrow_j}$+$n_{\downarrow_j}$)] subject to the constraints $n_{\uparrow_i}$+$n_{\downarrow_i}$=2, $n_{\uparrow_j}$+$n_{\downarrow_j}$=2 and 0$\leq$ $(\alpha+\beta)$ $\leq$2, ρ=α+β is band filling, and δq=$q_i - q_j$. e is the elementary charge.

Eq. (3) is sketched in Fig. 1, which has the following interpretation. In the case of α+β=0 or α+β=2, the CDW potential energy $E(\delta q)$ becomes the Rice-Sneddon potential energy and a material is an insulator with a CDW energy gap. In the case of 0< $(\alpha+\beta)$ <1 or 1< $(\alpha+\beta)$ <2, the potential energy has an arbitrary value larger than -(2$(eg)^2/c$) and a material becomes a semiconductor with charge disproportionation. In the case of α+β=1 and either $\alpha\neq$0 or $\beta\neq$0, the potential energy becomes zero and a metal-insulator transition occurs. It is difficult for this transition to occur because the transition point on the parabolic CDW-potential energy is unstable. This is the metal-insulator instability, which may be the reason why preparation of the metallic phase becoming a superconductor at a low temperature is difficult. Note that band filling is defined as 0< $\rho=(\alpha+\beta)$ $\leq$1 because 0< $\rho=(\alpha+\beta)$ $\leq$1 is equal to 1$\leq$ $\rho=(\alpha+\beta)$ <2.

2.2 Measurement effect

We consider only the semiconductor regime in Fig. 1 because the instability point does not reach. In the regime of $0< \rho = \alpha + \beta <1$, the charge difference, $|\delta q|$, between nearest neighbor sites is less than $2e$, which indicates that a charge of carrier in band should be fractional; $|\delta q|=2e[1-\rho]=2[e-e']$ where an effective fractional carrier charge, $e'=\rho e$ is given. However, the fractional effective charge concept is not accepted because the true $|\delta q|$ value is zero or 2 in a real system, but can be justified as the effect of measurement by means of measurement. When not measured, the concept of the effective charge is not defined. Eq. (3) is the effect of measurement when $0< \rho <1$. The fractional effective charge is defined by a probability for true charge to occupy nearest neighbor sites. ρ is a probability density to occupy nearest neighbor sites, as band filling, and can also represent the number of carriers, n, to the number of all lattices or atoms, L, in the measurement region (or a local region); $\rho=n/L$, (Fig. 2). The existence of carriers indicates that a metal-insulator transition occurs in a microscopical local region; a metal phase is formed in the region. The increase of ρ is the increase of the local metal region in Fig. 2 (a). Macroscopically, when a two-phase system, which is composed of the metal region with one electron per atom and the CDW insulator region with $|\delta q|=2e$, is measured, the measured data are averaged values of the two phases not true values (the effect of measurement) and show a semiconducting behavior. This judges that the measured material is a semiconductor experimentally, but, truly, indicates that the material is inhomogeneous. Thus, the metal-insulator instability explains the intrinsic inhomogeneity. Note that this consideration is based on the two-phase system without fluctuation or proximity effect between two phases. We introduce an example of the effect of measurement. Recently, Bozovic *et al.* [40] suggested no mixing of superconductivity of $La_{1.85}Sr_{0.15}CuO_4$ (LSCO) and antiferromagnetism of La_2CuO_4 (LCO) with the energy gap of about 2 eV, and an mid-gap of 1 eV in LSCO when holes are doped. When it is assumed that only the LSCO phase is measured because of no mixing of two phases, the mid-gap will be not measured. The mid-gap is attributed to the effect of measurement (or average) between the metal LSCO phase and the insulating LCO phase and is not true.

2.3 First-order metal-insulator transition

Next, as general features of high T_c superconductors regarded as a strongly correlated metal, charge doping to a Mott insulator results in metal phase, in which the extent of the metal phase increases with an increasing doping concentration up to an optimal doping. In order to explain the metal-insulator transition (MIT), the first-order transition in the strongly correlated system is introduced in the extended Brinkman-Rice (EBR) picture [43, 44]. The EBR picture predicted a first-order metal-Mott insulator transition in which a very low hole doping into a Mott insulator abruptly breaks down an energy gap in a sub band. Recently, it was experimentally

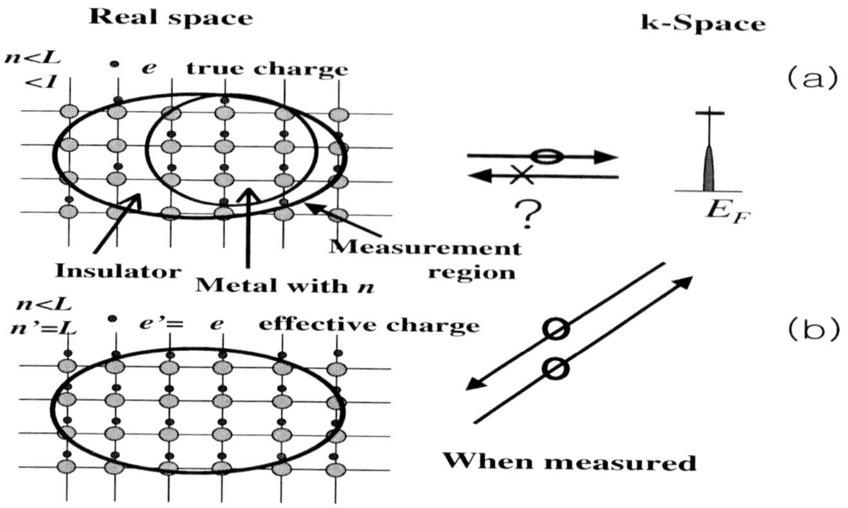

Figure 2: (a) An inhomogeneous system in the measurement region in real space. Transformation of real-space vs k-space. n is the number of carriers and L is the number of lattices, and ρ=n/L. Transformation from real-space to k-space is possible, reverse transformation is not. (b) When the system is measured, the averaged system is equivalence between two spaces. Spectral wight in k-space is maximum at ρ=1 and decreases with a decreasing ρ (or the extent of metal region).

proved [47] (Fig. 3, 4, 5). The Mott transition with doping causes an intrinsic inhomogeneity because of the divergence not to be perfect half filling in Eq. (4).

The divergence of the effective mass, m^*, of a quasi particle, in the EBR picture, is given by

$$\frac{m^*}{m} \equiv \frac{1}{1-(U/U_c)^2} = \frac{1}{1-\kappa^2\rho^4}, \tag{4}$$

where m is the bare electron mass, U/U_c is $\kappa\rho^2 \neq 1$, κ is the strength of the on-site Coulomb energy between carriers when ρ=1, and $0< \rho \leq 1$ is band filling. Eq. (4) is well fitted in a real metallic system and the effect of measurement for an inhomogeneous system [43, 44]. However, true metallic characteristics in the homogeneous metal region with ρ=1 are determined by the correlation strength κ_{BR} in the BR picture [48]. In addition, m^* is regarded as the two-dimensional DOS [44].

Finally, it is concluded that high-T_c superconductors are intrinsically inhomogeneous.

3 Extended BCS Density of States

The well-known BCS DOS of Eq. (6), which is applied to a homogeneous su-

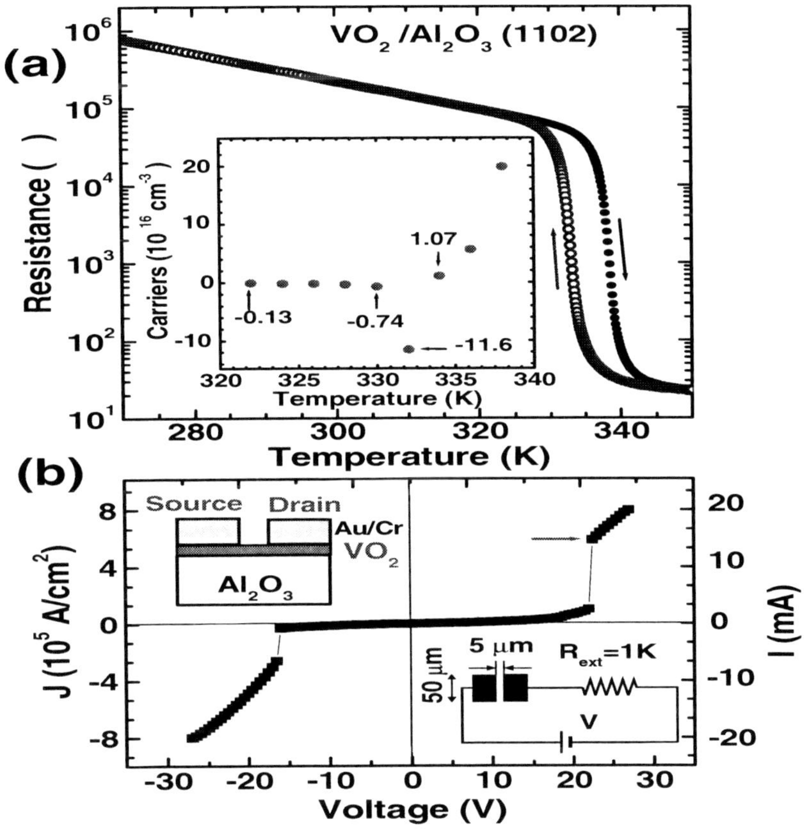

Figure 3: (a), Temperature dependence of the resistance of a Mott insulator, VO_2, film. An abrupt first-order MIT at a critical temperature $T_c \approx 340$ K is clearly shown. The inset in Fig. (a) shows the number of carriers obtained by Hall measurements. A change of carriers from holes to electrons is shown at 332 K, which is a metal-insulator transition. The minus sign indicates that the carriers are holes. Fig. (b), Current-density J vs. voltage V curve measured by a VO_2 based two-terminal device. An abrupt MIT is shown. The inset in Fig. (b) is a circuit with 1 KΩ and a layout of a two-terminal device. At the metal-insulator transition points, band filling is regarded as the critical ρ=0.99982 which corresponds to a hole doping content ($\triangle\rho$=1-ρ) of 0.018% and κ=1 in Eq. 4. ρ was evaluated from Hall data in inset of Fig. (a). This suggests that the first-order MIT occurs by hole doping of a very low concentration into conduction band, as indicated in Eq. 4. See reference 47.

perconductor and defined at 0 K, cannot be applied to experimental data measured in an inhomogeneous superconductor, which does not define k-space, so that the DOS must be converted into a DOS of a homogeneous superconductor (Fig. 2 (b)). Here, metal phase on homogeneous superconductors imply that there is no charge difference between nearest neighbor sites, for example when there is one electron per atom in the electronic structure (Metal region in Fig. 2 (a)). When the carriers in the metal phase of the inhomogeneous superconductor are averaged over all atomic (or lattices) sites in the measurement region, it is possible to change the inhomogeneous superconductor into a homogeneous one with a carrier of an effective charge. Then, the effective charge of the carrier is given as a fractional charge, $e' = \rho e$, where $0< \rho(=n/L)\leq 1$ is band filling, n is the number of carriers in the metal phase and L is the number of lattices [43, 44]. The number of bound charges, $n_b = L - n$, is bound in the insulating phase with a pseudogap; the total charges are conserved even in the inhomogeneous superconductor. The effective charge is justified only by means of measurement, that is, when not measured, the effective charge becomes the elementary true charge in the metal phase.

In the tunnelling conductance ($\frac{dI}{dV}$), the observed energy gap, $\triangle_{obs}$, is given by

$$\triangle_{obs} = eV_{bias} = \triangle_i/\rho, \tag{5}$$

from substituting e with e'. $\triangle_{obs}$ increases as ρ decreases and is an averaged value of the intrinsic true energy gap, $\triangle_i$, over a measurement region (Fig. 6). $\triangle_i$ is attributed to pairing of two electrons of true charge when ρ=1, is constant irrespective of the extent of ρ, and is determined by the minimum bias voltage.

The BCS DOS, tunnelling conductance in the inhomogeneous superconductor, is given by

$$N_s(E)/N_n = Re\left(\frac{E}{\sqrt{E^2-\triangle^2}}\right), \tag{6}$$

$$= Re\left(\frac{E}{\sqrt{E^2-(\triangle_i/\rho)^2}}\right), \tag{7}$$

where $\triangle_i$ is $\triangle_s$ in an s-wave superconductor, $\triangle_s\cos(2\phi)$ in a d-wave superconductor, and E is an applied bias energy (or voltage). Considering the broadening effect, E is substituted with $E = E - i\Gamma$ where Γ is the broadening parameter [9]. Eq. (7) is valid in $|E| \geq \triangle$ in the s-symmetry case and is averaged by phase angle ϕ in the d-symmetry case. Eq. (7) has a coherence peak at the energy gap which increases with decreasing ρ, (Fig. 7); this, the unsolved problem [29, 49, 50] in the tunnelling conductance, is explained. It was experimentally demonstrated that analogous to Bi-2212, the energy gap in Bi-2201 monotonically increases with a decreasing hole concentration [51]. Eq. (7) and the coherence peak energy when ρ=1

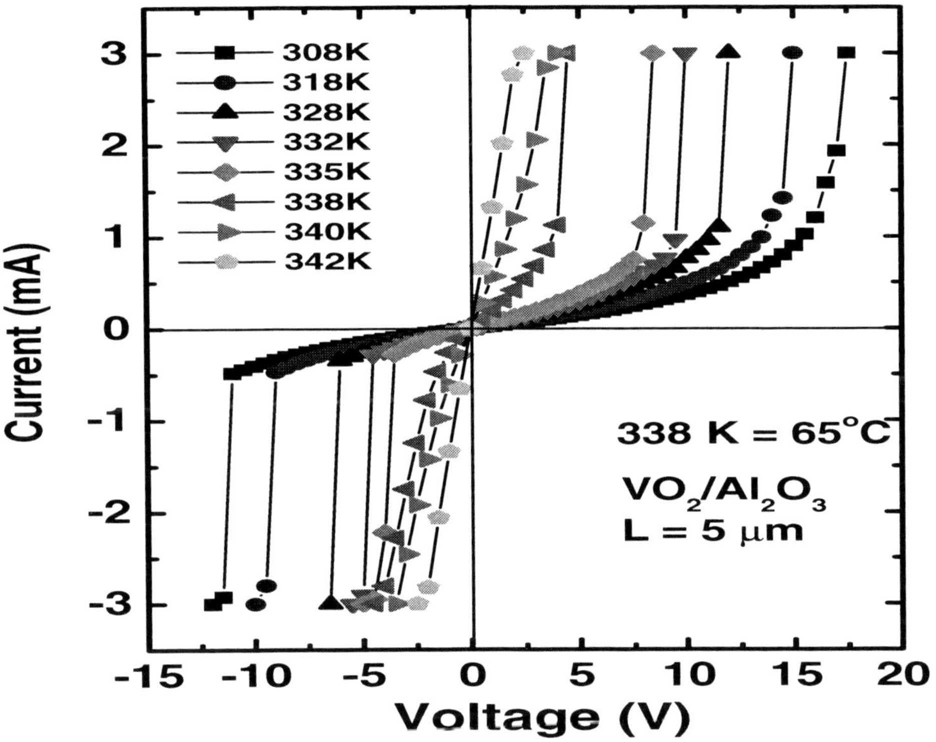

Figure 4: Temperature dependence of the abrupt MIT observed at a VO_2 based two-terminal device in a cryostat above room temperature. Near $T_c \approx 340$ K shown in Fig. 3a, the abrupt first-order MIT, jump, disappears and Ohmic behavior appears, which indicates that the first-order MIT observed by temperature in Fig. 3a is reproduced. The MIT voltage decreases with increasing temperature.

are regarded as the intrinsic DOS and $\triangle_i$, respectively. The broadening parameter is always zero at 0 K when ρ=1. Eq. (7) and the peak energy when $0 < \rho < 1$ imply an averaging of the intrinsic DOS and $\triangle_i$ over the measurement region, which is the effect of measurement. This is because a tunnelling spectrum observed by STM is the averaged spectrum over the Fermi surface.

When $|\frac{eV_{bias}}{\triangle}| < 1$ for a conductance curve, the DOS for the s-wave pairing symmetry has flat bottom regions, while the DOS for the d-wave symmetry has a V shape near zero-bias voltage and a peak width near the peak, (Fig. 7 (b)). This is not used for judging pairing symmetry in this research. When $|\frac{eV_{bias}}{\triangle}| > 1$, the DOS for the s-wave symmetry has a much wider peak-width than the DOS for d-wave symmetry, (Fig. 7 (c)). Furthermore, even theoretical calculations for the superconductor-insulator-superconductor junctions in a d-wave superconductor showed a peak width of the coherence peak when $|\frac{eV_{bias}}{\triangle}| < 1$ rather than when $|\frac{eV_{bias}}{\triangle}| > 1$ [52, 53]. The peak width plays a decisive role in judging pairing symmetry. When $|\frac{eV_{bias}}{\triangle}| = 1$ (or gap edge peak), the magnitude of the d-wave DOS, $N_s(0)/N_n \approx 5$, which is given by numerical calculations and is less than the values near the divergence in the s-wave DOS, (Fig. 7 (b) and see the caption), because the DOS is averaged over phase angles of $d_{x^2-y^2}$ symmetry. This indicates that quasi particles are distributed inside the peak energy, but exist at the peak in the case of the s-wave. The true measured $N_s(E)/N_n$ cannot reach the calculated value 5 and may be less than a value 2 because there is no outside peak width above the value 2. $N_s(E)/N_n$ is an experimental coherence-peak height to a background value. Moreover, note that N_n in the normal state decreases as ρ decreases [44].

Bi-2212 superconductors have been judged as d-wave superconductors by analysis of conductance curves near zero-bias voltage [15, 54]. However, this analysis contains a fatal error in which a pseudogap in the data, in which the effect of the two phases was merged, was not removed. For a tunnelling conductance measured for Bi-2212 thin films, a low temperature pseudogap (LTPG) has no coherence peak and gap widths of 30-35 meV corresponding to nearly the superconducting energy gap of optimal doped crystals [55]. Similar analysis's were given by several groups [50, 56, 57]. This indicates that two DOS curves overlap when $|\frac{eV_{bias}}{\triangle}| < 1$, and that the coherence peak is only the superconducting energy-gap peak without LTPG. Thus, we can judge pairing symmetry through observations of the magnitude and shape of the coherence peak for a conductance without the dip-hump structure from experimental data measured at a local superconducting region of $\rho \approx 1$ and Γ=0, although the dip-hump structure is a universal feature of high-T_c superconductors [32, 51]. It has been suggested that the dip-hump structure is a high-energy pseudogap with a V-shape near zero-bias voltage [58, 59]. The analysis is also explained in Fig. 8.

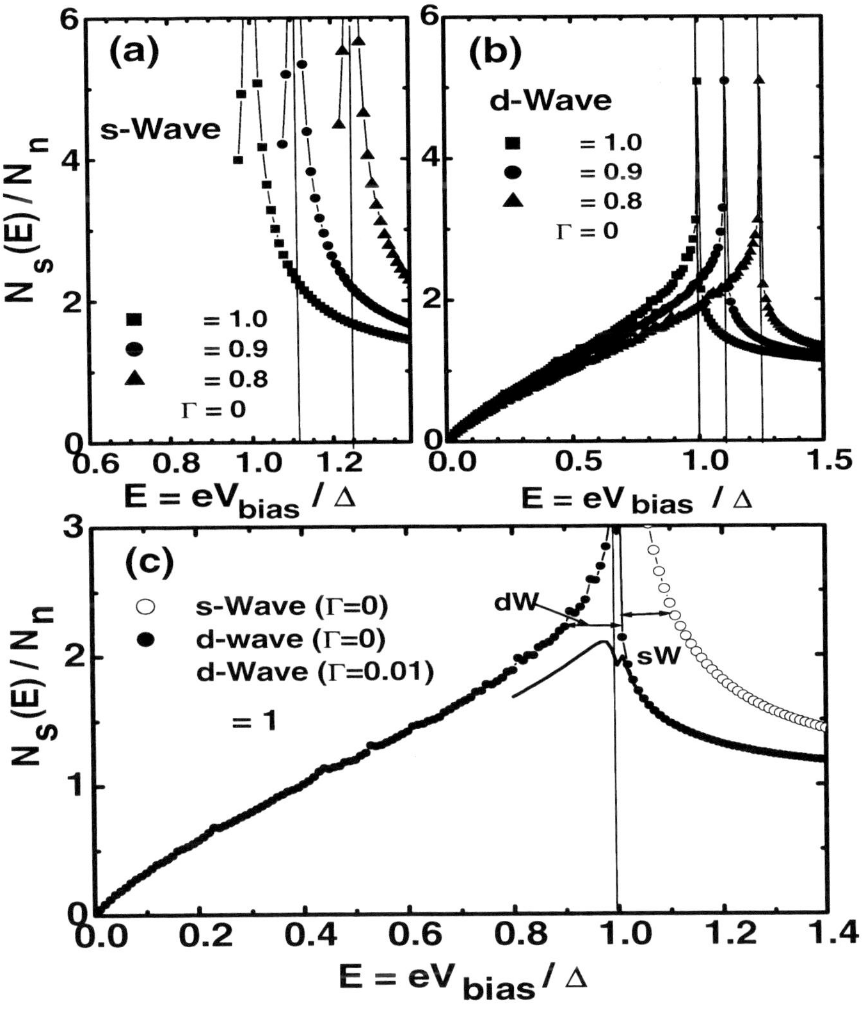

Figure 5: (a) Band filling, ρ, dependence of the s-wave DOS of Eq. (7). $\frac{N_s(E)}{N_n} = 0$ is assumed in $|\frac{(E=eV_{bias})}{\triangle}| < 1$. Peak curves when $|\frac{eV_{bias}}{\triangle}| < 1$ are just given for a comparison to curves when $|\frac{eV_{bias}}{\triangle}| > 1$. (b) Band filling dependence of the d-wave DOS of Eq. (7). The DOS's were precisely calculated from $\frac{N_s(E)}{N_n} = \frac{1}{2\pi}\int \frac{N_s(E,\phi)}{N_n} d\phi$ with $\triangle = \triangle_s cos(2\phi)$ and $\Gamma = 0$ by numerical analysis not using complete elliptic integrals. Divergences in calculations were ignored because the divergences have no derivative width ($d\phi = 0$). (c) Comparison of s and d-wave DOS's with $\Gamma = 0$ and $\Gamma = 0.01$. sW denotes the s-wave width and dW represents the d-wave width.

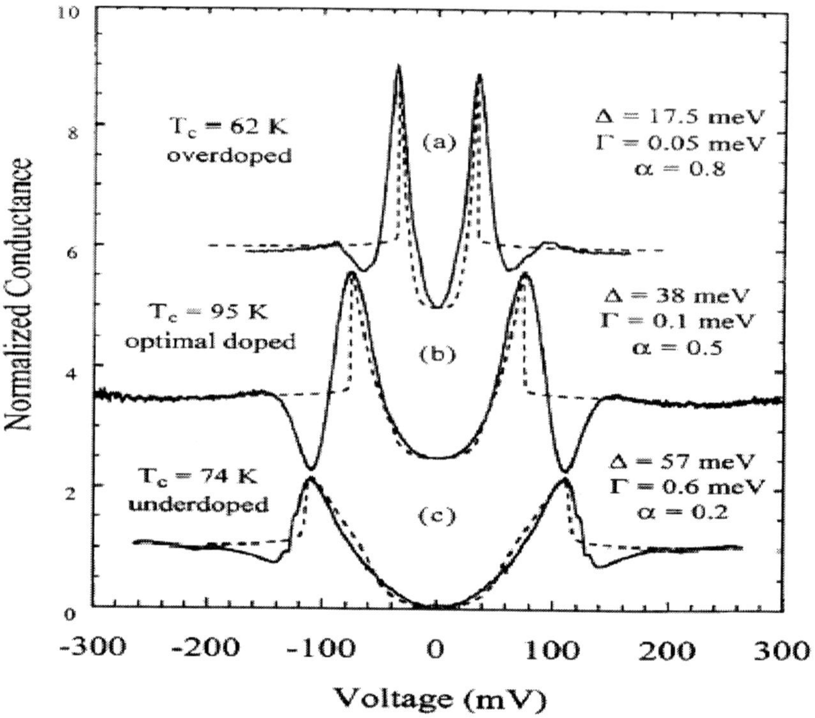

Figure 6: Zasadzinski *et al.* Phys. Rev. Lett. 87 (2001) 67005. Fig. (a) deviates from the d-wave DOS and the peak width is wide, which seems to follow the s-wave DOS as mentioned. Figs. (b) agrees with the d-wave DOS at zero bias, but the peak width does not fit the d-wave DOS. Fig. (c) agrees with the d-wave DOS. When there are two phases, DOS's of two phases are overlapped near zero bias, but the peak widths are separated. We can say that pairing symmetry of optimal-doped and over-doped crystals is s-wave. This analysis differs from Zasadzinski *et al.*.

4 Identity of the Gap Anisotropy

On the other hand, the photoemission spectra and tunnelling conductance are the DOS measured in k-space and real-space, respectively. The photoemission spectra have a much larger insulating effect than spectra measured by STM because the size of the X-ray beam cannot be reduced to less than 30 Å. However, angle-resolved photoemission spectroscopy (ARPES) gives information on DOS at a node and a non-node.

Although the gap anisotropy has been suggested as evidence of the d-wave symmetry [1], on the contrary it indicates, according to Eq. (5), that $\rho_{\Gamma-Y}$ for the small gap at a node $\Gamma - Y$ is larger than $\rho_{\bar{M}}$ for the large gap at $\bar{M}$ of (π,0). The

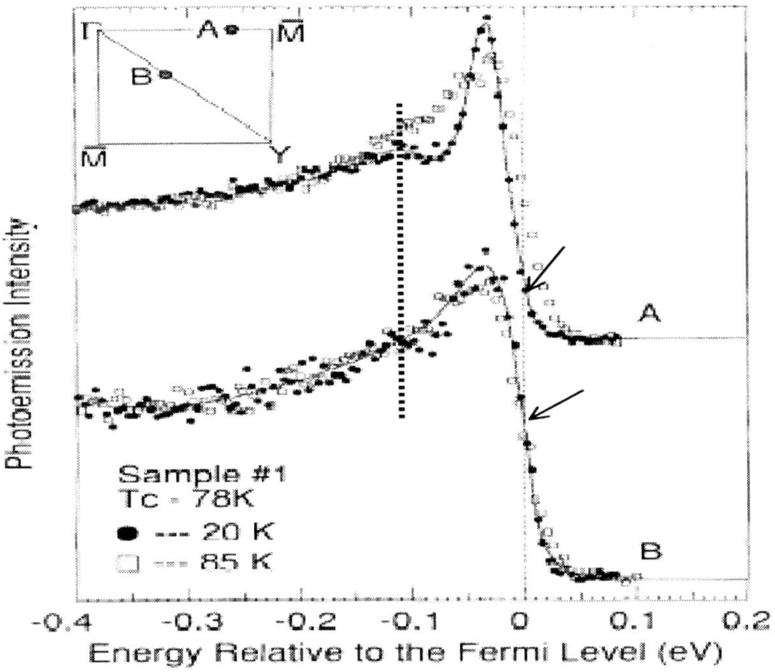

Figure 7: Shen *et al.*, Phys. Rev. Lett. 70 (1993) 1553. Figure shows the absence of the hump at the node, which indicates that pairing symmetry of an insulating phase is *d*-wave. Anisotropic gap with the non-zero small gap at the node was proposed by Shen *et al.*, which is attributed to the inhomogeneity and is not evidence of the *d*-wave symmetry.

large $\rho_{\Gamma-Y}(=\rho_{\bar{M}}+\frac{n_b}{l}\approx 1)$ is because bound charges, n_b, become carriers when the hump structure in the spectra disappears at the node $\Gamma-Y$; transition from insulator (region A in Fig. 10) with the pseudogap to metal occurs. As an example, Fig. 9 shows the absence of the hump at the node (a dot line), which indicates that the pseudogap of an insulating phase A has the *d*-wave symmetry (Fig. 10). The coherence peak of the small gap in Fig. 9 is not clear at the node, but an arrow of the Fermi-level point at the node (curve B) is at higher position than that at the non-node (curve A). This indicates that the energy gap at the node is smaller than that at the non-node, which is the gap anisotropy. The observed gap anisotropy is the effect of measurement and results from the inhomogeneity, because the gap anisotropy of a true $\triangle_i$ cannot be measured for inhomogeneous superconductors. A clear coherence peak at the node with $\rho\approx 1$ was observed with a small gap, $\triangle\leq 10$ meV [60 − 62], and the small gap is much closer to the true gap of $\triangle_i$ than the large gap at $\bar{M}$; $\triangle_i\leq 10$ meV for an optimal-doped Bi-2212.

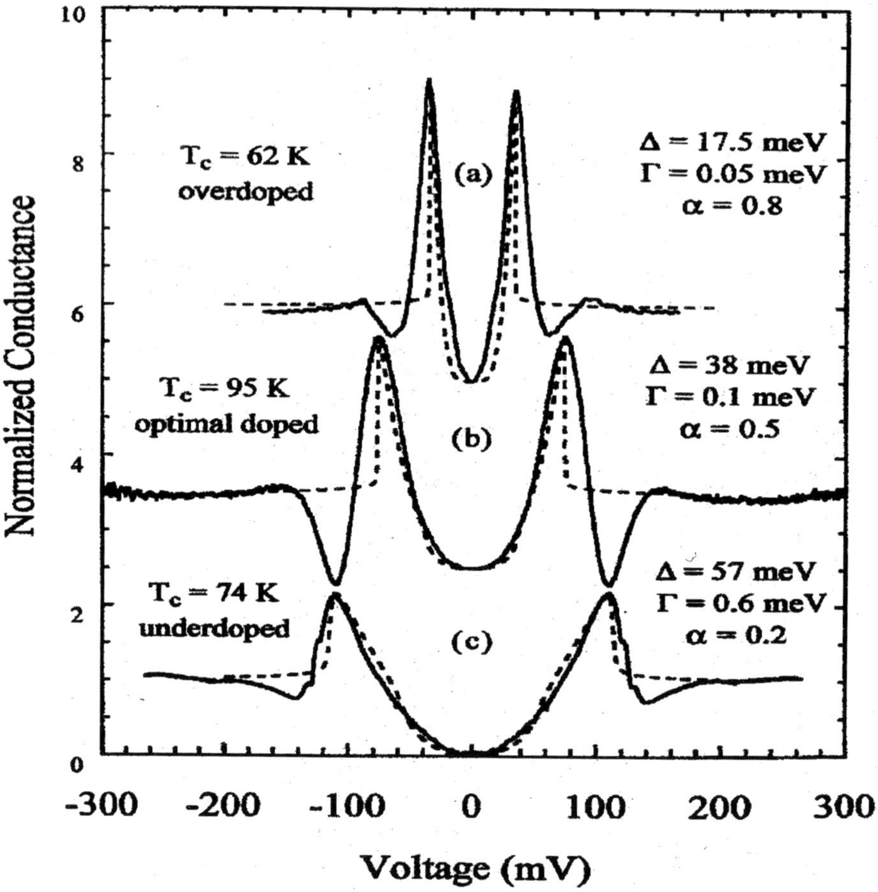

Figure 8: An inhomogeneous high-T_c superconductor is composed of the metal phase and the d-wave insulating phase, on the basis of Shen's data in Fig. 9. Between A region and B region is not dispersive.

As another example, Kohsaka *et al.* [63] measured anisotropic gaps at the node and the non-node for an underdoped $Ca_{2-x}Na_xCuO_2Cl_2O_2$ (CNCCO) single crystals at x=0.19 by ARPES. Spectra of the insulator of CNCCO with x=0 and a superconductor of CNCCO with x=0.1 showed the *d*-wave symmetry and the gap anisotropy, respectively, in Fig. 2c of their paper. Spectral weight of the superconductor spectrum is dispersive and broad, but the small gap coherence peak without a dip-hump structure is intense. Rather than their analysis, the gap anisotropy can be explained in terms of Eq. (5) and Fig. 6, which indicates that ρ_{node} at the node is greater than $\rho_{non-node}$. The dispersion and broadness of the spectral weight is attributed to an average of all DOSs in a measurement region (real space) which includes a homogeneous and an inhomogeneous regions.

Note that the energy gap observed by STM is larger than the small gap observed at the node by ARPES, because the averaged STM gap over the Fermi surface is an average of the small gap at a node and the large gap at a non-node. The observed dip-hump structure in the tunnelling spectra [51] comes from the non-node $\bar{M}$. Furthermore, when the hump structure disappears at nodes and non-nodes, the gaps become isotropic due to the same ρ. The isotropic gaps in the structures without humps were experimentally observed, although the observation depended on the properties of the cleaned sample surface [2]; the metal phase with $\rho = 1$ at the sample surface is unstable because of the metal-insulator instability [42]. Electronic Raman scattering also showed the isotropic gaps measured in an over-doped Bi-2212 crystal [14]. The isotropic gap is evidence of *s*-wave symmetry.

We comment on the suggestion "the nodal states play no rule in the superconductivity" in abstract of Valla *et al.* [61]. They observed the behavior in which the peak width of a momentum distribution curve (MDC) measured at the Fermi surface below T_c is on the linear which is the temperature dependence of peak widths measured in the normal state, for the optimally doped Bi-2212 single crystal, as shown in Fig. 2B of their paper. This is the reason of their suggestion. The suggestion is right only in assuming that pairing symmetry of Bi-2212 is $d_{x^2-y^2}$ wave and the gap disappears at the node. However, Fig. 3A of their paper [61], Shen's data in Fig. 9, Kaminski's data [60] show that the magnitude of the small gap at the node is not zero although it is small. For this reason, there are no carriers for superconductivity at the Fermi surface. Thus, the observed peak width below T_c is not related to the superconducting state, which is differ from their suggestion. We think that the behavior is due to an impurity carrier because data [31 – 34] of STM show several phases not explained in an inhomogeneous Bi-2212 superconductor.

Recently, McElroy *et al.* [5] showed an anisotropic superconducting gap measured at a Bi-O surface for slightly over-doped Bi-2212, which agrees closely with Ding's gap [64] measured for an under-doped crystal, analyzed and measured by Fourier transform scanning tunnelling spectroscopy (FT-STS). The anisotropic gap is an average of all energy gaps in a local region of $640 Å^2$ including an inhomogeneous region as well as a homogeneous region in real-space (Fig. 2), though it was suggested that a homogeneous superconducting region is within $30\AA$ [31−34]. The fact that the averaged anisotropic gap agrees with Ding's gap measured by ARPES indicates that slightly over-doped Bi-2212 crystal is very inhomogeneous, such as Ding's under-doped crystal, and that the superconducting property of its surface (BiO plane) was very suppressed. Thus, because the averaged gap is not the intrinsic true gap, the anisotropic gap observed by ARPES and FT-SIS cannot be chosen as evidence of the d-wave symmetry. In order to obtain a reliability of data measured by ARPES and FT-SIS, the measurement point should be selected on CuO_2 plane of an over-doped crystal, because the over-doped crystal has little insulating phase and is more homogeneous. In addition, It has been known that the BiO plane shows generally the semiconducting gap structure [65], and that the superconducting property at the surface [66] is suppressed. In addition, the gap anisotropy decreased with an increasing doping content, from under-doped to over-doped crystals [67]. Thus, the gap anisotropy is not intrinsic but the effect of measurement.

5 Extended Ambegaokar-Baratoff Theory

The Josephson I_cR_n product decreases with an increasing superconducting gap [30]. This also creates a problem in determining the extent of the s-wave component in $s+d$ mixed pair states. Many investigations indicated that the Josephson product in c-axis Josephson pair (or intrinsic Josephson) tunnelling experiments is much smaller than the all-s-wave Ambegaokar-Baratoff limit [29, 68 − 75]. On the basis of this experimental result, it has been interpreted that the ratio of the s-wave component to the full d-wave one in the $s + d$ mixed states is very small. In this section, band-filling (or doping) dependence of the Josephson supercurrent and the Josephson product at T=0 K are given by means of measurement explained in previous sections; this is an extension of Ambegaokar - Baratoff Josephson current and product.

Ambegaokar and Baratoff [76] derived the Josephson tunnelling supercurrent on the basis of BCS theory for an s-wave homogeneous superconductor. The supercurrent at T=0 K was given by

$$J = \frac{\pi}{2} R_n^{-1} \triangle, \tag{8}$$

where $R_n = (2\pi h/e^2T)$, T is the tunnelling matrix, and $\triangle$ is a superconducting energy gap.

In an inhomogeneous superconductor, the averaged metallic system has the electronic structure of one effective charge per atom, which is mathematically equivalent to the electronic structure of the metal used in the BCS theory. The metal for k-space used in the BCS theory has the electronic structure of one electron per atom in real space. The Josephson current and product derived in the Ambegaokar and

Baratoff theory can be used without formula's change even in the inhomogeneous superconductor by replacing true charge by the effective charge because the averaged effective charge is invariant under transformation. In addition, a similar calculation has been given when the Brinkman-Rice picture was extended [44]. Thus, the observed supercurrent, J_{obs}, is given by substituting e in R_n and $\triangle$ with $e' = \rho e$ and $\triangle_{obs}=\triangle_i/\rho$ by

$$J_{obs} \equiv (\frac{e^2 T}{4h})\rho\triangle_i = \rho J_i, \tag{9}$$

where J_i is the intrinsic supercurrent. The observed Josephson product is also given by using Eq. (5) by

$$J_{obs}R_n \equiv \frac{\pi}{2}\rho^2\triangle_{obs} \equiv \frac{\pi}{2}\rho\triangle_i = \rho J_i R_n, \tag{10}$$

where $\triangle_i$ is constant.

When ρ =1, Eq. (9) and Eq. (10) are the intrinsic supercurrent and the intrinsic product (or Ambegaokar and Baratoff product) occurring due to true charges, respectively. When 0< ρ <1, the equations correspond to the averages of the intrinsic supercurrent and the intrinsic product over the measurement region and are the effect of measurement. Eq. (9) and Eq. (10) are the extended Ambegaokar - Baratoff Josephson current and product, respectively.

The Josephson product of eq. (10), which decreases with decreasing ρ, fits well the experimental data measured by break junctions (Fig. 11). This explains the fact that the observed Josephson product decreases with an increasing energy gap [30, 78], and that $Bi_2Sr_2CaCu_2O_{8+x}$ (Bi-2212) crystals are inhomogeneous, which is a general characteristic of high-T_c superconductors [31,32,33,34,42,78] and the reason why the Ambegaokar - Baratoff product is not applied directly to experimental data. The *d*-wave superconductive components do not exist in the homogeneous metal region in Bi-2212 crystals. Note that Mourachkine [78] discussed that the decrease of the product with the increasing gap is not intrinsic effect and due to inhomogeneity. ρ dependence in Eq. (10) comes from Eq. (9), which agrees with a result observed by the intrinsic Josephson junction [72]. Note that the magnitude of the intrinsic product is basically very small because $\triangle_i$ is small. Considering that the anisotropy of the number of carriers in the c-axis and ab-plane is large ($\rho_{c-axis} << \rho_{ab-plane}$), the product observed in the c-axis is naturally much less than that in the ab-plane. Thus, the observed small Josephson products [29, 68 75, 78] can be explained by Eq. (10). Additionally, for a Josephson junction by two superconductors with different energy gaps, the Josephson product derived by Anderson [77] is in the context of the above analysis.

We analyze the intrinsic gap of $Bi_2Sr_2CaCu_2O_{8+x}$ from experimental data, using Eq. (10). Irie *et al.* [72] suggested that $I_cR_n \approx$13.3 meV observed by the intrinsic Josephson junction is $\frac{1}{3}$ of the Ambegaokar-Baratoff product, $I_cR_n \approx$ 40 meV, using

$\triangle_{obs}$ ≈25 meV and Eq. (10) with ρ=1. The true Ambegaokar-Baratoff product is much less than 40 meV, when both $\rho \neq 1$ and $\triangle_{obs} \neq \triangle_i$ are considered. The intrinsic gap, $\triangle_i$ ≈8.5 meV, is obtained from the observed product, I_cR_n ≈13.3 meV by using Eq. (10) with ρ=1. The true intrinsic gap is slightly larger than 8.5 meV because ρ <1 slightly. Mourachkine [30,78] observed the maximum Josephson product of $I_cR_n \approx$ 26 meV for an over-doped crystal, which can be regarded as $\rho \approx 1$ without a pseudogap [79], at the minimum energy gap of $\triangle_{obs}$ ≈21 meV. The intrinsic true gap, $\triangle_i \approx$ 16.5 meV, is obtained by Eq. (4) with ρ=1. The intrinsic true gap is less than that analyzed by Mourachkine. Thus, we conclude that the analyzed intrinsic gap is in $8.5 < \triangle_i < 17$ meV.

6 Application to the Josephson Current

In order to evaluate the flux quantization caused by the Josephson current predicted in the Josephson-π junction theory [6], Eq. (9) is applied to the theory. The observed circulating current in an inhomogeneous superconducting ring is given when $I_{ij}L > \Phi_0$ without any external field [9] by

$$I_{obs} \equiv \rho I_i \approx \rho \frac{\Phi_0}{2L}, \tag{11}$$

where Φ_0 (=$h/2e$) is the flux quantum and L is a self-inductance of a superconducting ring. When $0< \rho <1$, the observed supercurrent, I_{obs}, is an average of the intrinsic supercurrent over the measurement region.

Tsuei *et al.* [9, 80, 81] and Sugimoto *et al.* [11, 82] analyzed the half-flux quantum from a flux observed by a scanning superconducting-quantum-interference-device (SQUID) loop for frustrated (or π loop) $YBa_2Cu_3O_{7-\delta}$ (YBCO) films deposited on a tricrystal substrate, and emphasized the observation of the half-flux quantum as evidence of the *d*-wave symmetry. However, they did not consider ρ in Eq. (11) in their analysis of the experimental data; they assumed ρ=1. The ρ effect differs from the disorder effect applied by Tsuei *et al.* [9]. We regard the YBCO films as inhomogeneous superconductors of $0< \rho <1$. When L, evaluated by Tsuei *et al.*, is used, an intrinsic flux to be evaluated, $\Phi_i/2$, should be larger than $\Phi_0/2$; $\Phi_i = \frac{1}{\rho}\Phi_0 > \Phi_0$ [83]. When Φ_i=Φ_0 and $\rho \neq 1$ in Eq. (11), a flux value to be observed should be less than $\Phi_0/2$. The half-flux quantum can be observed only when ρ=1. Note that L is independent of ρ which comes from the supercurrent. In contrast, their analyzed flux values have a smaller error, $(\frac{1}{\rho} - 1)(\Phi_0/2)$, than the expected intrinsic flux value. To estimate ρ near the triple junction, it is thought that the characteristic of the superconducting ring is not good due to the presence of surface stresses on the substrate at a triple junction which was revealed as either concentrated or deconcentrated [84, 85]. As evidence, the frustrated YBCO film around a triple junction does not show the Meissner effect (expulsion of flux) in

Fig. 17 (c) of reference 80. Thus, the inhomogeneity effect cannot be ignored because ρ in the ring is smaller than that at a region away from junctions. The true observed flux is about $\frac{1}{3}\Phi_0$ not $\frac{1}{2}\Phi_0$, as shown in Fig. 2 (a) of reference 81, which indicates $\rho \neq 1$. Nielsen *et al.* [22] also observed the flux value less than $0.3\Phi_0$ for the paramagnetic Meissner effect (PME; single-π junction) in Nb-Al_2O_3-Nb Josephson-junction arrays, which indicates $\rho \neq 1$. Finally, the intrinsic flux to be evaluated can be regarded as $\frac{1}{2}\Phi_0$. In addition, Tsuei and Kirtley [80, 86] also measured the half-flux quantum for ring, disk and blanket films.

However, Kirtley *et al.* [81] and Sugimoto *et al.* [11] observed the change of flux direction near T_c, which is not explained by the π-junction theory, and also observed in the PME of BKBO [20], Nb [21], YBCO [23] superconductors (Fig. 12d). Note that the change of the flux direction indicates that the magnetic property of a superconductor changes from paramagnetic (or ferromagnetic) to diamagnetic. Koblischka *et al.* [23] suggested that the PME in an artificial granular YBCO film is attributed to field trapping on the basis of the observation of the upturn near T_c. Nielsen *et al.* [22] and Leo *et al.* [87] suggested that the PME can arise from magnetic screening in multiply connected superconductors. These are reasons why we do not think that the observed half flux occurs due to the triple-π junctions in the superconducting ring.

7 Flux Trap

We also comment on a flux trap of the magnetic modulation experiment [88] using Pb-YBCO dc SQUIDs, on the basis of our observation of the PME for BKBO [20]. Wollman *et al.* [88, 89] mentioned that the trapping of magnetic vortices is observed in the experiment, but does not affect the corner measurement. Klemm [90] commented on the singular demagnetization effects associated with the corners of very thin samples. We suggest that what has influence on results at the corner measurement is a trapped flux but not its quantity, because the PME is observed although its quantity is very small [20]. The flux trap is independent of sample geometry and size and is observed even in grains of a size of 1μm (Fig. 13) [20]. For a polycrystal and a film, a flux is trapped easily, but comes out easily when an external field disappears. On the contrary, for a high quality single-crystal, it is difficult to trap a flux [20]. However, once a flux is trapped even though the quantity is small, the flux remains closed in the crystal even when not in an external field (Fig. 12) [20]. This causes the effect of the π junction, the half flux due to the π-phase shift. Because Wollman's experiments measured minimum resistances (or maximum currents) with varying flux [88], the flux can be trapped easily into a sample even in a very low field. Note that the superconducting state measuring the maximum currents, as explained in Fig. 1 (b) of reference 88 (Fig. 14), is not a perfect condensed state; the superconductors do not perfectly shield or expel a flux. Thus, a flux in the YBCO crystal rather than the Pb film can be trapped.

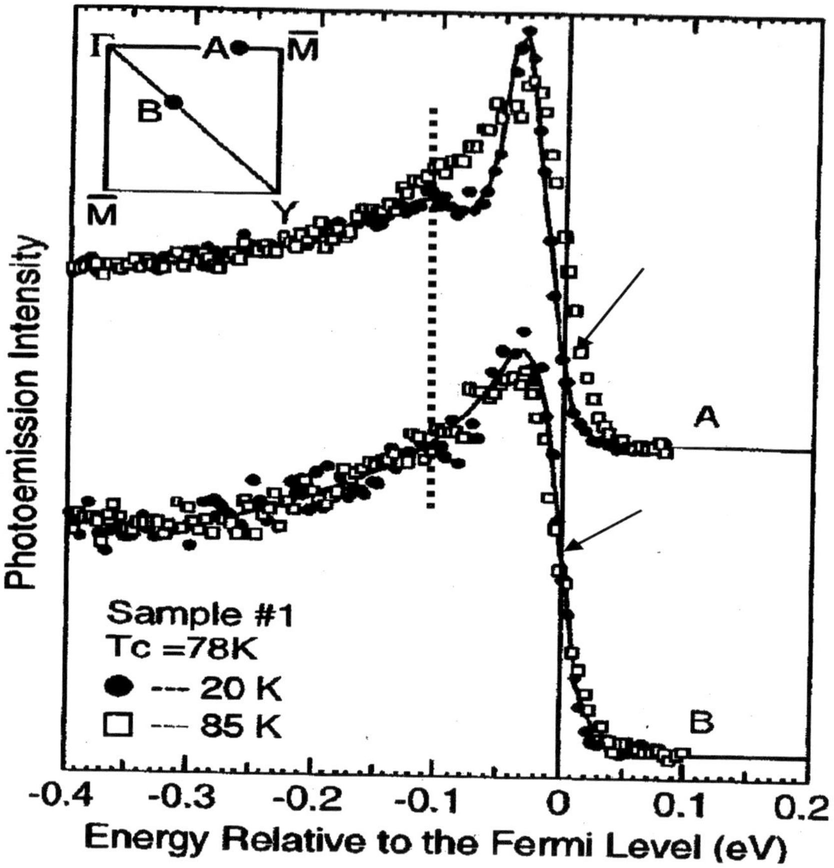

Figure 9: For a very high quality $Ba_{0.63}K_{0.37}BiO_3$ single crystal [20], the temperature dependence of field-cooled (FC) susceptibilities. With increasing field, FC susceptibilities decrease in Figs. a, b and c. A FC susceptibility at a strong magnetic field of 1,500Oe is diamagnetic, which indicates that a trapped flux does not come out easily. Fig. d shows the trapping process near T_c.

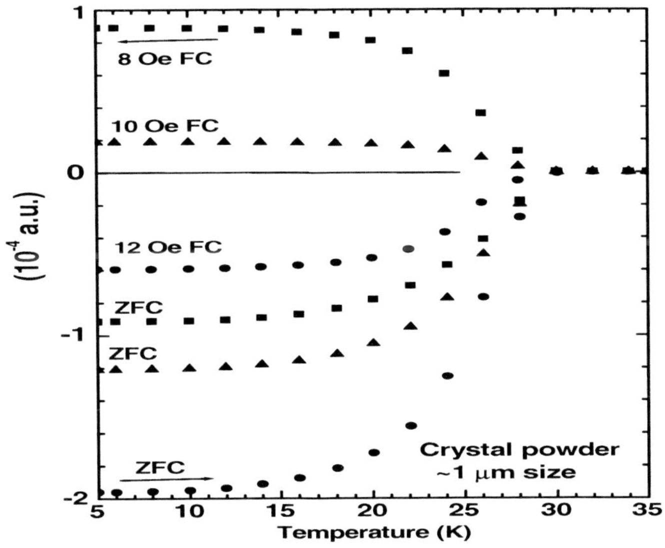

Figure 10: Temperature dependence of the field cooled and zero-field cooled susceptibilities of a BKBO single-crystal powder with ~ 1 μm size.

This can also account for the minimum current, a small V shape, or the maximum resistance, a small peak, near zero flux for single modulation experiments [88]. This analysis is different from Wollman *et al.*'s comments [89]. In addition, the PME and the half-flux quantum due to the π-phase shift have been predicted simultaneously in the π-junction theory [6, 80]. Nevertheless, it has been revealed that the PME occurs by a trapped flux [20 − 23].

8 Discussions to Other d-Wave Results

In addition, Klemm [91] shows that a tightbinding $\xi(k)$, to which the anisotropic extended s-wave order-parameter is applied, fits well into Takano's whisker data [16, 92] in contrast to Li's data [93]. This indicates that Takano's data is not able to be explained by only the d-wave theory. Takano's data are the angle dependence of the c-axis Josephson current which can be regarded as evidence of the d-wave symmetry.

We found that Li's whisker [93] was annealed in an enough oxygen atmosphere, while Takano's whisker [16, 92] in not enough. Li's whisker can be regarded as an over-doped whisker, while Takano's whisker as an under-doped one which can have an insulating phase with a pseudogap. This author thinks that the angle dependence of $J(\theta)$ measured by Takano *et al.* came from the insulating phase. When whisker is made in an enough oxygen atmosphere, the whisker can show more the intrinsic $J(\theta)$ because an overdoped crystal has only slight or no insulating phase [79]. Thus,

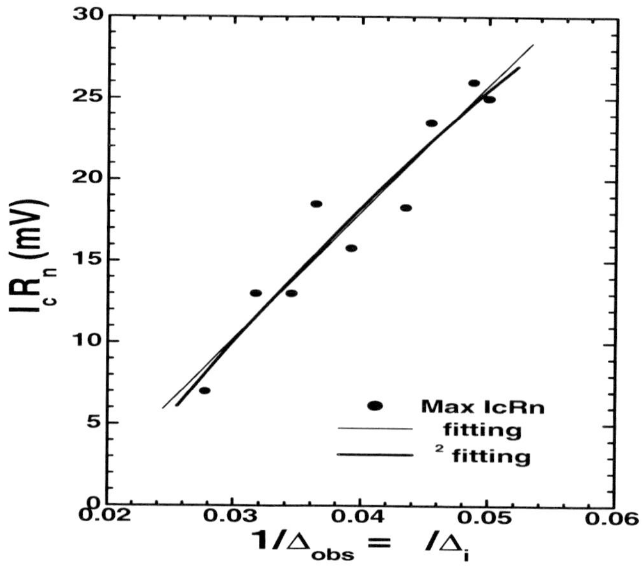

Figure 11: This shows fittings of the maximum I_cR_n data shown by Mourachkine [78]. An inverse energy gap as x-axis, on the basis of Eq. (5), is taken to fit the ρ dependence. Even though it is not easy to distinguish a more good fitting between linear and square fittings with respect to ρ, it can be interpreted that the ρ^2 fitting of Eq. (10) is more satisfied.

the Li data without the angle dependence of $J(\theta)$ indicating s-wave symmetry may show rather the intrinsic characteristic than the Takano data.

The strong spin-fermion model [94] for a homogeneous d-wave superconductor of $\rho = 1$ proposed both the dip-hump structure and the broad coherence peak. However, according to the model, although the coherence peak and the dip-hump structure should disappear at the same time at the node $\Gamma - Y$, only the dip-hump structure disappeared [1], while the coherence peak remained [61–63]. This indicates that the model does not explain the experimental data.

The zero-bias conductance peak (ZBCP) as evidence of the d-wave symmetry, theoretically suggested by Kashiwaya *et al.* [95] and Tanaka and Kashiwaya [96], was observed in a thin film and an under-doped crystal by tunnelling experiments [12, 13, 97]. They assumed that the crystals used had a single phase with ρ=1. However, we insists that the ZBCP came from the d-wave insulating phase for the inhomogeneous superconductors, because Kohen *et al.* [34] could not observe the ZBCP on overdoped [110] oriented $Y_{0.8}Ca_{0.2}Ba_2Cu_3O_{7-\delta}$ films [98] by planar tunneling or point contact measurements; overdoped crystals have only slight or no d-wave insulating phase [79]. In addition, Ekino *et al.* [99] indicated that the ZBCP observed with break-junction tunnelling is attributed to the interface of the break junction.

For fully oxygenated YBCO films and a very high quality YBCO crystal, experimental data of the penetration depth fit an exponential temperature below a third of T_c, which can be explained in terms of the s-wave theory [26, 100]. The linear and T^2 temperature dependencies of the penetration depths at low temperatures have been observed for a large inhomogeneous or oxygen deficient samples [17, 101−103]. When Klein *et al.* [100] applied experimental data to a formula with a weak exponential temperature dependence of the penetration depth, a small energy gap of $\triangle$=6 meV was used. This indicates that the superconducting true gap is not large. In addition, the "giant" Josephson current through the superconductor-normal-superconductor (S-N-S) junction where the barrier N' is an underdoped cuprate is the giant Josephson proximity effect [104]. This was explained by the intrinsic inhomogeneity of the cuprates [105].

9 Conclusion

In conclusion, for inhomogeneous high-T_c superconductors, the necessity of the measurement theory is proposed. The increase of a doped content, ρ, indicates the increases of metal phase in Fig. 2(a) in real space. Measured superconducting gaps in experiments are the effect of measurement and are not true. The true gaps are measured only when ρ=1, but not able to be measured in real crystals because of the intrinsic inhomogeneity. The analyzed true superconducting gap for Bi-2212 is within 8.5< $\triangle_i$ <17meV and its pairing symmetry is s-wave. The d-wave symmetry is observed in under-doped or oxygen deficient crystals. In addition, the high T_c for the small energy gap leads to b=$2\triangle_i/k_BT_c$ <4; T_c=93K and $\triangle_i$ <10meV for Bi-2212, b is less than 4. The fact that m^*/m as the 2-dimensional DOS is explained by the extended Brinkman-Rice picture [44] indicates that high T_c superconductors are strongly correlated. Finally, high-T_c superconductivity is attributed to the on-site Coulomb energy and its mechanism is within the context of the BCS theory.

Acknowledgements

We acknowledge Prof. H. J. Lee for valuable comments.

References

[**1**] Z. X. Shen, D. S. Dessau, B. O. Wells, D. M. King, W. E. Spicer, A. J. Arko, D. Marshall, L. W. Lombardo, A. Kapitulnik, P. Dickinson, S. Doniach, J. DiCarlo, A. G. Loeser, and C. H. Park, *Phys. Rev. Lett.* 70 (1993) 1553.
[**2**] H. Ding, J. C. Campuzano, K. Gofron, C. Gu, R. Liu, B. W. Veal, and G. Jennings, *Phys. Rev. B* 50 (1994) 1333.
[**3**] Y. Kohsaka, T. Sasagawa, F. Ronning, T. Yoshida, C. Kim, T. Hanaguri, M. Azuma, M. Takano, Z. X. Shen, and H. Takagi, *cond-mat/0209339.*
[**4**] T. Sasagawa, F. Ronning, Y. Kohsaka, K. M. Shen, T. Yoshida, M. Azuma, M. Takano, Z. X. Shen, H. Takagi, *Physica C* 388-389 (2003) 307.
[**5**]K. McElroy, R. W. Simmonds, J. E. Hoffman, D. H. Lee, J. Orenstein, H. Eisaki, S. Uchida, and J. C. Davis, *Nature* 422 (2003) 592.
[**6**] M. Sigrist and T. M. Rice, *J. Phys. Soc. Jpn.* 61 (1992) 4283.

[**7**] D. A. Wollman, D. J. Van Harlingen, W. C. Lee, D. M. Ginsberg, and A. J. Leggett, *Phys. Rev. Lett.* 71 (1993) 2134.
[**8**] D. A. Wollman, D. J. Van Harlinggen, J. Giapintzakis, and D. M. Ginsberg, *Phys. Rev. Lett.* 74 (1995) 797.
[**9**] C. C. Tsuei, J. R. Kirtley, C. C. Chi, L. S. Y. Jahnes, A. Gupta, T. Shaw, J. Z. Sun, and M. B. Ketchen, *Phys. Rev. Lett.* 73 (1994) 593.
[**10**] C. C. Tsuei and J. R. Kirtley, *Rev. Mod. Phys.* 72 (2000) 969.
[**11**] A. Sugimoto, T. Yamaguchi, and I. Iguchi, *Physica* C367 (2002) 28.
[**12**] I. Iguchi, W. Wang, M. Yamazaki, Y. Tanaka, and S. Kashiwaya, *Phys. Rev.* B62 (2000) R6131.
[**13**] J. Y. T. Wei, N. C. Yeh, W. D. Si, and X. X. Xi, *Physica B* 284-288 (2000) 973.
[**14**] C. Kendziora, R. J. Kelley, and M. Onellion, *Phys. Rev. Lett.* 77 (1996) 727.
[**15**] M. Oda, C. Manabe, and M. Ido, *Phys. Rev. B* 53, 2253 (1996).
[**16**] Y. Takano, T. Hatano, A. Fukuyo, A. Ishii, M. Ohmori, S. Arisawa, K. Togano, and M. Tachiki, *Phys. Rev.* B65 (2002) R140513.
[**17**] W. N. Hardy, D. A. Bonn, D. C. Morgen, R. Liang, and K. Zhang, *Phys. Rev. Lett.* 70 (1993) 3999.
[**18**] T. Hasegawa, M. Nantoh, A. Takagi, W. Yamaguchi, M. Ogino, M. Kawasaki, J. P. Gong, H. Koinuma, K. Kitazawa, *Physica B* 197 (1994) 617.
[**19**] Q. Li, Y. N. Tsay, M. Suenaga, R. A. Klemm, G. D. Gu, and N. Koshizuka, *Phys. Rev. Lett.* 83 (1999) 4160.
[**20**] H. T. Kim, H. Minami, W. Schmidbauer, J. W. Hodby, A. Iyo, F. Iga, and H. Uwe, *J. Low Tem. Phys.* 105 (3/4) (1996) 557; cond-mat/0206432.
[**21**] P. Kostic, B. Veal, A. P. Paulikas, U. Welp, V. R. Todt, C. Gu, U. Geiser, J. M. Williams, K. D. Carlson, and R. A. Klemm, *Phys. Rev. B* 53 (1996) 791.
[**22**] A. P. Nielsen, A. B. Cawthorne, P. Barbara, F. C. Wellstood, C. J. Lobb, R. S. Newrock, and M. G. Forrester, *Phys. Rev. B* 62 (2000) 14380.
[**23**] M. R. Koblischka, L. Pust. N. Chikumoto, M. Murakami, B. Nilsson, and T. Claeson, *Physica B* 284-288 (2000) 599.
[**24**] A. Kohen, Y. Dagen, and G. Deutscher, *Physica C* 349 (2001) 53.
[**25**] Y.Eltsev, K.Nakao, Y.Yamada, I.Hirabayshi, N.Koshizuka, *Physica C* 367 (2002) 24.
[**26**] H. T. Kim, K. Y. Kang, and S. K. Han, *IEEE Trans. Appl. Supercon.* 11 (2001) 3415.
[**27**] J. A. Skinta, M. S. Kim, T. R. Lemberger, T. Greibe, M. Naito, *Phys. Rev. Lett.* 88 (2002) 207005.
[**28**] R. Kleiner, M. Mößle, W. Walkenhorst, G. Hechtfischer, K. Schlenga, and Paul Müller, *Physica C* 282-287 (1997) 2435.
[**29**] M. Miyakawa, J. F. Zasadzinski, L. Ozyuzer, P. Guptasarma, D. G. Hinks, C. Kendziora, and K. E. Gray, *Phys. Rev. Lett.* 83 (1999) 1018.
[**30**] A. Mourachkine, *J. Supercond.* 14 (2001) 375.
[**31**] S. H. Pan, J. P. O'Neel, R. L. Badzey, C. Chamon, H. Ding, J. R. Engelbrecht, Z. Wang, H. Eisaki, S. Uchida, A. K. Gupta, K.-W. Ng, E. W. Hudson, K. M. Lang, and J. C. Davis, *Nature* 413, 282 (2001).
[**32**] T. Cren, D. Roditchev, W. Sacks and J. Klein, *Eryophys. Lett.* 54, 84 (2001).
[**33**] C. Howald, P. Fournier, and A. Kapitulink, *Phys. Rev. B* 64, 100504 (R) (2001).
[**34**] K. M. Lang, V. Madhavan, J. E. Hoffman, E. W. Hudson, H. Eisaki, S. Uchida, and J. C. Davis, *Nature* 415, 412 (2002).
[**35**] H. T. Kim, K. Y. Kang, W. J. Kim, Y. N. Choi, B. J. Kim, and Y. C. Kim, *J. Korean Phy. Soc.* 39 (2001) 1013.

[**36**] A. Chainani, T. Yokoya, T. Kiss, S. Shin, T. Nishio, and H. Uwe, *Phys. Rev. B* 64 (2001) 180509(R).
[**37**] B. J. Kim, Y. C. Kim, H. T. Kim, K. Y. Kang, and J. M. Lee, in press *Physica C*.
[**38**] V. M. Krasnov, A. Yurgens, D. Winkler, P. Delsing, and T. Claeson, *Phys. Rev. Lett.* 84, 5860 (2000).
[**39**] N. Miyakawa, J. F. Jasadzinski, M. Asano, D. Henmi, S. Oonuki, K. Sasaki, T. Kaneko, L. Ozyuzer, and K. E. Gray, *Physica C* 357-360, 126 (2001).
[**40**] I. Bozovic, G. Logvenov, M. A. J. Verhoeven, P. Caputo, E. Goldobin, and T. H. Geballe, *Nature* 422 (2003) 873.
[**41**] D. Budelmann, J. Holmlund, J. Andreasson, H. Rodriguez, J. Bäckström, L. Börjesson, H. Adrian, U. Merkt, and M. Rübhausen, *Phys. Rev.B* 67 (2003) 140507(R).
[**42**] H. T. Kim, *Phys. Rev.* B 54 (1996) 90.
[**43**] H. T. Kim, *Physica C* 341-348 (2000) 259.
[**44**] H. T. Kim, *New Trends in Superconductivity* (Ed. J. F. Annet and S. Kruchinin, Kluwer, 2002), *NATO Science Series* Vol. II/67, p. 137; cond-mat/0110112.
[**45**] H. T. Kim, *J. Phys. Soc. Jpn* 71 (2002) 2106.
[**46**] T. M. Rice and L. Sneddon, *Phys. Rev. Lett.* 47 (1981) 689.
[**47**] H. T. Kim, B. G. Chae, D. H. Youn, S. L. Maeng, G. Kim, K. Y. Kang, and Y. S. Lim, *New J. Physics* 6 (2004) 52 (Online at http://www.njp.org/).
[**48**] W. F. Brinkman and T. M. Rice, *Phys. Rev. B* 2 (1970) 4302.
[**49**] N. Miyakawa, P. Guptasarma , J. F. Zasadzinski, D. G. Hinks, and K. E. Gray, *Phys. Rev. Lett.* 80 (1998) 157.
[**50**] Ch. Renner, B. Revaz, J.-Y. Genoud, K. Kadowaki, and Ø. Fisher, *Phys. Rev. Lett.* 80 (1998) 149.
[**51**] N. Miyakawa, J. F. Zasadzinski, M. Asano, D. Henmi, S. Oonuki, K. Sasaki, T. Kaneko, L. Ozyuzer, and K. E. Gray, *Physica C* 357-360 (2001) 126.
[**52**] D. Coffey and L. Coffey, *Phys. Rev. Lett.* 70 (1993) 1529.
[**53**] H. Won and K. Maki, *Phys. Rev. B* 49 (1994) 1397.
[**54**] J. F. Zasadzinski, L. Ozyuzer, N. Miyakawa, K. E. Gray, D. G. Hinks, and C. Kendziora, *Phys. Rev. Lett.* 87 (2001) 067005.
[**55**] T. Cren, D. Roditchev, W. Sacks, J. Klein, J.-B. Moussy, C. Deville-Cavellin, and M. Lagues, *Phys. Rev. Lett.* 84 (2000) 147.
[**56**] Z.Wang, J.R. Engelbrecht, S.Wang, H. Ding, S.H. Pan, *Phys. Rev. B* 65 (2002) 64509.
[**57**] V.M. Krasnov, A.E. Kovalev, A.Yurgens, D. Winkler, *Phys. Rev. Lett.* 86 (2001) 2657.
[**58**] A. Yurgens, D. Winkler, T. Claeson, S.-J. Hwang, and J.-H. Chey, *Physica C* 362 (2001) 286 (2001).
[**59**] Yu. I. Latyshev, T. Yamashita, L. N. Bulaevskii, M. J. Graf, A. V. Balatsky, and M. P. Maley, *Phys. Rev. Lett.* 82 (1999) 5345.
[**60**] A. Kaminski, J. Mesot, H. Fretwell, J. C. Campuzano, M. R. Norman, M. Randeria, H. Ding, T. Sato, T. Takahashi, T. Mochiku, K. Kadowaki, and H. Hoechst, *Phys. Rev. Lett.* **84** (2000) 1788.
[**61**] T. Valla, A. V. Fedorov, P. D. Johnson, B. O. Wells, S. L. Hulbert, Q. Li, G. D. Gu, and N. Koshizuka, *Science* **285** (1999) 2110.
[**62**] R. J. Kelley, C. Quitmann, M. Onellion, H. Berger, P. Almeras, and G. Margaritondo, *Science* **271** (1996) 1255.
[**63**] Y. Kohsaka, T. Sasagawa, F. Ronning, T. Yoshida, C. Kim, T. Hanaguri, M. Azuma, M. Takano, Z. X. Shen, and H. Takagi; *cond-mat/0209339*.
[**64**] H. Ding, M. R. Norman, J. C. Campuzano, M. Randeria, A. F. Bellman, T. Yokoya,

T. Takahashi, T. Mochiku, and K. Kadowaki, *Phys. Rev. B* 54 (1996) R9678.
[**65**] T. Hasegawa, M. Nantoh, A. Takagi, W. Yamaguchi, M. Ogino, M. Kawasaki, J. P. Gong, H. Koinuma, and K. Kitazawa, *Physica B* 197 (1994) 617-623.
[**66**] N. Kim, Y. J. Doh, H. S. Chang, and H. J. Lee, *Phys. Rev. B* 59 (1999) 14639.
[**67**] R. J. Kelley, C. Quitmann, M. Onellion, H. Berger, P. Almeras, and G. Margaritondo, *Science* 271 (1996) 1255.
[**68**] M. Mößle and R. Kleiner, *Phys. Rev. B* 59, 4486 (1999).
[**69**] R. Kleiner, M. Mößle, W. Walkenhorst, G. Hechtfischer, K. Schlenga, and P. Mueller, *Physica C* 282-287 (1997) 2435.
[**70**] L. Ozyuzer, J. F. Zasadzinski, C. Kendziora, K. E. Gray, *Phys. Rev. B* 61 (2000) 3629.
[**71**] A. Irie and G. Oya, *Physica C* 367 (2002) 393.
[**72**] A. Irie, T. Mimura, M. Okano, and G. Oya, *Supercond. Sci. Technol.* 14 (2001) 1097.
[**73**] R. Kleiner, A, S. Katz, A. G. Sun, R. Summer, D. A. Gajewski, S. H. Han, S. I. Woods, E. Dantsker, B. Chen, K. Chr, M. B. Maple, R. C. Dynes, and J. Clarke, *Phys. Rev. Lett.* 76 (1996) 2161.
[**74**] A.G. Sun, D.A. Gajewski, M.B. Maple, R.C. Dynes, *Phys. Rev. Lett.* 72 (1994) 2267.
[**75**] H. Arie, K. Yasuda, H. Kobayashi, I. Iguchi, Y. Tanaka, and S. Kashiwaya, *Phys. Rev. B* 62 (2000) 11864.
[**76**] V. Ambegaokar and A. Baratoff, *Phys. Rev. Lett.* 10 (1963) 486: *Phys. Rev. Lett.* 11 (1963) 104 (Erratum).
[**77**] P.W. Anderson, *Lectures on the many-Body Problem* (Academic,New York,1964), p.113.
[**78**]A. Mourachkine, *High-Temperature Superconductivity in Cuprates: The Nonlinear Mechanism and Tunneling Measurements*, (Kluwer Academic, 2002).
[**79**]J. L. Tallon and J. W. Loram, *Physica C* 349 (2001) 53.
[**80**]C.C.Tsuei and J. R. Kirtley, *Rev. Mod. Phys.* 72 (2000) 969.
[**81**]J. R. Kirtley, C.C.Tsuei, and K. A. Moler, *Science* 285 (1999) 1373.
[**82**]I. Iguchi, private communication.
[**83**] The flux in the right hand of Eq. (5) is equal to the half-flux quantum observed by experiments; $\rho(\Phi_i/2) = (\Phi_0/2)_{obs}$, where Φ_i is an intrinsic flux to be evaluated and $(\Phi_0/2)_{obs}$ is a value observed by Tsuei *et al.* and Sugimoto *et al.*. Thus $\Phi_i = \frac{1}{\rho}\Phi_0 > \Phi_0$ due to $0< \rho <1$.
[**84**] C. R. Chen, S. X. Li, J. L. Wen, and W. P. Jia, *Mater. Sci. Eng.* A282 (2000) 170.
[**85**]S. Care and A. Zaoui, *Acta Mater.* 44 (1996) 1323.
[**86**]C.C.Tsuei and J. R. Kirtley, *Physica C* 367 (2002) 1.
[**87**] C.D. Leo, G.Rotoli, P.Barbara, A.P. Nielsen, C.J. Lobb, *Phys. Rev. B* 64 (2001) 144518.
[**88**]D. A. Wollman, D. J. Van Harlingen, W. C. Lee, D. M. Ginsberg, and A. J. Leggett, *Phys. Rev. Lett.* 71 (1993) 2134.
[**89**]D. A. Wollman, D. J. Van Harlingen, A. J. Leggett, *Phys. Rev. Lett.* 73 (1994) 1872.
[**90**] R. A. Klemm, *Phys. Rev. Lett.* 73 (1994) 1871.
[**91**] R. A. Klemm, *Phys. Rev. B* 67 (2003) 174509.
[**92**] Y. Takano, Y. Hatano, M. Ohmori, S. Kawakami, A. Ishii, S. Arisawa, S.-J. Kim, T. Yamashita, K. Togano, and M. Tachiki, *Proceedings of the MOS2002*, to be published.
[**93**] Q. Li, Y. N. Tsay, M. Suenaga, R. A. Klemm, G. D. Gu, and N. Koshizuka, *Phys. Rev. Lett.* 83 (1999) 4160 (1999).
[**94**] A. Abanov and A. V. Chubukov, *Phys. Rev. B* **61** (2000) R9241.
[**95**] S. Kashiwaya, Y. Tanaka, M. Koyanagi, H. Takashima, and K. Kajimura, *Phys. Rev. B* **51** (1995) 1350.

[**96**] Y. Tanaka and S. Kashiwaya, *Phys. Rev. Lett.* **74** (1995) 3451.
[**97**] J.Y.T. Wei, N.-C. Yeh, D.F. Garrigus, M. Strasik, *Phys. Rev. Lett.* **81** (1998) 2542.
[**98**] A. Kohen, Y. Dagan, and G. Deutscher, *Physica C* **341-348** (2000) 687.
[**99**] T. Ekino, Y. Sezaki, and H. Fujii, *Phys. Rev. B* **60** (1999) 6916.
[**100**] N. Klein, N. Tellmann, H. Schulz, K. Urban, S. A. Wolf, and V. Z. Kresin, *Phys. Rev. Lett.* 71 (1993) 3355.
[**101**] C. Panagopoulos, J. R. Cooper, T. Xing, G. B. Peacock, and I. Gameson, *Phys. Rev. Lett.* 79 (1997) 2320.
[**102**] J.R. Cooper, C.T. Chu, L.W. Zhou, B. Dunn, G. Gruner, *Phys. Rev. B* 37 (1988) 638.
[**103**] Z. Ma, R. C. Taber, L. W. Lombardo, A. Kapitulnik, M. R. Beasley, P. Merchant, C. B. Eom, S. Y. Hou, and J. M.Phillips, *Phys. Rev. Lett.* 71 (1993) 781.
[**104**] K. Devin and A. Kleinsasser, *Supercond. Sci. Technol.* 9 (1996) 227.
[**105**] V. Kresin, Yu. Ovchinnikov, and S. Wolf, *Appl. Phys. Lett.* 83 (2003) 722.

Processing and Characterization of MgB_2

Adriana C. Serquis and Xiaozhou Liao
Superconductivity Technology Center, Los Alamos National Laboratory
Los Alamos, NM 87545

We review our recent progress on the processing, structures and properties of MgB_2. In particular, we have used a *magnesium vapor infiltration process* (MVIP) to make high quality MgB_2 powder. We present detailed studies of the field and temperature dependence of the magnetization as well as scanning and transmission electron microscopy characterizations of samples prepared under different conditions. We compare the environmental stability, the critical current densities (J_c) and the creep relaxation rates of MgB_2 samples with different microstructures. The MgB_2 samples synthesized by MVIP were found to contain nanometer-sized $Mg(B,O)_2$ precipitates. Magnetization data show that such precipitates act as effective flux pinning centers, without deteriorating other superconducting properties such as T_c. The sizes and distribution of these precipitates can be controlled through processing, providing an attractive way to introduce flux pinning centers.
We also review our results on the effect of heat treatments on the microstructure, magnetization and transport properties of MgB_2 wires prepared by the powder-in-tube method. We discuss the optimization of the annealing conditions that strongly improve the connectivity by eliminating most of the microcracks present in the un-annealed wires. On the other hand, hot isostatic pressed (HIPed) wires have a higher J_c than the annealed wires, especially at high temperatures and magnetic fields, and higher irreversibility field. The improvement is attributed to a high density of structural defects, which are the likely source of vortex pinning.

Introduction

Since the discovery of superconductivity in MgB_2 with the critical temperature (T_c) at 39 K,[1] the highest T_c observed for a binary compound, considerable progress has been made in understanding the fundamental properties of this compound and in investigating the possibilities of using this simple material for technological applications (i.e. magnets and electronic devices). The relatively high critical temperature, low cost, and possible absence of weak links[2] that limit the critical current density, J_c, make this material an excellent candidate for the fabrication of wires and tapes that may compete with other superconductors (e.g. Nb-based or Bi-Sr-Ca-Cu-O superconductors).

There is a considerable consensus in the basic properties of MgB_2 regarding the structural, magnetic and transport properties that have been reviewed by several authors.[3,4,5] MgB_2 has a hexagonal structure with lattice parameters a=3.08 Å and c = 3.52 Å, as shown in Fig. 1. It contains honeycomb boron layers, which are separated by hexagonal close-packed layers of magnesium. The observed decrease in T_c with pressure[6] and the isotope effect[7] are consistent with the BCS theory. The main mechanism proposed for the high T_c in MgB_2 based on band-structure calculations.[8,9,10,11] These theories suggest that superconductivity in MgB_2 results from strong electron-phonon interactions and the presence of a high phonon frequency associated with the motion of the light boron atoms, with a distinctive feature: the simultaneous existence of two energy gaps in the same material.

Although MgB_2 had already been available from chemical suppliers before it was found to exhibit superconducting properties, the quality of commercially available MgB_2 powder is not as high as desired. Despite the fact that MgB_2 is a simple binary compound (only three atoms per hexagonal unit cell), it is hard to make by conventional methods because (1) elemental Mg has a high vapor pressure and (2) MgB_2 decomposes rather than melts at high temperature and ambient pressures. This has naturally led to the investigation of optimal MgB_2 synthesis processes. Various synthesis processes have been reported and it is now clear that different sample preparation methods lead to materials with different superconducting properties. However, available results are still far from being optimal. Better understanding of process-structure-property relationship and further improvement of synthesis processes for better superconductivity in MgB_2 are needed. In sections III and IV of this paper, we review the characteristics of high quality MgB_2 samples prepared by *magnesium vapor infiltration process* (MVIP).[12,13] We present detailed studies of the field and temperature dependence of the magnetization, as well as scanning electron microscopy (SEM) and transmission electron microscopy (TEM) characterization of samples prepared under different conditions.[14]

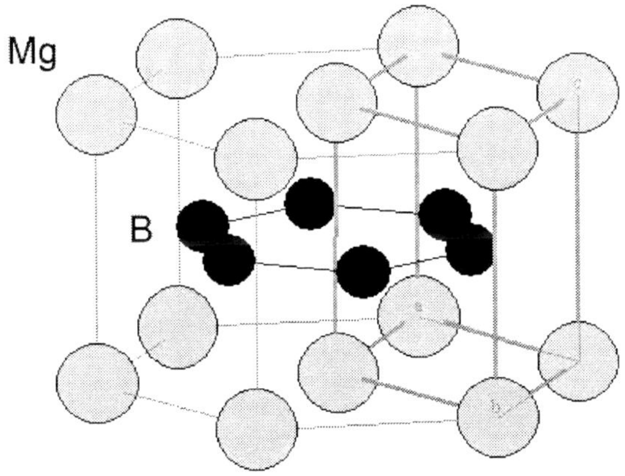

Figure 1. Crystal structure of MgB_2.

The interest for the commercial applications of MgB_2 superconductor are mainly based on (1) the potential for low-cost production of wires using easily-scalable techniques such as powder-in-tube, and (2) the possibility of high critical currents due to the absence of weak-link behavior at grain boundaries (GB). However, to make practical devices, it is essential to understand several features like the stability of MgB_2 under service environment, and how to increase the current carrying capability of MgB_2 (including the temporal stability of supercurrents).

Regarding the stability of MgB_2, we notice that most high-temperature superconductors are highly sensitive to water and moisture.[15,16] Therefore, it is important to explore how exposing MgB_2 to air and water will affect its superconductivity. Zhai *et al.*[17] studied the degradation of superconducting fraction in MgB_2 films by exposure to water and have observed that the T_c of the films remains unchanged throughout the degradation process. Little has been reported on the chemical stability of MgB_2, especially on its sensitivity to O_2, H_2O and CO_2 in ambient conditions. Observations on the MgB_2 reaction with air by other researchers suggested the presence of surface boron oxides[18] and magnesium oxide layers covering the MgB_2 grains.[19] Our results reviewed in section III (b) indicate that depending on synthesis conditions, some MgB_2 samples degrade with time when exposed to ambient conditions[20,21] This degradation is related to a surface decomposition as observed by X-ray Photoelectron Spectroscopy (XPS). We observed the formation of oxidized Mg, primarily in the form of a Mg hydroxide, the increase of C and O contents, and the reduction of B concentration in the surface layer of MgB_2 samples, which agree with the observation of Aswal *et al.*[22] In contrast, samples prepared by MVIP remain stable after exposure to ambient conditions for several months.

The critical current density (J_c) of the newly found superconductor MgB_2 was initially poor, especially in high magnetic fields (H), [2] much like in the early days of high T_c superconductors. To increase J_c, it is necessary to understand which structural features are the relevant pinning centers, and how to overcome the poor connectivity between grains. Concerning the first question, likely sources of vortex pinning include grain boundaries[23] (although the experimental evidence is inconclusive) and intra-grain defects.[24,25,26] The second question involves other aspects such as the influence of porosity, the formation of MgO phase at grain boundaries, and the grain connectivity.

Many types of crystal defects, such as dislocation networks,[27] stacking faults,[28] grain boundaries,[29,30] and non-superconducting impurity phases, can act as effective flux pinning centers in high T_c superconductors. A variety of techniques have been used to create crystal defects acting as local flux pinning centers in high-T_c superconductors, including chemical doping,[31] and ion,[32,33] neutron,[34] pulse-laser[35] and electron[36,37] irradiation. Some of these techniques have also been successfully applied to the MgB_2 system.[38,39] Although these techniques increase J_c, they might also introduce a negative effect on T_c.[37,40] Furthermore, many of these techniques are complex and need extra procedures and/or expensive facilities for sample processing. In section IV we review the characteristics of nanometer-sized $Mg(B,O)_2$ precipitate defects presented in the MgB_2 samples synthesized by MVIP.[23,25,41] A detailed TEM investigation on the structures and compositions of the precipitates is presented. We also discuss the effect of the precipitates in different size ranges on flux pinning. Magnetization data show that such precipitates act as flux pinning centers, without affecting other superconducting properties such as T_c. The sizes and distribution of these precipitates can be controlled through processing, providing an attractive way to introduce flux pinning centers.

The question of grain connectivity is more relevant for MgB_2 wires and tapes required for applications, in which fabrication and processing conditions strongly affect microstructures and current carrying capability. The most promising technique for the production of wires or tapes seems to be the powder-in-tube (PIT) method,[42] because of the ceramic-like properties of MgB_2. In this method, MgB_2 powder or a mixture of Mg and B powders with stoichiometric composition are packed in a metal tube, cold worked into wires or tapes, and usually heat-treated afterwards. A key issue on which there is no agreement in the literature is the optimization of the heat treatment parameters. Although some post-annealing appears to be necessary to achieve higher J_c,[43,44,45] some authors reported detrimental effects of heat treatments in the performance of MgB_2 wires or tapes.[46,47] In section V, we review the main results obtained in MgB_2 wires prepared by PIT, and we establish a clear relationship among annealing conditions, modifications in the microstructure, and changes in J_c.[48,49,50,51] We summarize the main conclusions in section VI.

Experimental

Sample preparation

The MgB_2 bulk samples were prepared by solid-state reaction using different processes (see Table I). Amorphous boron powder (-325 mesh, 99.99% Alfa Æsar) and Mg turnings (99.98% Puratronic) were used as starting materials. Samples A-B were prepared by MVIP[12] using an atomic ratio of Mg:B = 1:1, varying synthesis temperatures and times, under flowing Ar (using three different sets of heat treatment parameters). The boron powder was pressed into pellets with dimensions of 5 mm diameter x 4 mm thickness. For sample A, boron pellets and Mg turnings were wrapped in Ta foil and placed in an alumina crucible inside a tube furnace under ultra-high purity (UHP) Ar, heated for one hour at 900°C, slowly cooled down at the speed of 0.5°C/min to 500°C, heated again for one hour at 900°C, slowly cooled again down to 500°C, and then furnace cooled to room temperature. Sample B was also placed in an alumina crucible inside a tube furnace under UHP Ar, heated at 900°C for one hour and fast cooled to room temperature without exposure to air. Sample C was sealed in a quartz tube under UHP Ar atmosphere and placed into the furnace. This sample was heated for one hour at 900°C, slowly cooled down at 0.5°C/min to 600°C and then removed and quenched in water. For comparison, we have prepared another sample of MgB_2 (Sample D), starting with a stoichiometric mixture of boron and magnesium following the standard procedure of other authors as described elsewhere.[7]

Table I - Synthesis parameters and Tc for MgB_2 bulk samples.

Sample	Starting Materials & Processing States	Mg:B	Temp	Time	Cooling	Annealing
A	Mg turnings + B powder pellets	1:1	900°C	2 h	slow	Ar flux
B	Mg turnings + B powder pellets	1:1	900°C	1 h	fast	Ar flux
C	Mg turnings + B powder pellets	1:1	900°C	1 h	quenched	Quartz tube
D	Mg turnings + B powder	1:2	950°C	2 h	fast	Quartz tube
A-HIP	Sample A HIPed	--	1000°C	2 h	fast	P=200 MPa

Part of sample A was ground into powder and hot isostatically pressed (HIPed) at 200 MPa to form the HIPed sample (A-HIP). The HIPing was carried out in an ABB Mini-HIPer unit using a cycle cooling under pressure with a maximum temperature of 1000°C, as described elsewhere.[13,52,53,54]

For the PIT MgB_2 wires, commercially available MgB_2 powder (-325 mesh, 98% Alfa Æsar), with additional 5 at.% Mg powder (-325 mesh, 99.8% Alfa Æsar) as extra source of magnesium, was ball milled for two hours and packed into stainless steel tubes 304 with inner and outer diameters of 4.6 and 6.4 mm, respectively, under Ar atmosphere. The tubes were cold-drawn (with an intermediate annealing) into round wires several-meters-long with final external diameter of 0.8-1.4 mm. Details about the heat treatments of MgB_2 wires are described in section VI (see Table IV).

Sample characterization

Powder X-ray diffraction (XRD) data were collected using a Scintag XDS2000 Θ–2Θ powder diffractometer. XRD suggests that all samples are mainly MgB_2 with small amount of MgO. Sample surface morphology and microstructures were investigated using a JEOL 6300FX SEM equipped with an X-ray energy dispersive spectrometer (EDS).

Samples for TEM investigation were prepared by grinding the MgB_2 pellets or wires mechanically to a thickness of about 30 μm and then further thinning to a thickness of electron transparency using a Gatan precision ion polishing system with Ar^+ accelerating voltage of 3.5 kV. TEM bright-field diffraction contrast imaging and electron diffraction investigations were carried out using a Philips CM30 TEM working at 300 kV. High-resolution transmission electron microscopy (HREM) investigations were carried out using a JEOL 3000F TEM working at 300 kV. Composition analysis and elemental mapping were performed in a JEOL 2010F TEM with a field emission gun working at 200 kV. The JEOL 2010F is equipped with an Oxford EDS system and a Gatan image filtering system. The elemental maps were obtained using energy-filtered imaging (EFI) and the three-window technique was used for background removal.[55] The boron K-edge at 188 eV in the electron energy loss spectrum was used for boron mapping, and the centers of two pre-edge windows were set at 148 and 168 eV with a slit width of 20 eV. Oxygen maps were obtained using the oxygen K-edge at 532 eV with the centers of two pre-edge windows set at 492 and 512 eV, respectively, with a slit width of 20 eV. To avoid the channeling effect when collecting EDS and electron energy loss spectra (EELS),[56] strong diffraction conditions were avoided by orienting the specimen away from any main zone-axis. Strong diffraction conditions were also prevented in the elemental mapping because the background removal procedure in the three-window technique is unable to totally eliminate the intensity changes caused by diffraction contrast variations that occur between images acquired at different energy losses, leaving artifacts in the final EFI.[57,58]

A Quantum Design SQUID magnetometer was used to investigate the dc magnetization, M, of bulk, powder and wire samples. M vs. temperature (T) was measured at magnetic field H = 10-20 Oe after zero field cooling (ZFC) and field cooling (FC). Magnetization loops M(H) were measured between 5 K and 40 K (i.e., slightly above the T_c of MgB_2). When measuring PIT wires the 40 K loops were used to discount the stainless steel contribution. In all cases the stainless steel exhibits hysteresis only for $H < 1000$ Oe, and its magnitude is very low when compared with the superconductor hysteresis. From the superconducting contribution of the 5-30K loops the magnetic J_c was calculated using the Bean critical state model[59] in those cases where it was appropriate (see below).

A sample for X-ray Photoelectron Spectroscopy (XPS) was prepared by hot isostatic pressing (HIP), since this technique is advantageous in producing fully dense bulk MgB_2 samples suitable for surface analysis. All high resolution XPS spectra were collected with a Physical Electronics 5600ci XPS system equipped with an Omni IV hemispherical capacitor analyzer in retarding mode of operation and a pass energy of 23.5 eV; details of sample preparation and collection data are given elsewhere.[19] Atomic concentrations were calculated for the XPS spectra using the following relative sensitivity factors determined for the XPS system used: B1s 0.171, C1s 0.314, O1s 0.733, Mg2p 0.167.

The dc transport critical current, I_c, of MgB_2 wires was measured at 4 K and 26.5 K, with the wires immersed in liquid He and Ne, respectively, with the field H applied perpendicular to the wire axis. Cu-tape current contacts were soldered on the stainless steel, which was previously electroplated with Cu on the contact regions to improve the wetting. We found that the I-V curves of short pieces of wire (~3-4 cm) frequently exhibit an initial ohmic behavior. This is a consequence of the poor connectivity between the MgB_2 and the stainless steel, which results in a transfer length for the current a couple of cm long, so some current is always flowing through the stainless steel. For this reason we performed all transport measurements on pieces ~10 cm long, where this artifact was minimized and the I-V curves showed no ohmic background. Voltage contacts were placed ~1 cm apart, and we defined I_c using a 1 μV criterion.

Superconductivity in MgB_2 bulk samples

Superconducting transition and surface morphology

Figure 2 shows the magnetization data of the as-made MgB_2 bulk samples. It is seen that Samples A, A-HIP, and B have very sharp transitions and the T_c onset slightly changes after HIPing, due to a strain effect.[51] The broadening in the transition corresponding to samples C and D are related to poor connectivity and small grain size, as it was confirmed by SEM observations (see Table II).

Figures 3(a), (b), (c) and (d) show the surface morphology of samples A, B, C, and D, respectively. Well-developed grains of around 0.3-5 μm can be seen on the surface of samples A and B. However, the grains are not well connected on the surface. Sample C presents the smallest grains and the worst connectivity, while sample D is a powder. In contrast, the grains in the A-HIP sample (Fig. 3 (e)) are well compacted. The high density of the HIPed sample makes it possible to prepare a polished shiny surface of mirror quality (Fig. 3 (f)).

The transition broadening in samples C and D can be explained by the penetration length $\lambda(T)$ and its dependence on temperature, which follows the relationship:

$$\lambda(T) = \frac{\lambda(0)}{\sqrt{1-(T/Tc)^2}} \quad (1)$$

where $\lambda(0)$ = 110-180 nm, for MgB_2.[3] Therefore, the penetration length can be significantly larger than the particle size at temperatures near T_c (leading to transition broadening) and decreases with temperature. It can be seen that isolated particles with sizes less than 1 μm exist in both samples (Fig. 3(c) and (d)). These particles are smaller than the penetration length near T_c, and a lower temperature is needed to expel the magnetic field from most of the particles volume, giving rise to the transition broadening.

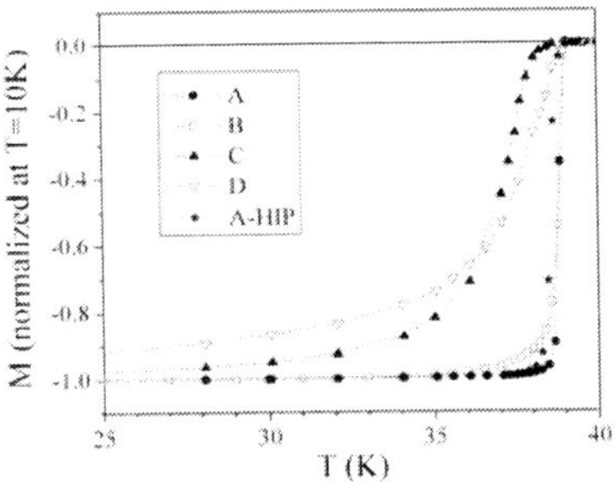

Figure 2. Magnetic susceptibility of as-made MgB_2 samples A, B, C, D and A-HIP (described in Table I) as a function of temperature. A constant magnetic field of 10 Oe was applied.

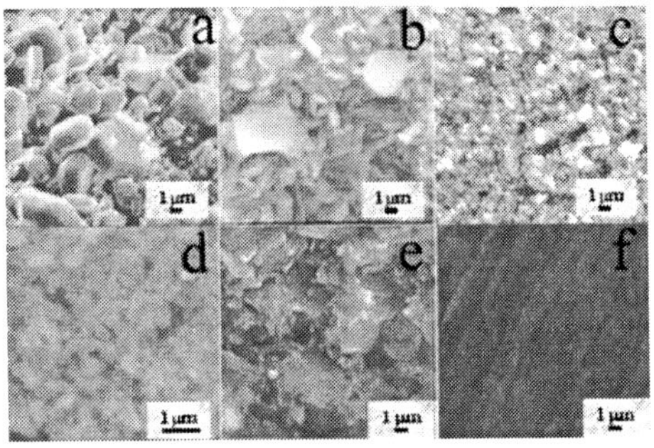

Figure 3. SEM micrographs of MgB_2 samples: (a) A, (b) B, (c) C, (d) D, (e) A-HIP and (f) polished A-HIP samples.

Table II - Tc, and grain size (observed by SEM) for MgB_2 samples.

Sample	T_c [K]	$T_c^{(10\text{-}90\%)}$[K]	Grain size [m]
A	38.9	0.4	0.5-5.0
B	38.9	0.8	0.3-3.0
C	38.8	4.3	0.1-0.5
D	38.9	10.3	0.2-1.0
A-HIP	38.8	0.5	

Environmental stability

To study the stability of MgB_2 under ambient conditions, we measured the superconducting transition of the same samples A – D several times at a time interval of a few months. Figures 4 (a), (b) and (c) plot the ZFC dc magnetization vs. temperature for samples A, C, and D, respectively, measured at different times. It is seen that Sample A, which was prepared with excess Mg and had larger grain sizes, remained stable for several months under ambient conditions. The same behavior is observed in samples B and A-HIP. In contrast, samples C and D underwent a slow degradation. Figure 4 (b) shows that the superconducting fraction of sample C at 10 K was reduced by ~13% and the superconducting transition became broader (ΔT_c =15.3 K). The behavior of sample C was similar to sample B, with a reduction of the superconducting fraction by ~10 %. The XRD patterns of samples A, B, and D suggest no structural change with time, while the XRD patterns of sample C show the decrease of the MgB_2 phase intensity and the presence of a new very broad peak (in the 30-40 2θ region), which corresponds to the formation of an amorphous phase (see Fig. 5). Similar results were reported by Aswal et al.,[21] who studied the degradation behavior of polycrystalline MgB_2 superconductor exposed to water and ambient atmosphere. They found that prolonged exposure to water completely destroys superconductivity.

Optical microscopic and XRD analyses of their samples indicate that, on exposure to water, the material becomes amorphous like.

To study the nature of MgB_2 degradation, we performed XPS analysis on sample A- HIP, which is fully dense and therefore is suitable for surface analysis. The surface cleaned by Ar ion sputtering (estimated 300 Å of material removed) was taken as the intrinsic state, hereafter referred to as the initial one. XPS shows that the initial MgB_2 still has residual O and C present. The initial Mg-to-B ratio is lower than 1:2, which may indicate the presence of Mg vacancies in the external layer of the samples.

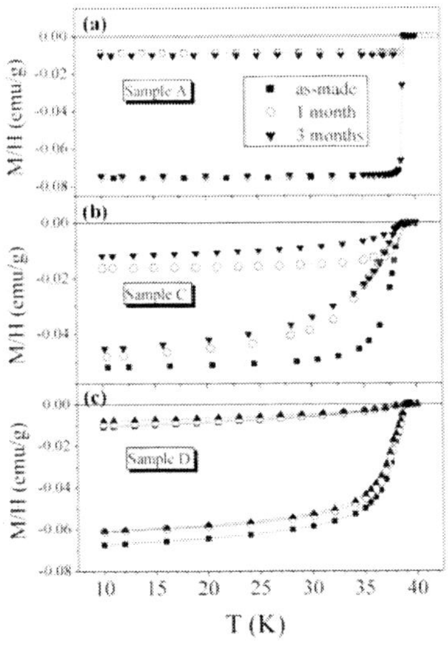

Figure 4- Magnetic susceptibility of MgB_2 samples A, C and D as a function of temperature for different ageing times. A constant magnetic field of 10 Oe was applied.

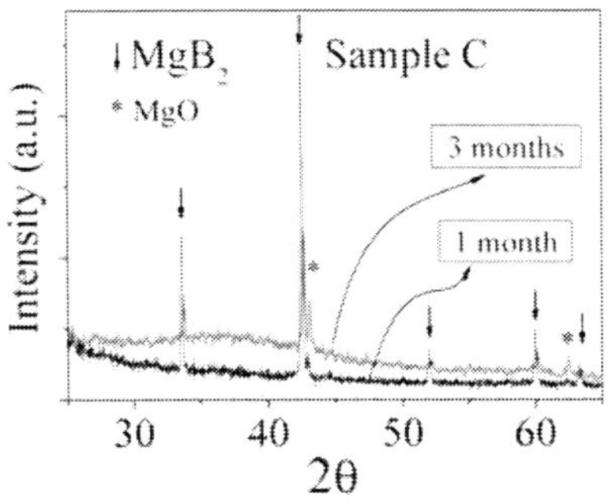

Figure 5- XRD pattern of the MgB_2 Sample C after 1 and 3 months.

The relative atomic concentrations of Mg, B, C, and O as a function of time are shown in Fig. 6. Most of compositional changes took place within the first 12 hours of exposure to air. The surface layer appeared to reach a constant composition in approximately 400 hours of air exposure. The relative Mg content in the surface layer dropped only slightly at a short exposure time (5 minutes), and then remained relatively constant. The B content, however, dropped rapidly and the O and C amounts climbed rapidly at short exposure time. This suggests that B in the MgB_2 was replaced by O and C containing species through reaction with O_2, CO_2 (and possibly also other C containing species), and H_2O in air. The increase in C content was also evidenced by the increase of the C1s peak intensity with air exposure, and the addition of oxidized C (but not fully $MgCO_3$ like) after longer exposure time. Likewise, the O1s peak intensity grew with increasing air exposure, and there was a shift to higher binding energy from 531.1 eV to 532.0 eV. The binding energies for sample A-HIP and the standards are summarized in Table III. We also observed a relatively broad O1s feature that suggests the presence of several chemically distinct oxygen species, in agreement with the observation of B_2O_3 and MgO by other authors.[17,18] The Mg2p photoemission line, which has a relatively insensitive binding energy with chemical environment,[60] showed only a slight shift to higher binding energy with air exposure. Similarly, the B1s photoemission line showed only slight increases in binding energy with increasing air exposure. In both the Mg2p and the B1s cases, the greatest changes in chemical state took place within the first 12 hours of exposure.

In addition to the photoemission lines, the x-ray excited Mg KLL Auger transition was monitored. With increasing air exposure, the low energy feature at 302.1 eV, which is the signature of the intrinsic MgB_2, dropped in intensity, while the feature at 306.6 eV, which is the signature of oxidized Mg, increased in intensity (see Fig. 7 (a)). In order to sort out the specific chemical state of this oxidized Mg, several standards were examined. Figure 7 (b) shows the Mg KLL spectra for MgO, $MgCO_3$, $Mg(OH)_2$, and spectra acquired from an initial sample (sputter cleaned) and from a sample exposed to air for 1278 hours, hereafter referred to as air-exposed. Of the three oxidized Mg standards, the $Mg(OH)_2$ most closely matches the peak location in the air-exposed spectrum and the energy of the Mg2p photoemission line (see Table III). Therefore, we believe that the major degradation product in the MgB_2 from air exposure is $Mg(OH)_x$. However, it is also possible that the oxidized magnesium is in a mixed chemical environment, having some components of MgO and Mg oxycarbon in addition to the Mg hydroxide. Thus, a Mg oxy-hydroxide layer was formed on the surface of the sample. It is also possible that Mg oxy-hydroxide was formed at the grain boundaries in polycrystalline samples. These results are in agreement with those reported by Aswal *et al.*,[21] who also observed through XPS the formation of $Mg(OH)_2$, $MgCO_3$ and B_2O_3, even at room temperature.

By assuming homogeneous Mg oxy-hydroxide overlayer thickness on the surface of the air-exposed sample, the thickness was calculated to be about 20 Å, based on the ratio of the Mg KLL line intensity contribution from the intrinsic MgB2 lineshape and the contribution from the Mg hydroxide intensity from the Mg(OH)2 standard lineshape.61 Assuming a spherical grain, the percentage of oxy-hydroxide is only 0.1% for a grain with a diameter of 5 μm, but 6 % for a grain with a radius of 0.1 μm. Therefore, large-grained or well-sintered samples (e.g. Samples A, B,

Table III - Binding energies for MgB_2 sample A-HIP, Mg metal, MgO, $Mg(OH)_2$, and $MgCO_3$.

Binding energies (eV)	**Mg2p**	**MgKLL**	**O1s**	**B1s**
MgB_2 sputtered	50.1	302.1	531.1	187.2
MgB_2 air exposed	50.7	306.6	532.0	187.5
Mg metal	49.7	301.0		
B metal				189.4
MgO standard	49.4	304.6	529.5	
$Mg(OH)_2$ standard	50.3	306.2	531.8	
$MgCO_3$ standard	51.3	307.2	532.5	

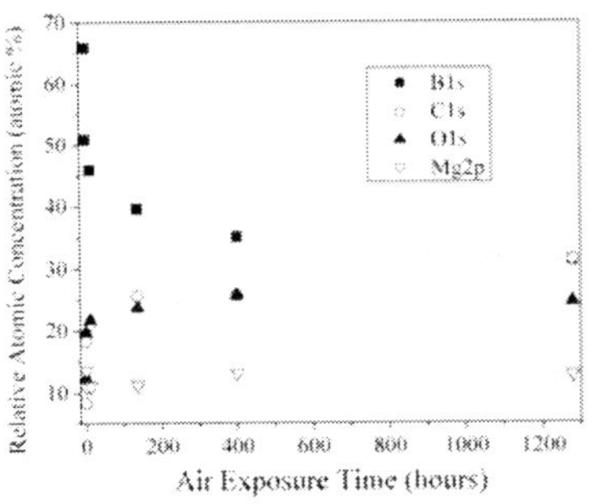

Figure 6. Relative atomic concentration (%) as a function of air exposure time for sample A-HIP.

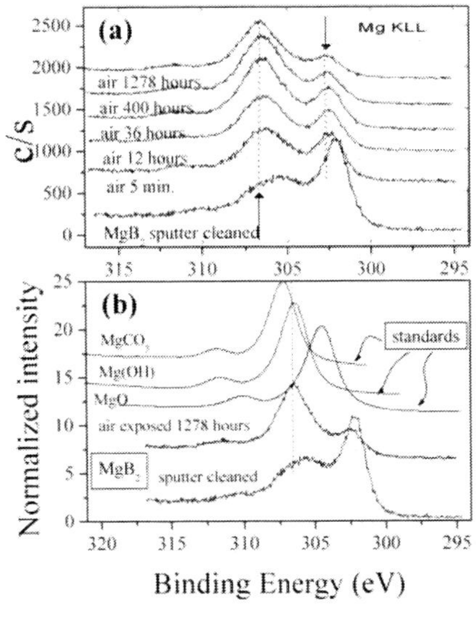

Figure 7. (a) XPS spectrum of Mg KLL for MgB_2 sample A-HIP after different air exposure times; (b) Mg KLL spectra for the MgO, the $Mg(OH)_2$, and the $MgCO_3$ standards, and the initial and air-exposed spectrums of (a).

and A-HIP) will not be affected by these surface reactions. However, a significant fraction of the samples will degrade in samples with smaller grain sizes (e.g. samples C and D). Schmidt *et al.*[62] suggested that chemical modifications of the surface (e.g. MgB_2 reaction with water) could potentially produce a layer with a lower T_c. These authors also suggested that if Mg vacancies are present in the near-surface regions, H^+ could enter the vacant Mg^{2+} positions in the MgB_2 structure, or possibly form MgO.[11] To investigate if the Meissner degradation effect was related to Mg vacancies in MgB_2 samples, we determined the Mg occupancy by Rietveld analysis of powder XRD data of these samples using the computer program GSAS.[63] It was found that all these samples had Mg vacancies lower than 0.01, much lower than 5% reported previously in other samples.[51] However, it is necessary to point out that XRD analysis does not accurately determine the Mg vacancies in the surface layer. The excess Mg in the initial formulation of the samples could help to prevent the presence of Mg vacancies, and might also have played a role in the formation of well-sintered samples of high quality.

In summary, the degradation of MgB_2 in air was caused by a surface decomposition as observed by XPS. Upon air exposure, the surfaces and possibly also the interfaces oxidized, and more specifically in this case, hydroxylated, to form magnesium oxy-hydroxide. Samples with small grain sizes and that are not well sintered are more susceptible to degradation when exposed to air. High-quality stable samples can be synthesized using our method, which requires the presence of excess Mg in an open atmosphere under Ar flux.

Critical current and microstructure in MgB_2 bulk samples

Microstructures and defects

In this section we present a microstructural study of the defects presented in samples A, B, and C prepared by MVIP. The synthesis conditions of these samples have been described in Table I. Instead of using the four-index notation system, we will be using the three-index notation system to index the hexagonal MgB_2 crystal in this work.

Figure 8(a) shows a typical [010] zone-axis bright-field TEM image of a MgB_2 crystallite in sample A. The (001) plane of the crystallite parallels to the vertical edges of the figure and a (100) plane parallels to the horizontal edges of the figure. A large number of precipitates with a size range from about 10 nm up to larger than 100 nm are seen within the MgB_2 crystallite.[64] The fact that most of the precipitates appear dark in Fig. 8(a) implies that these precipitates are also under zone-axis imaging conditions. This was confirmed by nano-beam electron diffraction analysis of the precipitates. Figure 8(b) shows a typical [010] zone-axis bright-field TEM image of a MgB_2 crystallite in sample B, revealing only a few precipitates with sizes smaller than 50 nm, some are marked with black arrows, within the MgB_2 crystallite. In contrast, Fig. 8(c), a typical [010] zone-axis bright-field TEM image of a MgB_2 crystallite in sample C, shows no precipitate.

A rough estimation from typical images of sample A (see Fig. 8(a)) suggests that the densities of the precipitates with size ranges from 10 nm to 50 nm and from 50 nm to 100 nm are ~ $10^{15}/cm^3$ and ~ $10^{14}/cm^3$, respectively. Precipitates with the smallest sizes are spherical (see a typical example marked with "1") while precipitates with medium sizes are elliptical (see a typical example marked with "2"). Precipitates larger than 50 nm show clear facets (see a typical example marked with "4"). Note that the size-range of spherical and elliptical precipitates is partially overlapped. Evidence shows that elliptical precipitates could be formed through the coalescence of two closely located spherical precipitates during their growth process (see a typical example marked with "3").

The factors that affect the shape of a precipitate are interfacial energy and strain energy. As will be discussed later, smaller precipitates have the same lattice structure, a similar lattice parameter (electron diffraction cannot tell the difference in lattice parameter), and the same crystal orientation as the MgB_2 matrix. Therefore, strain energy is negligible. Since the crystal lattices of smaller precipitates and the matrix match very well in all interfacial planes, the interfacial energy should not vary much with the orientation of the interface between the smaller precipitates and the matrix. Therefore the smaller precipitates take the spherical shape, which has the smallest interfacial area (and therefore the smallest total interfacial energy).[65] However, with increasing precipitate size, the chemical difference between the precipitates and the MgB_2 matrix increases (see discussion on precipitate composition later). As a result, it is possible that interfaces along some specific planes [for example, (100)] have lower interfacial energy and the larger precipitates tend to become faceted along these planes.

The composition of the precipitates was investigated using EDS taken from very thin areas at sample edge. Figure 9 shows the EDS results of (a) the MgB_2 matrix, (b) a small precipitate of about 30 nm in diameter, and (c) a large faceted precipitate. A trace amount of oxygen is seen in the MgB_2 matrix while the oxygen content is higher in the small precipitate and only magnesium and oxygen signals are seen in the large precipitate.

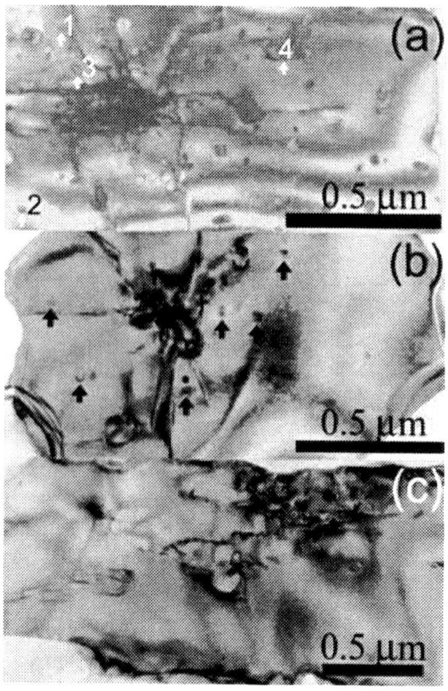

Figure 8. [010] zone-axis bright-field diffraction contrast images of a MgB_2 crystallite in (a) sample A, (b) sample B, and (c) sample C. In sample A, a high density of precipitates with different shapes and sizes are clearly seen. Some precipitates are labeled with "1", "2", "3", and "4" and indicated with arrows, demonstrating the change of shape with size and coalescence during the growth of the precipitates. Some precipitates in sample B are also indicated by arrows

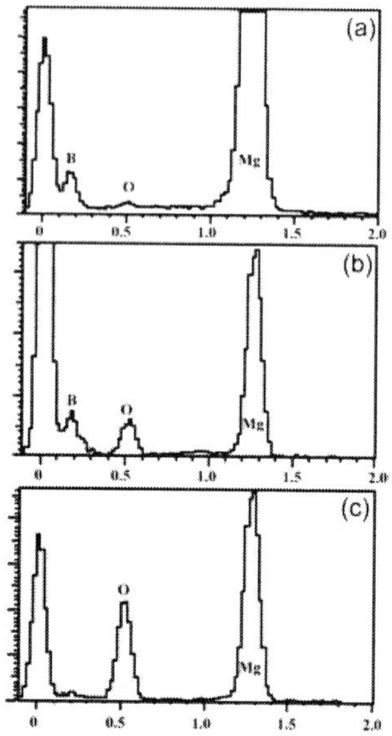

Figure 9- EDX spectra of (a) the MgB_2 matrix, (b) a small precipitate, and (c) a large faceted precipitate.

Because of the small precipitate sizes, signals from the surrounding matrix material might contribute to the EDS spectrum in Fig. 9 (b) and therefore, from the EDS spectrum itself, one cannot conclude that the precipitates is made up of magnesium, boron, and oxygen. Because precipitates include much more oxygen than the MgB_2 matrix, it is expected that the different chemical environments between the precipitates and the matrix will result in different near edge fine structures in the boron K-edge spectra, if the precipitate does contain boron. To confirm that small precipitates do contain boron, EELS analysis was carried out. The boron K-edge spectra obtained from the MgB_2 matrix and a small precipitate are shown in Fig. 10 (a) and (b), respectively. The boron K-edge fine structure in Fig. 10 (a) obtained from MgB_2 matrix is very similar to that of MgB_2 reported by Klie *et al.*[25] while clear difference is seen in Fig. 10 (b): the shoulder indicated by an arrow in (a) becomes a small peak in (b), also indicated by an arrow. The difference between the boron K-edge fine structures in Fig. 10 (a) and (b) directly proves that boron exists in the precipitate.

The fact that large precipitates contain mainly magnesium and oxygen while small precipitates contain all three elements (magnesium, boron, and oxygen) implies that the composition in precipitates varies with precipitate size. The oxygen content increases, while the boron content decreases, with increasing precipitate size, indicating the substitution of boron with oxygen. Unfortunately, it is not possible to quantitatively determine the composition-size relationship because influence from the matrix unavoidably affects the composition investigation of very small precipitates. Quantitative analysis of the EDS spectra in Fig. 9 using magnesium oxide (MgO) located at the MgB_2 grain boundaries as the standard sample suggests that the oxygen : magnesium ratio in the MgB_2 matrix is about 0.05, while the oxygen : magnesium ratio measured from the small precipitate is about 0.46. Given the fact that smaller precipitates have the same basic lattice structure as the MgB_2 matrix (see below), it is expected that the composition of the small precipitate remains the form of $Mg(B,O)_2$. Therefore, the composition of the precipitate that gives the spectrum in Fig. 9 (b) should be $MgB_{1.54}O_{0.46}$. Given the possibility that signals from the surrounding MgB_2 matrix material might contribute to the EDX spectrum in Fig. 9 (b), the real oxygen content in the precipitate might be higher than 0.46.

Oxygen in the sample is believed to have come from flowing UHP Ar during the MgB_2 synthesis process. A trace amount of oxygen in the UHP Ar, which was used as the protective gas, could dissolve into the MgB_2 at high synthesis temperatures. It is believed that MgB_2 has relatively high oxygen solubility at the synthesis temperature. When temperature decreased during the cooling process, the solubility of oxygen decreased, forcing the oxygen out of the MgB_2 lattice to form Mg(B,O) precipitates.

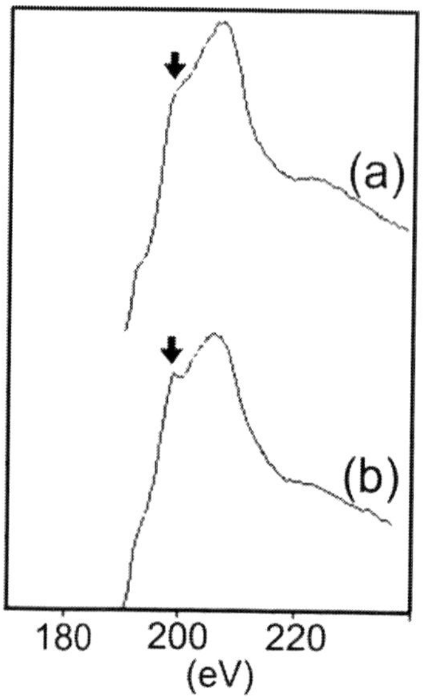

Figure 10- EELS spectra taken from (a) the MgB_2 matrix and (b) a small precipitate showing difference in the detailed shape of boron K-edge. The position indicated by an arrow has changed from a shoulder in (a) to a peak in (b).

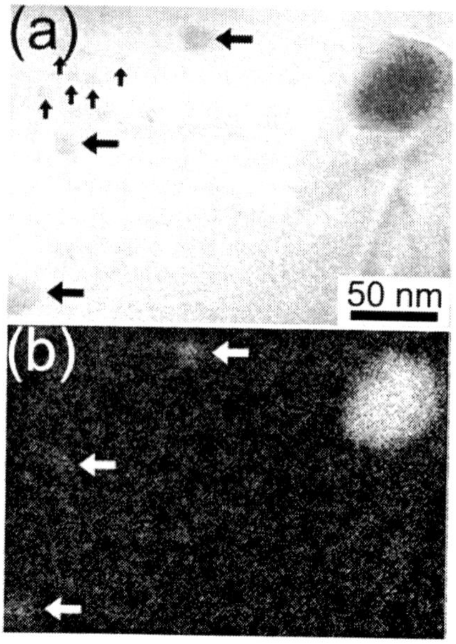

Figure 11- EFI images of (a) a boron map and (b) an oxygen map. Large arrows indicate precipitates with size range of 10 to 20 nm. Small arrows indicate precipitates in the size range of around 5 nm.

Figure 11(a) shows a typical elemental map of boron. The dark areas in Fig. 11(a), which imply less boron content than the matrix, indicate the locations and the sizes of precipitates. Three different precipitate size ranges are seen in Fig. 11(a): (1) the largest precipitate with a dimension of around 50 nm located at the upper-right corner of the image; (2) three medium-sized precipitates with dimensions of around 10 to 20 nm indicated by three large arrows; and (3) a few very small precipitates with dimensions of about 5 nm forming a precipitate cluster at the upper-left corner of the image, as indicated by small arrows. Note that the small precipitates show very poor image contrast in Fig. 11(a) and are not seen by the conventional diffraction contrast image in Fig. 8. The reasons contributing to the poor contrast might include: (1) the difference in boron contents between the small precipitates and the surrounding matrix is small and (2) contribution from the matrix further smears out the contrast. Figure 11(b) is a typical elemental map of oxygen taken from the same area as Fig. 11(a). The areas appearing dark in Fig. 11(a) are bright in the oxygen map, consistent with the above mentioned conclusion that boron is substituted by oxygen. However, because of the poor intensity, no small precipitate is seen in Fig. 11(b). The observation in Fig. 11 pushes down the lower limit of observed precipitate dimension from about 10 nm seen in Fig. 8(a) to about 5 nm. Although there are less very small precipitates than the precipitates with the sizes in the range of 10 ~ 50 nm, the local density of the very small precipitates, as shown in Fig. 11(a), is much higher than that of larger precipitates. This implies that ripening (some precipitates grow larger at the expense of others) happened during the growth of these precipitates, much like the precipitation processes observed in other systems.

Large angle tilting electron diffraction experiments on the precipitates suggest that medium- to small-sized precipitates have the same basic lattice structure and orientation as their MgB_2 matrixes. No difference in lattice parameters between the precipitates and the matrix can be detected by conventional electron diffraction patterns. However, extra satellite diffraction spots are seen in some directions (see, for example, Fig. 15), implying the structural modulation nature of the precipitates. Most precipitates are more visible and appear darker than their MgB_2 matrices in bright-field diffraction contrast images when the MgB_2 matrices are under some main zone-axes (see, for example, the [010] image in Fig. 8) imaging conditions. This is because the precipitates have the same orientation as the MgB_2 and the substitution of boron by oxygen makes the precipitates stronger in electron scattering.

HREM images taken from various main zone-axes (e.g. [010], [001], [1-$\bar{1}$1], and [101]) further confirm that the precipitates have the same basic lattice structure as the MgB_2 matrix. Typical examples of HREM images of precipitates are shown in Fig. 12. Figure 12(a) shows an HREM image of a precipitate taken along a [010]. The precipitate is spherical with a diameter of about 15 nm. The precipitate shows the same rectangular lattice fringes as the surrounding matrix. Figure 12(b) illustrates the [001] HREM image of another precipitate with a diameter of around 30 nm. To see more clearly the lattice fringes of the precipitate and its surrounding matrix area in Fig. 12(b), an area marked by a white rectangle is enlarged and demonstrated in Fig. 12(c), which shows exactly the same hexagonal lattice fringes inside and outside the precipitate.

HREM images in Fig. 12 demonstrate that the precipitates have the same *basic* structure as the MgB_2 matrix. However, the partial replacement of boron by oxygen in the precipitates does

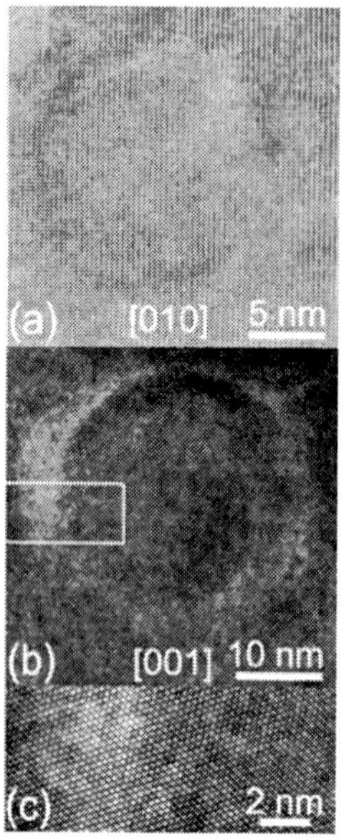

Figure 12- HREM images of precipitates taken from (a) a [010] direction and (b) the [001] direction. The area marked with a white rectangle in (b) is enlarged and shown in (c).

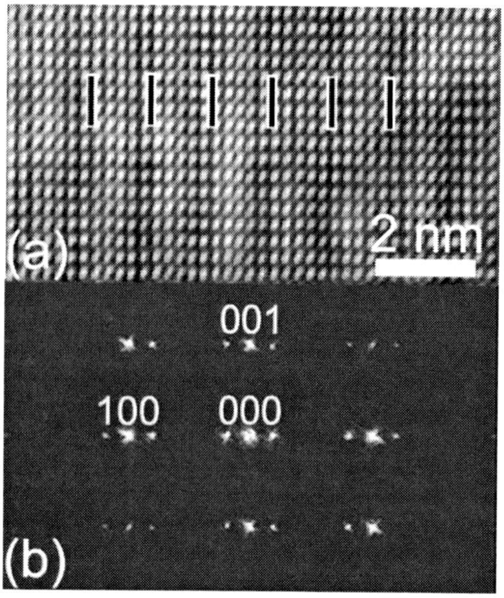

Figure 13- (a) A [010] HREM image showing basic lattice fringes, which are the same as the MgB_2 matrix, and periodic contrast change marked with black bars; (b) Fourier transformation of (a). Satellite diffraction spots are seen along $[100]^*$ with a period of $1/5[100]^*$.

affect their structures as evidenced by extra satellite spots along some directions in their electron diffraction patterns. This is also reflected in HREM images from several directions. Figure 13(a) shows a [010] HREM image of a precipitate providing an evidence of structural modulation. A periodic contrast change is superimposed on two-dimensional lattice fringes, which are the same as the fringes observed in its surrounding MgB_2 matrix.[23] The periodic contrast change, appeared as dark-and-bright stripes, is along [100] and the period is five times that of the MgB_2 crystal-lattice constant along [100]. This period is further confirmed by Fig. 13(b), the Fourier transformation of Fig. 13(a), which shows satellite diffraction spots along $[100]^*$ with a vector equals to $1/5[100]^*$. The fact that the dark and bright stripe areas have the same two-dimensional lattice fringes implies that the crystal structure at these areas remains the same. The periodic contrast difference is caused by periodic composition (oxygen and boron) variation, with the dark areas having higher oxygen content. Therefore, the precipitates are of the basic MgB_2 crystal structure with compositional modulation.

Note that Moiré fringes generated by two overlapping crystals can also present similar image contrast as shown in Fig. 13(a). However, 20% lattice mismatch between the two overlapping crystals is needed to have Moiré fringes with the period shown in Fig. 13(a). The 20% lattice mismatch is much larger than the very small lattice difference between the precipitate and the matrix. Furthermore, a typical HREM image of Moiré fringes normally appears differently at the bright and dark areas (see, for example, ref. [66]), which is not the case in Fig. 13(a).

Figure 14(a) is another example of a [010] HREM image showing compositional modulation superimposing on the basic structure of MgB_2. A spherical precipitate with a diameter close to 15 nm demonstrates slightly darker contrast than its surrounding matrix in Fig. 14(a). The precipitate/matrix boundary is highlighted using white stars and an area marked with a white rectangle is enlarged and inserted on the upper right corner of Fig. 14(a), showing clearly the same basic structure between the precipitate and the matrix. However, dim stripes are seen within the precipitate along the direction indicated by a white line drawn within the precipitate. Fourier transformations of the image from the matrix area and from the precipitate are shown in Fig. 14(b) and (c), respectively. Besides the basic spots shown in Fig. 14(b), extra satellite spots are seen in Fig. 14(c) with a vector of about [-0.26, 0, 0.39]*.

Obviously, the modulations shown in Fig. 13 and Fig. 14 are different. In fact, more than one type of modulated structures have been found in precipitates. An evidence is shown in a [010] electron diffraction pattern in Fig. 15, where extra satellite diffraction spots along the [001]* with a vector of about 2/5[001]*are seen. Because the [001]* is unique in the hexagonal MgB_2 structure and because no extra satellite spot along [001]* is seen in Figs. 13 and 14, it is concluded that the diffraction pattern shown in Fig. 15 comes from a structure that is different from the structure(s) that give rise to the Figs. 13 and 14. It is believed that different oxygen contents are responsible for the different modulations in precipitates.

It is found that the synthesis parameters significantly affect the density and structure of the precipitates. Longer oxygen exposure time at the high temperature of 900°C increases the density

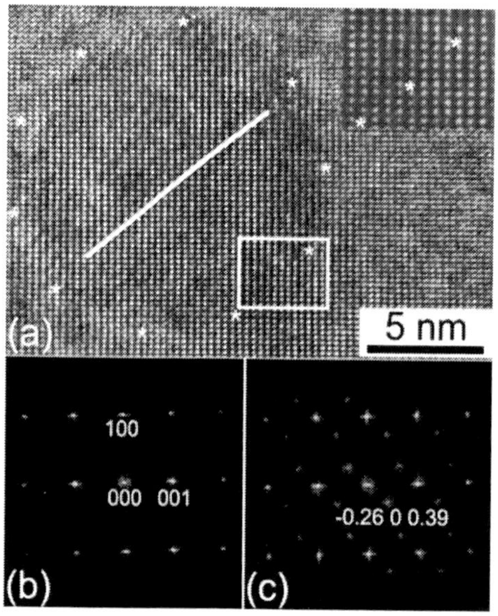

Figure 14. (a) An HREM image along [010] direction. A spherical precipitate with a diameter of about 15 nm and with darker contrast than the MgB_2 matrix is clearly seen. The precipitate boundary is highlighted using white stars. Weak stripe contrast along the direction marked by a white line is seen in the precipitate. A magnified image at the precipitate-matrix boundary marked by a white rectangle is shown at the upper right corner, which attests to the coherent nature of the precipitate and the same basic structure of the matrix and the precipitate. (b) Fourier transformation of the matrix. (c) Fourier transformation of the precipitate showing satellite spots with a vector of [-0.26, 0, 0.39]*.

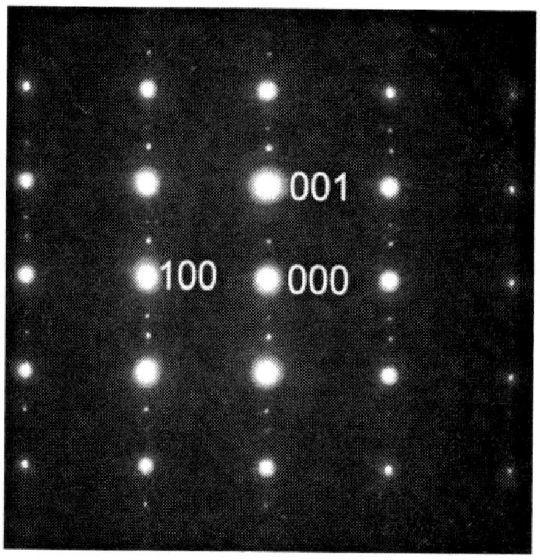

Figure 15. A [010] diffraction pattern of a precipitate showing modulation satellite spots along [001]* with a period of roughly 2/5[001]*.

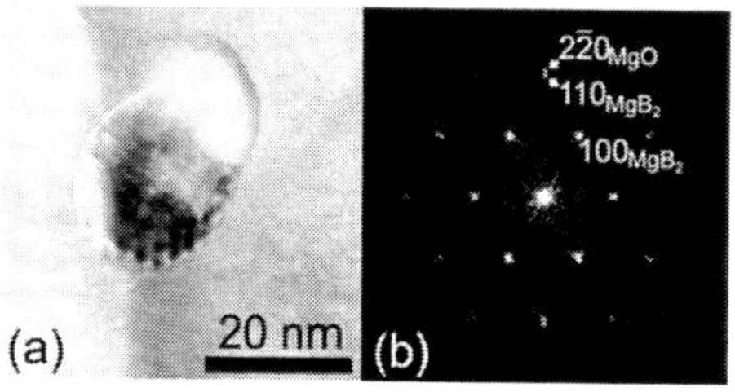

Figure 16. (a) An HREM image of a MgO precipitate and the surrounding MgB_2 matrix (shown in a lower magnification) and (b) its Fourier transformation showing the orientation relationship between the MgO precipitate and it MgB_2 matrix.

of the precipitates but no significant change in the average precipitate size has been observed. This is beneficial for improving flux pinning. However, longer oxygen exposure time also increases the amount of MgO at grain boundaries, which acts as "weak link" and therefore is undesirable. Therefore, it is important to balance between good flux pinning and good grain boundary connections in choosing synthesis parameters. Longer exposure to trace amount of oxygen at high temperatures also results in the transformation of the precipitates from the hexagonal $Mg(B,O)_2$ phase with compositional modulations to the face-centered cubic MgO phase, implying $Mg(B,O)_2$ is not a stable phase at high temperature in an environment containing trace amount of oxygen. The orientation relationship between the resulting MgO precipitates and the MgB_2 matrix revealed by an HREM image and its Fourier transformation in Fig. 16 is: $[001]_{MgB2}$ // $[111]_{MgO}$, and $(110)_{MgB2}//(1\text{-}10)_{MgO}$ (note that planar distance $d(110)_{MgB2} = 0.154$ nm while $d(220)_{MgO} = 0.149$ nm. The lattice mismatch between $d(110)_{MgB2}$ and $d(220)_{MgO}$ is only 3.2%). In fact, Zhu *et al.*[67] have also reported that the precipitates in their MgB_2 samples are MgO. A possible reason for the small MgO precipitate sizes after longer time high temperature annealing (ripening did not happen) is that MgO is a very stable compound. Once it forms, the energy barrier for it to dissociate for the oxygen to migrate to form large precipitates is very high.

While random oxygen substitution for boron results in a lower T_c in MgB_2,[39] it is interesting to note that both samples A, B, and C have a T_c onset of ~39 K, implying little oxygen content within the superconducting phase in either sample. As we will see in the next section J_c of sample A is larger than the J_c of samples B and C, indicating an improvement in the flux pinning. Since there is no big difference between the dislocation densities of all samples (see Fig. 8), the large number of precipitates in sample A is the likely crystalline defect responsible for the strong flux pinning in this sample.

Magnetization critical current densities

In the previous section we showed that, due to the specimen preparation process (exposure to residual oxygen from UHP Ar at high synthesis temperatures followed by slow cooling), oxygen atoms in samples A and B were dissolved into MgB_2 and then segregated to form coherent nanometer-sized $Mg(B,O)_2$ precipitates within the MgB_2 matrix. To determine the effect of these precipitates on the flux pinning properties, we performed magnetization measurements to calculate the field dependence of the critical current density of samples with different densities of precipitates.

Inter-grain J_c

We measured magnetization loops on pellets of similar size for samples A, B, C, and A-HIP. $J_c(H)$ was determined using the Bean critical state model[59] for a long parallelepiped:

$$J_c(H) = \frac{20 \times \Delta M(H)}{a(1 - a/3b)} \quad (1)$$

where a and b are the dimensions of the parallelepiped perpendicular to the magnetic field H and ΔM is the width of the magnetization loop.

Figure 17 shows the dependence of J_c on H for all the samples. It can be seen that J_c at low fields for samples A and B is very similar and about one order of magnitude larger than the J_c of sample C. This may indicate an improvement of either the intra-grain flux pinning, the inter-grain connectivity, or both, and it is important to discriminate between these possibilities.

A TEM bright-field image of the sample A, which reveals poor connectivity among the MgB_2 grains, is shown in Fig. 18(a). The white areas in the figure are pores, and the dark areas have been proven by electron diffraction to be MgO. Sample B presents a similar morphology. However, as we have just mentioned, sample C has smaller grain size and even more porosity. Thus, at least part of the J_c improvement of A and B with respect to C was due to better inter-grain connectivity.

Data for sample A-HIP were also included in Fig. 17. The J_c at $H = 0$ is nearly the same for both samples A-HIP and A . However, the J_c in sample A-HIP shows significantly reduced field dependence. This improvement was also due to a better inter-grain connectivity. Figure 18(b) shows the excellent connectivity between the MgB_2 grains of sample A-HIP. Neither pores nor MgO are seen at MgB_2 grain boundaries. The MgO, seen at the MgB_2 grain boundaries in sample A (Fig. 18(a)), have been broken up and dispersed inside the MgB_2 grains in the form of fine MgO particles.[13] In addition, the dislocation density inside the MgB_2 grains is much higher in sample A-HIP than in sample A. Because of the non-zone-axis imaging conditions used for Figs. 18(a) and (b), the precipitates cannot be seen in these images.

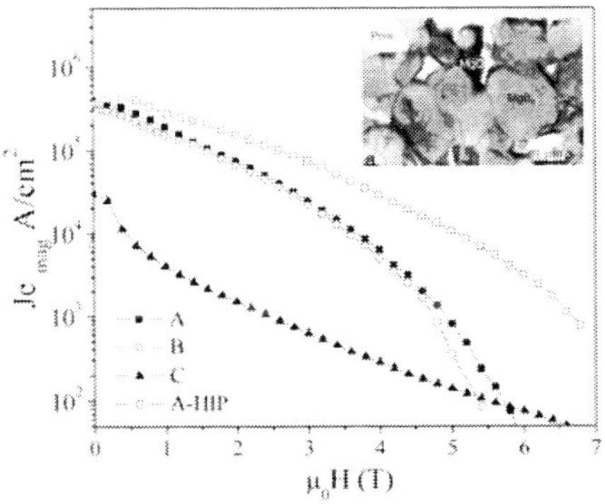

Figure 17- Magnetization J_c as a function of applied field at 5 K for MgB_2 bulk samples.

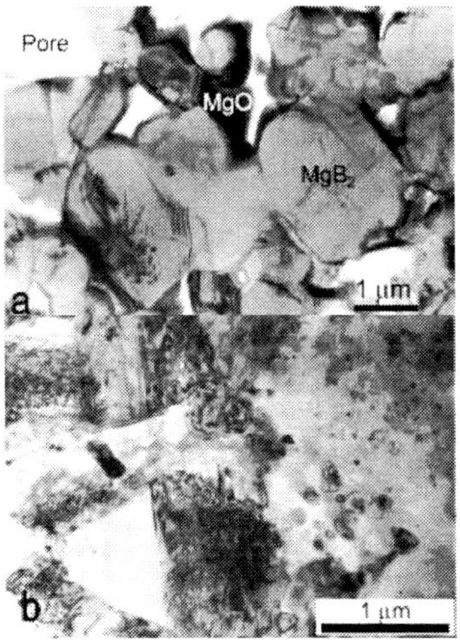

Figure 18. (a) A bright-field image of the un-HIPed sample reveals poor connectivity among MgB_2 grains. Pores and MgO at the grain boundaries of MgB_2 are seen; (b) A bright-field image of the HIPed sample shows that connectivity among the MgB_2 grains has been greatly improved. No pores are seen.

In summary, the weak connectivity between domains and the presence of impurities in the grain boundaries in the MgB_2 ambient temperature sintered sample seem to limit J_c at high fields, although not as severely as in high-T_c superconductors. The HIP process improves the field dependence of J_c through better connectivity of the grains, the generation of dislocations, and the destruction of MgO at MgB_2 boundaries. However, due to the inter-grain effects, the M(H) studies in pellets cannot clarify the effect of $Mg(B,O)_2$ precipitates on J_c.

Intra-grain J_c

In order to determine the influence of $Mg(B,O)_2$ precipitates on the intra-grain critical current density, we ground samples A, B, and C and dispersed the powders in clear epoxy with a volume fraction of ~2%. Particles from ground samples usually do not correspond to single crystals, but to

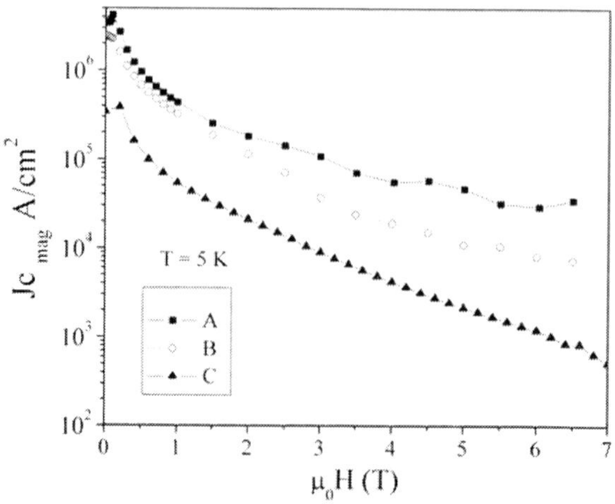

Figure 19. Magnetization J_c as a function of applied field at 5 K for MgB_2 powder samples dispersed in epoxy.

small agglomerates with some size distribution. SEM measurements of particles contained in thin sections cut from the epoxy suggest that the average particle dimensions $\langle d \rangle$ were between 4-5 μm depending on the samples. Assuming the agglomerates to be spherically shaped, we calculated the critical current densities by using a corrected expression of the Bean model for exponential size distributed particles [15]:

$$J_c(H) = \frac{30 \times \Delta M(H)}{4 \times \langle d \rangle} \tag{2}$$

The dependence of J_c on the applied magnetic field for powder samples dispersed in epoxy is plotted in Fig. 19. Now it is clear that sample A, the one with higher densities of precipitates according to Fig. 8, has higher values of J_c than sample B and much higher than sample C. This result suggests that the presence of $Mg(B,O)_2$ precipitates increases the pinning force in the grains. It is important to mention that the J_c dependence with field in these powders is also better than in the pellets.

As already discussed, the synthesis parameters significantly affect the density and structure of the precipitates. Longer oxygen exposure time at the high temperature of 900ºC increases the density of precipitates but no great change on precipitate size has been observed. This is beneficial for improving flux pinning. However, longer oxygen exposure time also increases the amount of MgO at grain boundaries, which acts as "weak link" and therefore is undesirable. Hence, it is important to balance between improving flux pinning and keeping good grain boundary connectivity in choosing synthesis parameters.

Precipitates as pinning centers

Inclusions in a superconductor can pin vortices by reducing or suppressing of the condensation energy within their volume, and more indirectly by creating defects such as stacking faults, dislocations and microcracks in the superconducting matrix. This second effect is relevant, for instance, in the case of inclusions of Y_2BaCuO_5 (the "221" phase) in $YBa_2Cu_3O_7$. In our samples, in contrast, the inclusions (i.e. precipitates) are coherent with the matrix lattice, with a remarkable absence of surrounding matrix defects, so pinning is likely to arise only from the first mechanism. Thus, the elementary pinning energy of one defect, u_p, is given by the difference between the condensation energy of a vortex core sitting on top of the defect and far away from it, $u_p = \eta(H_c^2/8\pi)V$, where $\eta \leq 1$ indicates the fraction of suppression of the order parameter ($\eta = 1$ for a non-superconducting inclusion), V is the pinned volume of the core, and $H_c = \Phi_0/(2\sqrt{2}\pi\xi\lambda)$ is the thermodynamic critical field. Here Φ_0 is the flux quantum, ξ is the coherence length, and λ is the penetration depth. If the radius of the inclusion, R, is smaller than the radius of the vortex core, $\sqrt{2}\xi$, then $V = (4\pi/3)R^3$, else $V = 2\pi\xi^2 R$. The elementary pinning force f_p is the maximum gradient in u_p, and it can be estimated as u_p divided by the distance over which the order parameter recovers. Taking into account the sharpness of the defect-matrix interfaces, we can assume that even for $R > \sqrt{2}\xi$ such recovery takes place over the shortest possible distance, namely $\sim \xi$. (This is equivalent to say that in the large defects pinning occurs essentially at the interface.) We thus obtain $f_p = (\eta/6)H_c^2R^3/\xi$ for $R < \sqrt{2}\xi$ and $f_p = (\eta/4)H_c^2R\xi$ for $R > \sqrt{2}\xi$.

The critical current density is $J_c = cF_p/B$, where c is the speed of light, F_p is the pinning force per unit volume, and B is the magnetic induction. In general, the relation between F_p and f_p is highly nontrivial. However, for very low defect density we can make a very crude estimate of F_p by simply summing up the individual pinning forces. This is clearly an overestimate, as both the cost in elastic energy and the partial cancellation of the forces produced by the random distribution of defects will tend to reduce F_p. In this approximation, the contribution of defects of a certain radius is $F_p(R) \sim f_p(R)N_p(R)$, where $N_p(R)$ is the number of vortex-defect interactions per unit volume. Let us first consider that R is much smaller than the inter-vortex distance a =

$1.075(\Phi_0/B)^{1/2}$. In this limit, N_p can be approximated as the fraction $2\pi\xi^2 B/\Phi_0$ of the total number of defects of that size per unit volume, $n_p(R)$, that lay within the cores. By combining the above relations we can write the critical current density due to defects of radius R as $J_c(R) \sim (\sqrt{3}/2)\pi\eta(R)[Rsn_p(R)]J_0$, where $s = R^2$ for $R < \sqrt{2}\xi$ and $s = (3/2)\xi^2$ for $R > \sqrt{2}\xi$, and where to facilitate the numerical comparisons we have introduced the depairing current density $J_0 = cH_c/(3\sqrt{6}\pi\lambda)$. For T=0, using $\lambda \sim 110$ nm and $\xi \sim 4$ nm, we obtain $H_c \sim 5100$ Oe and $J_0 \sim 2\text{x}10^8$ A/cm^2.

As mentioned in section IV, the density of the precipitates with the size range of 10 nm < D < 50 nm, or 5 nm < R < 25 nm, is ~ 10^{15} defects/cm^3. We also know that in defects of these sizes a large fraction of the boron has been replaced by oxygen, so we can assume that the superconductivity is very strongly suppressed in them, thus $\eta \sim 1$. Taking an average radius R = 15 nm we get J_c(15 nm) ~ $2\text{x}10^5$ A/cm^2, which is in excellent agreement with the results in Fig. 23 (sample A has $J_c \sim 5\text{x}10^5$ A/cm^2 for T = 5 K and $H \sim 0$). Considering the crudeness of our estimates, we conclude that these defects are good candidates to be one of the main sources of vortex pinning in our samples, and the controlled increase in their density may result in an increase in J_c.

In contrast, the smallest defects are probably rather inefficient. It is of course a general rule that defects much smaller than ξ are poor vortex pins. Taking $R \sim 2.5$ nm, we find J_c(2.5nm) ~ $8.5\text{x}10^{-12}$ η(2.5nm) n_p(2.5nm) A/cm^2. The density of these defects is hard to estimate, as they are difficult to see in the TEM images. We can take the inverse approach and find that, assuming η = 1, we need $n_p \sim 2\text{x}10^{16}$ cm^{-3} to obtain a contribution similar to the larger defects. This n_p is too large, certainly well above the observed density. On top of that, these small defects have a much smaller oxygen content, suggesting that $\eta \ll 1$ and thus further reducing J_c.

Finally, we have to consider the largest defects. We observe about 10^{14} defects/cm^3 with 25 nm < R < 50 nm. Taking R = 40 nm we obtain J_c(40 nm) ~ $5\text{x}10^4$ A/cm^2, smaller than the contribution of the "medium size" defects, but still significant. On the other hand, for fields above ~ 3 KOe the vortex spacing becomes smaller than the diameter of these defects, so each one can pin more than one vortex. Thus, these large defects may become comparatively more important as H increases. Detailed studies of the field and temperature dependence of pinning are required to clarify this point. Additional vortex pinning may arise from the grain boundaries, but the analysis of that contribution is beyond the scope of the present study.

Flux creep

One prominent feature of high T_c superconductors is a rapid decay of critical currents in the mixed state, which arises from easy movement of vortices ('giant flux creep') that are depinned either by thermal activation or by quantum tunneling.[68] In contrast, it was found that for a substantial range of field and temperature, the mixed-state supercurrent density is highly stable in time in MgB_2.[69]

Here we present a study of the time relaxation of the irreversible magnetization, $m_{irr}(t)$, as a function of H and T, and current density (J) dependence of the normalized time (t) relaxation rate, S=dln$J$/dln$t$, in our microstructurally well-characterized samples A and A-HIP. For each temperature and field we measured the decay from both the lower and upper branches of the isothermal hysteresis loops M(H). Fig. 20 shows a typical example for sample A-HIP of the raw data ln$|m_{irr}|$ as a function of ln(t+ t_0), at H=3T and T=7K, with an excellent linear fits and good coincidence (whitin 10%) between lower and upper branches. The normalized relaxation rate S as determined from lower and upper branches coincide for all measured temperatures (S = dln$|m_{irr}|$/dln(t)). A plot of S as a function of T in several applied fields for both samples is given in Fig. 21. It can be seen that the decay rate in sample A-HIP is lower than in sample A, which is consistent with a higher flux pinning in sample A-HIP observed in the previous section. If we compare with the behavior of other superconductors (see Fig. 22), the encouraging result is that the decay rate of MgB_2 lies below most of other superconductors and our sample has even lower values than previously reported result on MgB_2.[69]

Powder in tube MgB_2 wires

In this section we review the results on many MgB_2 wires prepared by PIT and annealed under different conditions. Table IV summarizes the annealing parameters and the lengths of all MgB_2 PIT wires analyzed in this section.

Table IV - Annealing parameters and lengths for all wires.

Wire	Atmosphere	Temperature	Time	Rate heat-cool	Length
A-0	----	----	----	----	10 cm[(a)]
A-1	Ar	900°C	15 min.	10 °C/min - 0.5°C/min	10 cm
A-2	Vacuum	900°C	30 min.	35 °C/min – gas quench	annealed: 6 m measured: 10 cm[(b)]
A-3	Ar-HIP	900°C	30 min.	10 °C/min - 5°C/min	10 cm[(b)]

[(a)] A-0 is the initial un-annealed sample. The original portion had ~7 m from which all samples were cut.

[(b)] For measurements between 8-18 T the wire lengths were constrained to ~3-4 cm long.

Role of excess Mg and heat treatments on microstructure and J_c of MgB_2 wires

Fig. 23 shows transport I_c and J_c as a function of H for one piece of starting several-meters-long un-annealed wire, identified as A-0. Another non-adjacent piece of A-0 exhibits a very similar $I_c(H)$, indicating that an homogeneous wire was available for annealing studies. Also shown are magnetization and transport J_c for two annealed wires, A-1 and A-2, which will be discussed later.

Fig. 24 shows $4\pi M/H$ vs. T at $H = 20$ Oe after zero-field cooling (ZFC) for pieces of the three wires shown in Fig. 23. The $T_c \sim 37.5$ K is the same in all cases and only slightly lower than in bulk samples. The ZFC curve for A-0 exhibits the two-steps typical of weak-link behavior. At the lowest temperatures $4\pi M/H \sim -1$, indicating that the screening currents flow through the whole sample, but connectivity is gradually lost as T increases and the weak links appear to collapse at $T \sim 29$ K (see arrow). The substantial J_c values of A-0 at high fields (see Fig. 23) indicate that some fraction of the current paths does not contain weak links. However, it is also clear from Fig. 24 that the first goal of further processing should be to improve connectivity, rather than increasing pinning.

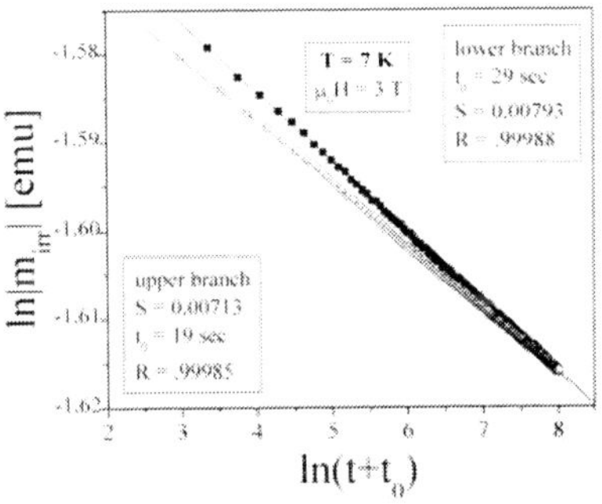

Figure 20. Raw data ln|m_{irr}| vs. ln($t+t_0$), at $\mu_0 H$=3T and T=7K, for sample A-HIP. In the inset texts are the parameters of linear fits for the upper and lower branches.

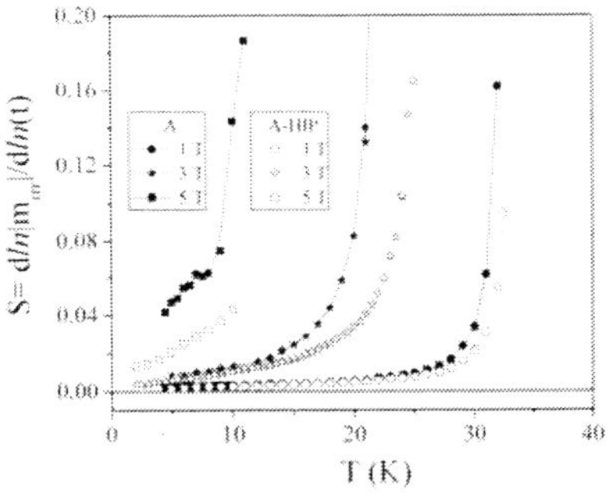

Figure 21. S as a function of T for samples A and A-HIP in applied fields $\mu_0 H$ = 1, 3 and 5 T.

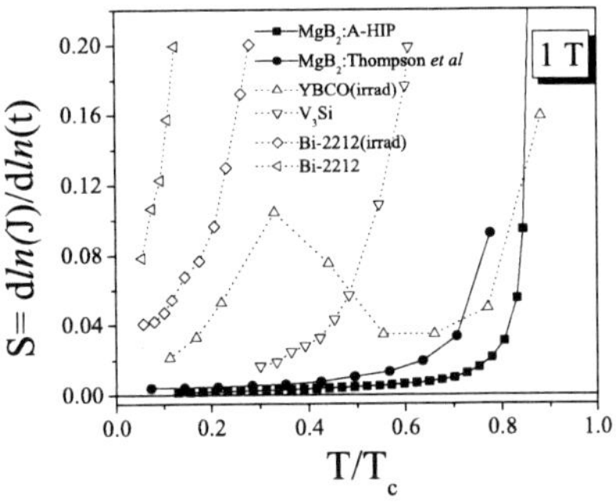

Figure 22. The normalized decay rate S as a function of reduced temperature T/T_c for several superconductors in and applied field of 1 T. Our MgB_2 HIPed sample is compared with those results presented by Thompson *et al.* in Ref. 69.

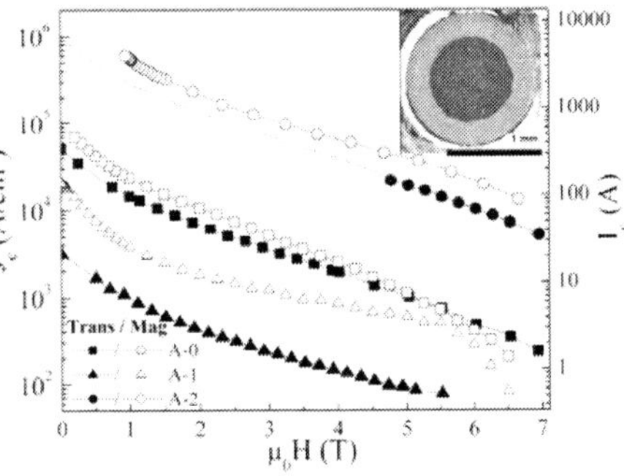

Figure 23. J_c vs. applied field at 4 K, for wires A-0, A-1 and A-2, as measured by transport (full symbols) and by magnetization (open symbols). Extrapolated J_c for A-2 is indicated by the dotted line. Inset: typical cross section of the wires as observed by SEM.

Wire A-1 is an example of an inappropriate heat treatment. In this case a 10 cm long wire was annealed in high purity flowing Ar. The temperature was increased at a rate of 10°C/min, then maintained at 900°C for 15 minutes, slowly cooled to 500°C at a rate of 0.5°C/min, then furnace cooled down to room temperature. While Fig. 23 shows that the transport J_c has decreased by an order of magnitude, the reduced screening fraction and the absence of the two steps in the ZFC curve in Fig. 24 indicates that the current carrying capability of the weak links has deteriorated.

A sharply contrasting result was obtained for wire A-2. Here a 6 m long wire was annealed in vacuum. The sample was heated at a rate of 35°C/min, kept at 900°C for 30 minutes, and gas quenched with Ar. Fig. 23 shows the transport J_c for a piece cut from A-2 after annealing, which is 20 times higher than the pre-annealing values. Only data above 4.75 T are shown, because at lower fields, I_c was so high that strong heating at the current contacts precluded the collection of reliable data. The dotted line in Fig. 23 is an extrapolation assuming the same H dependence as in A-0. Four other pieces of A-2 were also measured showing similar results (within 20%). Consistently, the ZFC data in Fig. 24 exhibit almost perfect screening with no hint of weak-link behavior, confirming that the J_c increase is mainly due to the improved connectivity.

Also shown in Fig. 23 (open symbols) are the J_c's of A-0, A-1 and A-2, as calculated from magnetization loops M(H) using the critical state Bean model and assuming uniform J_c flowing through the entire sample. The data was corrected for self-field effects, which are significant only for samples A-0 and A-2 at fields below 1 T. For these samples, the similar field dependence of transport and magnetization J_c, and the coincidence within a factor of 2 or better in the field region of overlap, demonstrate that in the transport measurements the current is flowing through most of the wire cross section. In contrast, the magnetization data corresponding to A-1 is very different from the transport values, because this sample is quite inhomogeneous and the Bean model should not be used for calculating the J_c in this case, as is discussed in detail elsewhere.[50]

SEM observations and EDS analysis showed no reaction between the MgB_2 and the stainless steel (see the inset of Fig. 23). The distribution of grain sizes can be estimated from dark field images such as those in Figs. 25 (a), (c) and (e), corresponding to A-0, A-1, and A-2, respectively. The observations are summarized as follows: (i) in all three samples, most MgB_2 crystals are of sub-micrometer sizes, and in some rare cases, the grain size can reach around one micron [e.g., the largest bright area in Fig. 25(c)]; (ii) a large density of grains even smaller than 0.1 μm is seen in A-0 and A-1, while A-2 has fewer of those; (iii) while A-0 and A-1 have similar grain size distribution, A-2 has a slightly larger average grain size. Contradictory claims regarding the effect of grain size on J_c can be found in the literature.[22, 70] Our results show that two orders of magnitude variations in transport J_c can be observed in wires with very similar grain sizes. If pinning by GB is important, the small grain size of our wires is desirable, but clearly the differences in their J_c cannot be attributed to changes in GB pinning. We have also seen a substantial and similar density of pores in the three samples. Fig. 25(f) shows just one example of pores in A-2. Similar images were obtained for A-0 and A-1. Thus, from the microstructural data we conclude that neither grain size nor porosity is relevant factors in determining J_c in our PIT MgB_2 wires.

The only significant microstructural difference observed is that wires A-0 and A-1 contain microcracks, while A-2 does not. Figs. 25 (b) and (d) show examples of microcracks in A-0 and A-1 respectively. For each one of the three wires we explored by TEM an area ~ 250 times that covered by Fig. 25 (b), in the shape of strips of ~ 900 x 10 μm, which approximately coincides with a wire diameter. In both A-0 and A-1 we observed around 5 microcracks in that area (which corresponds to about 300 microcracks in the whole wire cross section), while in A-2 we found none, suggesting at least one order of magnitude lower crack density. The microcracks in A-0 and A-1 extend over distances larger than ~ 10 μm width, i.e., they are much larger than the grain size and thus introduce a strong limitation to the flow of currents. From this we conclude that the main beneficial effect of the annealing of A-2 was the elimination of the microcracks.

To determine the reason for the deleterious effect of the annealing in A-1, we annealed a 2.5 cm piece of A-0, under similar conditions as in A-1 but for a shorter time. We then cut a series of ~ 5 mm long consecutive samples and measured their magnetization. We found[50] that both the connectivity (as parameterized by the double step ZFC as that of A-0 in Fig. 24) and the J_c were worst for the end samples and systematically improved in samples taken closer to the center. This suggests that the deterioration was due to a loss of Mg through the wire ends during annealing.

Although it is natural to associate microcracks with weak-link behavior, the worst connectivity of A-1 as compared to A-0 is not due to a larger density of cracks. Moreover, the microcracks in Figs. 25 (b) and (d) are too wide to act as weak links (they are just "open circuits" for all T and H). However, we can assume a continuous distribution of widths all the way down to atomic distances. Furthermore, the T_c for A-0, A-1 and A-2, as well as the short annealed pieces is the same (see Fig. 24). This implies that Mg loss is inhomogeneous, as homogeneous Mg loss results in a reduction in T_c.[71] The obvious inference is that the microcracks act as channels for easy Mg diffusion, and the deterioration of the weak link behavior is associated with Mg loss in the narrowest cracks and at GB. In contrast, the loss of Mg was precluded in A-2 for two reasons.

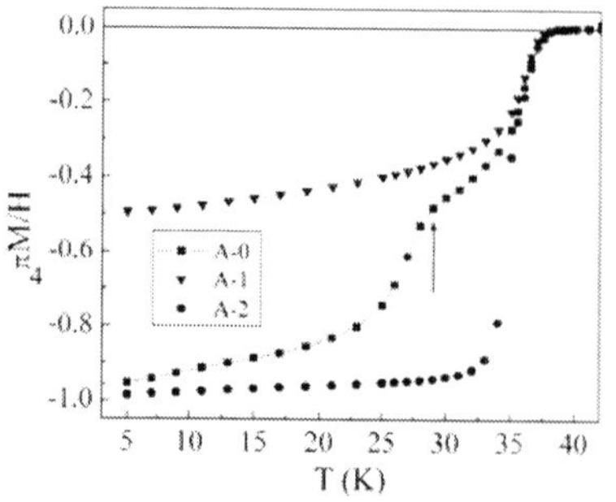

Figure 24. Zero Field Cooling (ZFC) dc magnetization as a function of temperature for as-drawn and annealed MgB_2 wires. The arrow indicates the collapse of the weak links.

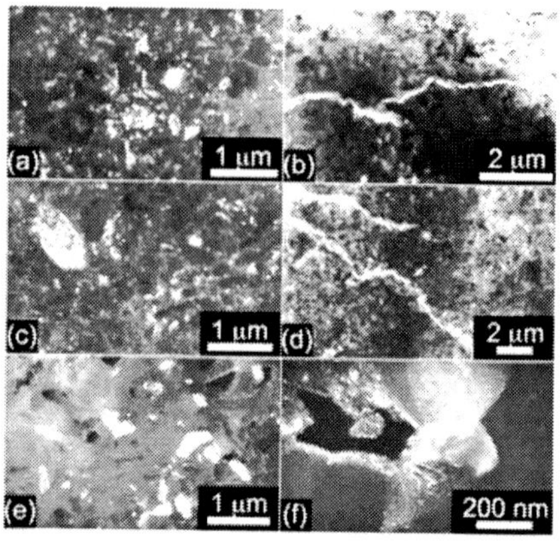

Figure 25. TEM dark field [(a),(c),(e)] and bright field [(b),(d),(f)] images, where (a) and (b) are from A-0, (c) and (d) from A-1, and (e) and (f) from A-2. As discussed in the text Figs. 3 (b) and (d) show examples of microcracks in A-0 and A-1 respectively, which were not observed in A-2.

First, the Mg loss occurs through the open wire ends (as demonstrated by the annealing of the short pieces), while this wire was very long, and the measured pieces were far from the edges. Second, the heating was very fast, thus reducing the Mg loss before the recrystallization temperature was reached. As a result, excess Mg is still available at that temperature to act as a sintering aid to eliminate the cracks.

Role of HIPing on microstructure and J_c of MgB_2 wires

Fig. 26 shows J_c obtained from magnetization, as a function of applied magnetic field in the 5-30 K temperature range for A-3, the HIPed wire and for A-2, a piece of an appropriately annealed wire (see previous section). Also shown in this figure are the transport values measured in liquid Ne at 26.5 K (diamond symbols, solid lines). For both samples, the data at 5 K was corrected for self-field effects, because this effect is important at fields below 1 T. The $J_c(H)$ at 5

K is similar for both samples and the extrapolated zero field J_c is higher than 10^6 A/cm^2. For higher temperatures and magnetic fields, J_c values of the HIPed wire are higher than those of the annealed wire, and the steep J_c drop with H is shifted to higher fields. For both samples, excellent agreement was found between the magnetization and transport values measured in liquid Ne at 26.5 K. These values are among the best reported for this range of temperature in MgB_2 PIT.[4]

Fig. 27 displays J_c vs. applied field for A-2 and A-3 wires as measured by magnetization (at 5 K) up to 7 T, and by transport (at 4K) up to 18 T. Again, a good correlation exists between magnetization and transport data indicating that both samples are quite homogeneous. The magnetization J_c for both samples is almost the same for fields below 4 T, but the difference increases with the applied field. The J_c is one order of magnitude higher for wire A-3 in fields greater than ~12 T. For transport measurements up to 7 T we used samples ~10 cm long in order to eliminate the initial ohmic behavior that we sometimes observed in the I-V curves of shorter wires. However, in the 8-18 T region the wire lengths were constrained to ~3-4 cm long, and these measurements frequently exhibited an initial ohmic behavior. This is a consequence of the poor connectivity between the MgB_2 and the stainless steel, which results in a transfer length 1-2 cm long for the current, so some current is always flowing through the stainless steel. This problem progressively disappears as I_c decreases with increasing H. In particular, transfer length and heating problems precluded the collection of reliable data for wire A-3 below 9 T. In the inset of Fig. 27, the J_c values of our PIT wires are compared with some of the best transport values reported in the literature (Refs. 24, [72], [73], [and 74]). The J_c of our wire A-3 is one of the best and only the SiC doped MgB_2 tape[24] has comparable values, indicating that the defects introduced by HIPing are as effective as SiC doping to enhance the pinning. Besides, the method based on HIPing can easily incorporate doping by SiC or other elements or compounds to provide synergistic effects for enhancement of pinning.

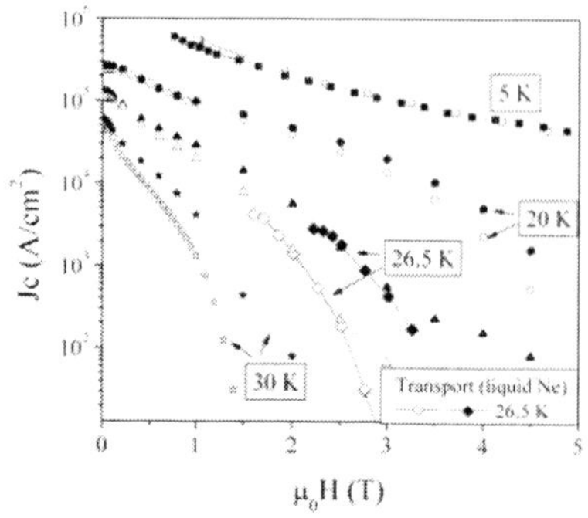

Figure 26- J_c vs. applied field for A-2 (open symbols) and A-3 (closed symbols) wires as calculated from magnetization loops in the 5-30 K temperature range. Values measured by transport in liquid neon at T= 26.5 K (diamond symbols, solid lines) are also included.

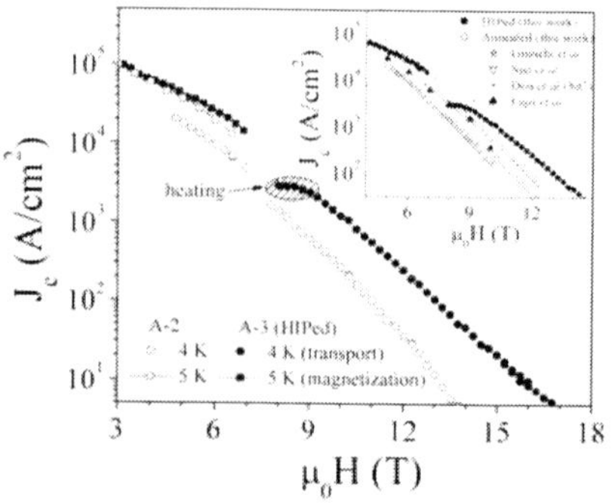

Figure 27- Jc vs. applied field for A-2 and A-3 wires as measured by transport (at 4K) and by magnetization (at 5 K). In the inset the Jc values of the same samples are compared with several values reported in the literature (Refs. 25, 72, 73, 74).

TEM investigations of both wires show[75] that (i) the average density of wire A-3 is a little higher than that of wire A-2, although some porosity is still present; (ii) the MgO at grain boundaries found in A-2, which reduces connectivity among grains, was not present in wire A-3, similarly to what we observed in bulk samples;[13] and (iii) a higher density of structural defects exists in wire A-3. These three differences contribute to the enhancement of J_c in wire A-3 as compared to A-2. However, the increase in J_c due to the reduction of porosity should be small and field independent. In particular, the high density of defects is the most likely reason for the improved pinning at high fields and for the higher H_{irr}. These defects include small angle twisting, tilting, and bending boundaries, which were introduced by the HIPing process, resulting in the formation of sub-grains within MgB_2 crystallites.

The MgB_2 crystallites normally are of a plate shape with the width on (001) up to 1 μm and the thickness along [001] up to 0.2 μm. Along the [001], the crystallites are usually divided into a few sub-grains with the sub-grain boundaries roughly parallel to (001) plane. The sub-grains can be easily identified in TEM when (001) is parallel to the electron beam direction, as shown in the grains marked with A, B, and C, respectively, in Fig. 28(a). There is usually small angle twisting along [001] and/or tilting around (001) between neighboring sub-grains, resulting in a high density of dislocations distributed in the sub-grain boundaries. Figure 28(b) shows an example of dislocations in a twisting/tilting sub-grain boundary in which black-white contrast appears roughly periodically at an interval of about 2.5 nm, as marked with black arrows, along the boundary. At the center of each black-white contrast point is a dislocation. Two black lines are drawn in Fig. 28(b), with each line parallel to the (001) of sub-grains I and II, respectively, indicating a 5° tilt between the two neighboring sub-grains. The high-resolution image in Fig. 28(b), in which one sub-grain is on a <100> zone-axis while the other is off zone-axis (showing only one-dimensional lattice fringes), suggests some twisting between the two neighboring sub-grains. The higher density of defects in the A-3 is obviously induced by the high temperature deformation during HIPing. The HIPing is a complex process that induces high strain deformation at the grain scale, thus creating intra-grain defects. At high H, where the pinning enhancement due to the HIPing is more significant, the distance between vortices is small (~15nm at 8T, ~11nm at 16T), so the defects involved must have a large density. The short separation between the observed dislocations thus makes them good candidates. Dislocations are known to act as pinning centers both in conventional superconductors[76] and in epitaxial $YBa_2Cu_3O_7$ thin films,[77,78] where they also form at low angle grain boundaries.

As we described in the previous section, appropriate annealing conditions improve J_c by more than one order of magnitude compared to as-drawn wire, and in this work we show that it also enhances the irreversibility field (H_{irr} > 13 T at 4 K, as shown in Fig. 27). The results for wire A-3 are even more promising for applications,[79] with high field J_c values around one order of magnitude higher than those of the annealed wire and H_{irr} ~ 17 T (at 4 K). This value is the largest reported in PIT MgB_2 wires or tapes, indicating that the defects produced by the HIPing process are effective as pinning centers.

Summary and conclusions

Throughout the work discussed in this review paper, very good correlations between processing, microstructure and superconducting properties are established for both MgB_2 bulk samples and wires.

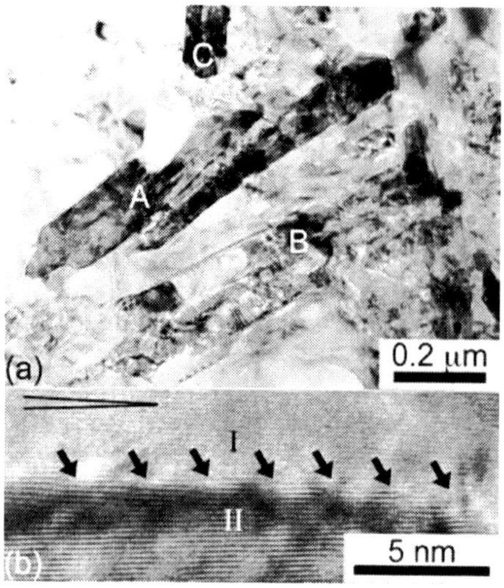

Figure 28. (a) Bright-field TEM image of wire A-3. Three crystallites, marked with A, B, and C, respectively, clearly show sub-grain boundaries roughly parallel to (001); (b) High-resolution TEM image of a twisting/tilting sub-grain boundary. Black arrows indicate the centers of black-white contrast points at which dislocations are located. Two black lines, each parallel to the (001) of sub-grains I and II, respectively, are drawn together, showing a 5° small angle tilt between the two neighboring sub-grains.

MVIP is an excellent specimen preparation process of bulk MgB_2 samples in two aspects: (1) compared with other MgB_2 samples, samples prepared by MVIP are stable under ambient conditions and (2) it is easy to introduce large amount of $Mg(B,O)_2$ precipitates, which act as effective flux pinning centers, into MgB2 matrix and therefore to increase J_c. The $Mg(B,O)_2$ precipitates are of the same basic structure as the MgB_2 matrix but with composition modulations. Long time exposure to oxygen at high temperatures results in the transformation of $Mg(B,O)_2$ precipitates to MgO with little change in precipitate sizes. Those precipitates with radius larger than ~ 5 nm (or diameters larger than ~ 10 nm) are relevant pinning centers in MgB_2. Another important advantage of our MgB_2 samples is that the decay rate of supercurrents is very low (lower than other previously reported data) indicating high stability in time over a significant temperature range.

A detailed analysis of the effect of different heat treatments on the microstructure, magnetization and transport properties of PIT MgB_2 wires has been presented. We have shown that the most beneficial effect of the annealing under an appropriate condition is the improvement of connectivity due to the elimination of microcracks. The presence of excess Mg in the initial MgB_2 powder helps to the re-crystallization process. In order to obtain high transport critical currents, the loss of Mg during the heat treatment must be precluded by annealing long wires with a high heating rate. HIPed MgB_2 wires were found to have a higher J_c than wires annealed at ambient pressure, especially at high temperatures and magnetic fields, and at higher irreversibility field (H_{irr}). The HIPed wires are promising for applications, with $J_c>10^6$ A/cm^2 at 5 K and zero field and $>10^4$ A/cm^2 at 1.5 T and 26.5 K, and H_{irr} ~ 17 T at 4 K. The improvement was attributed to a high density of structural defects, which are the likely source of vortex pinning. These defects, observed by TEM, include small angle twisting, tilting, and bending boundaries, resulting in the formation of sub-grains within MgB_2 crystallites.

Acknowledgments

The authors would like to thank Leonardo Civale, Yuntian Zhu, Fred Mueller, Dean Peterson, Alp Findikoglu, Roland Schulze, Marcelo Jaime, J. Yates Coulter, Huifang Xu, and Vitali Nesterenko for their tremendous contribution to the work presented in this paper.

This work was performed under the auspices of the US Department of Energy, Office of Energy Efficiency and Renewable Energy, as part of its Superconductivity for Electric Systems program.

References

[1] J. Nagamatsu, N. Nakagawa, T. Muranaka, Y. Sentani, and J. Akimitsu, *Nature* (London) **410**, 63 (2001).
[2] D. C. Larbalestier, L. D. Cooley, M. O. Rikel, A. A. Polyanskii, J. Jiang, S. Patnaik, X. Y. Cai, D. M. Feldmann, A. Gurevich, and A. A. Squitieri, *Nature* (London) **410**, 186 (2001).
[3] C. Buzea and T. Yamashita, *Supercond. Sci. Technol.* **14**, R115 (2001).
[4] R. Flükiger, H. L. Suo, N. Musolino, C. Beneduce, P. Toulemonde, and P. Lezza, *Physica C* **385**, 286 (2003).
[5] P. C. Canfield, S. L. Bud'ko, and D. K. Finnemore, *Physica C* **385**, 1 (2003) and other articles in the same issue.
[6] T. Tomita, J.J. Hamlin, J.S. Schilling, D.G. Hinks , and J.D. Jorgensen, *Phys. Rev. B* **64**, 092505 (2001).
[7] S. L. Bud'ko, G. Lapertot, C. Petrovic, C. E. Cunninghamy, N. Anderson, and P. C. Canfield, *Phys. Rev. Lett.* **86**, 091877 (2001).
[8] J. Kortus, I.I. Mazin, K.D. Belashchenko, V.P. Antropov, and L.L. Boyer, *Phys. Rev. Lett.* **86,** 204656 (2001).
[9] P. Ravindran, P. Vajeeston, R. Vidya, A. Kjekshus, and H. Fjellvag, *Phys. Rev. B* **64**, 224509 (2001).
[10] V. Milman and M. C. Warren, *J. of Physics: Condens. Mater* **13,** 5585 (2001).
[11] A.K.M.A. Islam and F.N. Islam; *Physica C* **363,** 189 (2001).
[12] *U.S. Patent: 6,511,943 B1.*
[13] A. Serquis, Y. T. Zhu, E. J. Peterson, J.Y. Coulter, D. E. Peterson, and F. M. Mueller, *Appl. Phys. Lett.* **79**, 4399 (2001).
[14] A. Serquis, X. Z. Liao, Y. T. Zhu, J.Y. Coulter, J.Y. Huang, J.O. Willis, D. E. Peterson, F. M. Mueller, N.O. Moreno, J. D. Thompson, V. F. Nesterenko, and S.S. Indrakanti, *J. Appl. Phys.* **92**, 351 (2002).
[15] M. F. Yan, R. L. Barns, H. M. O'Bryan, Jr., P. K. Gallagher, R. C. Sherwood, and S. Jin, *Appl. Phys. Lett.* **51**, 532 (1987).

[16] T. H. Buyuklimanli and J. H. Simmons, *Phys. Rev.* B **44**, 727 (1991).
[17] H. Y. Zhai, H. M. Christen, L. Zhang, M. Paranthaman, P. H. Fleming, and D. H. Lowndes, *Supercond. Sci. Technol.* **14**, 425 (2001).
[18] T. A. Callcott, L. Lin, G. T. Woods, G. P. Zhang, J. R. Thompson, M. Paranthaman, and D. L. Ederer, *Phys. Rev.* B **64**, 2504 (2001).
[19] H. Fujii, H. Kumakura, and K. Togano, *Physica* C **363**, 237 (2001).
[20] A. Serquis, R. K. Schulze, Y. T. Zhu, J.Y. Coulter, D. E. Peterson, N.O. Moreno, P. G. Pagliuso S.S. Indrakanti, V. F. Nesterenko, and F. M. Mueller, Mat. Res. Soc. Symp. Proc. **689**, 47 (2002).
[21] A. Serquis, R. K. Schulze, Y. T. Zhu, J.Y. Coulter, D. E. Peterson, and F. M. Mueller, *Appl. Phys. Lett.* **80**, 4401 (2002).
[22] D. K. Aswal, K. P. Muthe, Ajay Singh, Shahswati Sen, Kunjal Shah, L. C. Gupta, S. K. Gupta, and V. C. Sahni, *Physica* C **363**, 208 (2001).
[23] A. Gümbel, J. Eckert, G. Fuchs, K. Nenkov, K. H. Müller, and L. Schultz, *Appl. Phys. Lett.* **80**, 2725 (2002).
[24] X. Z. Liao, A. Serquis, Y. T. Zhu, J.Y. Huang, D. E. Peterson, F. M. Mueller, and H. F. Xu, *Appl. Phys. Lett.* **80**, 4398 (2002).
[25] S. X. Dou, J. Horvat, S. Soltanian, X. L. Wang, M. J. Qin, H. K. Liu, and P. G. Munroe, cond-mat/0208215 (2002), to be published in *ASC proceedings*, Houston (2002).
[26] R. F. Klie, J. C. Idrobo, N. D. Browning, A. Serquis, Y. T. Zhu, X. Z. Liao and F. M. Mueller, *Appl. Phys. Lett.* **80**, 3970 (2002).
[27] G. Yang, P. Shang, S. D. Sutton, I. P. Jones, J. S. Abell, C. E. Gough, *Phys. Rev.* B **48**, 4054 (1993).
[28] Z. L. Wang, A. Goyal, and D. M. Kroeger, *Phys. Rev.* B **47**, 5373 (1993).
[29] A. Díaz, L. Mechin, P. Berghuis, and J. E. Evetts, *Phys. Rev. Lett.* **80**, 3855 (1998).
[30] K. H. Müller, M. Nikolo, and R. Driver, *Phys. Rev.* B **43**, 7976 (1991).
[31] D. Shi, M. S. Boley, U. Whelp, J. G. Chen, and Y. Liao, *Phys. Rev.* B **40**, 5255 (1989).
[32] L. Civale, A. D. Marwick, T. K. Worthington, M. A. Kirk, J. R. Thompson, L. Krusin-Elbaum, Y. Sun, J. R. Clem, and F. Holtzberg, *Phys. Rev. Lett.* **67**, 648 (1991).
[33] B. Roas, B. Hensel, G. Saemann-Ischenko, and L. Schultz, *Appl. Phys. Lett.* **54**, 1051 (1989).
[34] A. Umezawa, G. W. Crabtree, J. Z. Liu, H. W. Weber, W. K. Kwok, L. H. Nunez, and H. Claus, *Phys. Rev.* B **36**, 7151 (1987).
[35] J. Eisenmenger, P. Leiderer, M. Wallenhorst, and H. Dötsch, *Phys. Rev.* B **64**, 104503 (2001).
[36] Y. Matsui, E. Takayama-Muromachi, and K. Kato, *Jpn. J. Appl. Phys.* **26**, L1183 (1987).
[37] J. Y. Lin, M. Gurvitch, S. K. Tolpygo, A. Bourdillon, S. Y. Hou, and J. M. Philips, *Phys. Rev.* B **54**, R12717 (1996).
[38] Y. Bugoslavsky, L. F. Cohen, G. K. Perkins, M. Polichetti, T. J. Tate, R. Gwilliam, A. D. Caplin, *Nature* (London) **411**, 561 (2001).
[39] Y. Zhao, Y. Feng, C. H. Cheng, L. Zhou, Y. Wu, T. Machi, Y. Fudamoto, N. Koshizuka, and M. Murakami, *Appl. Phys. Lett.* **79**, 1154 (2001).
[40] C. B. Eom, M. K. Lee, J. H. Choi, L. J. Belenky, X. Song, L. D. Cooley, M. T. Naus, S. Patnaik, J. Jiang, M. Rikel, A. Polyanskii, A. Gurevich, and X. Y. Cai, *Nature* (London) **411**, 558 (2001).
[41] R. F. Klie, J. C. Idrobo, N. D. Browning, A. Serquis, Y. T. Zhu, X. Z. Liao and F. M. Mueller, *Appl. Phys. Lett.* 80, 3970 (2002).
[42] S. Jin, H. Mavoori, C. Bower, and R.B. Van Dover, *Nature* (London) **411**, 563 (2001).
[43] B. A. Glowacki and M. Majoros, *Physica* C **372**, 1235 (2002).
[44] A. Matsumoto, H. Kumakura, H. Kitaguchi, H. Fujii, and K. Togano, *Physica* C **382**, 207 (2002).
[45] X. L. Wang, S. Soltanian, J. Horvat, A. H. Liu, M. J. Qin, H. K. Liu, and S. X. Dou, *Physica* C **361**, 149 (2001).
[46] B. A. Glowacki, M. Majoros, M. Vickers, J. E. Evetts, Y. Shi, and I. McDougal, *Supercond. Sci. Technol.* **14**, 193 (2001).

[47] K. J. Song, C. Park, N. J. Lee, H. M. Jang, H. S. Ha, S. S. Oh, M. H. Sohn, R. K. Ko, Y. K. Kwon, and J. H. Joo, to be published in *ASC proceedings*, Houston (2002).

[48] A. Serquis, L. Civale, D. L. Hammon, J. Y. Coulter, X. Z. Liao, Y. T. Zhu, D. E. Peterson, and F. M. Mueller, *Appl. Phys. Le*tt. **82**, 1754 (2003).

[49] A. Serquis, L. Civale, D. L. Hammon, J. Y. Coulter, X. Z. Liao, Y. T. Zhu, D. E. Peterson, and F. M. Mueller, *Appl. Phys. Lett.* **83**, 4401 (2002).

[50] L. Civale, A. Serquis, D. L. Hammon, X. Z. Liao, J. Y. Coulter, Y. T. Zhu, T. Holesinger, D. E. Peterson, and F. M. Mueller, to be published in ASC proceedings, Houston (2002) *IEE Transactions in Applied Superconductivity.*

[51] A. Serquis, L. Civale, D. L. Hammon, X. Z. Liao, J. Y. Coulter, Y. T. Zhu, D. E. Peterson, and F. M. Mueller, submitted to *J. Appl. Phys.*

[52] N. A. Frederick, Shi Li, M. B. Maple, V. F. Nesterenko, and S. S. Indrakanti, Physica C **363**, 1 (2001).

[53] S. S. Indrakanti, V. F. Nesterenko, M. B. Maple, N. A. Frederick, W. M. Yuhasz, and Shi Li, *Philos. Mag. Lett.* **81**, 849 (2001).

[54] V. F. Nesterenko, *cond-mat/0212543* (21 Dec 2002).

[55] L. Reimer, *Energy-Filtering Transmission Electron Microscopy*, Springer, Berlin, pp.347, (1995).

[56] D. B. Williams and C. B. Carter, Transmission Electron Microscopy, Plenum Press, New York (1996). P. 616

[57] F. Hofer, P. Warbichler, and W. Grogger, *Ultramicroscopy* **59**, 15 (1995).

[58] K. T. Moore, J. M. Howe, and D. C. Elbert, *Ultramicroscopy* **80**, 203 (1999).

[59] C.P. Bean, *Phys. Rev. Lett.* **8**, 250 (1962).

[60] J. Moulder, W. Stickle, P. Sobol, and K. Bomben, in *Handbook of X-ray Photoelectron Spectroscopy*, **2**nd edition, edited by J. J. Chastain (Perkin Elmer Corporation, *Physical Electronics*, 1992) and references therein.

[61] *Practical Surface Analysis, Auger and X-ray Photoelectron Spectroscopy*, **2**nd edition, edited by D. Briggs Briggs and M.P. Seah (John Wiley & Sons, New York, 1990), Vol. **1**.

[62] H. Schmidt, J. F. Zasadzinski, K. E. Gray, and D. H. Hinks, *Phys. Rev.* B **63**, 504(R) (2001).

[63] A.C. Larson and R.B. Von Dreele, GSAS, Generalized Structural Analysis System, *Document LAUR* 86-748, Los Alamos National Laboratory, Los Alamos, New Mexico, 1993.

[64] Note that only under a main zone-axis imaging condition can the precipitates be seen clearly.

[65] D. A. Porter and K. E. Easterling, *Phase Transformations in Metals and Alloys* [Van Nostrand Reinhold (International) 1981], p.150.

[66] D. B. Williams and C. B. Carter, *Transmission Electron Microscopy* (Plenum Press, New York 1996), p.449.

[67] Y. Zhu, L. Wu, V. Volkov, Q. Li, G. Gu, A. R. Moodenbaugh, M. Malac, M. Suenaga, and J. Tranquada, *Physica* C **356**, 239 (2001).

[68] G. Blatter, M. V. Feigel'man, V. B. Geshkenbein, A. I. Larkin, and V. M. Vinokur, *Rev. Mod. Phys.* **66**, 1125 (1994).

[69] J. R. Thompson, M. Paranthaman, D. K. Christen, K. D. Sorge, H. J. Kim, and J. G. Ossandon, *Supercond. Sci. Technol.* **14**, L17 (2001).

[70] S. Soltanian, X. L. Wang, I. Kusevic, E. Bavic, A. H. Li, M. J. Qin, J. Horvat, H. K. Liu, E. W. Collings, E. Lee, M. D. Sumption, and S. X. Dou, Physica C **361**, 84 (2001).

[71] A. Serquis, Y. T. Zhu, E. J. Peterson, J. Y. Coulter, D. E. Peterson, and F. M. Mueller, *Appl. Phys. Lett.* **79**, 4399 (2001).

[72] G. Giunchi, S. Ceresara, G. Ripamonti, A. DiZenobio, S. Rossi, S. Chiarelli, M. Spadoni, R. Wesche, and P. L. Bruzzone, *Supercond. Sci. Technol.* **16**, 285 (2003).

[73] H. L. Suo, C. Beneduce, M. Dhallé, N. Musolino, J. Y. Genoud, and R. Flükiger, Appl. Phys. Lett. **79**, 3116 (2001).

[74] H. Fujii, H. Kumakura, and K. Togano, *J. Mat. Res.* **17**, 2339 (2002).

[75] X. Z. Liao, A. Serquis, Y. T. Zhu, L. Civale, D. L. Hammon, D. E. Peterson, F. M. Mueller, V. F. Nesterenko, and Y. Gu, *cond-mat/0303009 (1 March 2003).*

[76] Hans Ullmaier, *Irreversible Properties of Type II Superconductors* (Springer-Verlag, New York, 1975), Chap. 5, p.83, and references therein.

[77] B. Dam, J. M. Huigbregste, F. C. Klaassen, R. F. C. Van der Geest, G. Dooms, J. H. Rector, A. M. Testa, S. Freisem, J. C. Martinez, B. Stäuble-Pümpin, and R. Griessen, *Nature* (London) **399**, 439 (1999).

[78] V. M. Pan and A. V. Pan, Low *Temperature Physics* **27**, 732 (2001).

[79] HIPing of macroscopically large solenoid type devices with very long wire needed for some practical application is possible with currently available production-sized HIP systems with sizes of workzone about 1 m.

Fabrication and Characterization of Superconducting MgB_2 Thin Films *In-Situ* Grown by dc Magnetron Sputtering

R. Di Capua [(a)], A. Andreone [(a)], A. Cassinese [(a)], F. Chiarella [(a)], E. Di Gennaro [(a)], G. Lamura [(a)], M.G. Maglione [(a)], L. Maritato [(b)], S.L. Prischepa [(b)], M. Salluzzo [(a)], M. Salvato [(b)], R. Vaglio [(a)]

[(a)] INFM-Coherentia and Dipartimento Scienze Fisiche, Università degli Studi di Napoli "Federico II", Napoli, Italy

[(b)] INFM-Coherentia and Dipartimento di Fisica "E.R. Caianiello", Università degli Studi di Salerno, Salerno, Italy

Abstract

In the present work, we report on the thin films fabrication and characterization of the recently discovered magnesium diboride (MgB_2) intermetallic superconducting compound.

High-quality c-axis oriented thin films were grown by a d.c. planar magnetron sputtering technique in a UHV system (10^{-7} Pa) equipped with 3 focused 2" magnetron sources. A precursor deposition step was followed by an in-situ annealing, in Mg atmosphere, at about 800°C in a In sealed Nb box. Superconducting samples were obtained both on MgO and Al_2O_3 (sapphire) single crystal substrates, 10 mm x 10 mm wide. The process is highly reproducible and can be easily scaled to produce large area films.

The best films showed maximum Tc = 35 K (onset), a transition width of 0.5 K, a residual resisitivity ratio up to 1.6, a low temperature critical current density Jc > 10^6 A/cm^2, with a thickness ranging between 0.5 μm and 1 μm.

The films were characterized by a variety of structural and electronic measurements.

Structural characterizations included profilometer, X-rays diffraction, SEM and AFM measurements. From them, a wide c-axis orientation was revealed, together with a granular structure of the surface.

Resistivity measurements in external magnetic field up to 8 T have been performed both in parallel and perpendicular configuration. The upper critical magnetic field vs. temperature behavior has been determined from the experimental data. Measurement of upper critical field showed, for the best samples, an anisotropy ratio of about 2.5, very close to the values observed for single crystals.

We measured the temperature and magnetic field dependencies of the critical current density Jc(H,T). Three-dimensional point like normal core pinning was evidenced by measurements of the magnetic dependence of the pinning forces independently from the superconducting and structural quality of the investigated films. The analysis of the experimental data in terms of the collective pinning model has pointed out the presence of a crossover magnetic field from a single vortex to a small vortex bundle pinning regime.

A ΔTc pinning mechanism, i.e., a pinning associated with spatial fluctuations of the transition temperature, has been evidenced by the temperature dependence of this crossover field, in agreement with previous observations performed on MgB_2 bulk materials.

In view of possible device applications, the microwave response has been studied in detail. We report and discuss the dependence of the surface impedance on temperature and r.f. field amplitude at 20 GHz and the temperature dependence of the penetration depth via a dielectric resonator technique.

1 Introduction

The recently discovered intermetallic superconducting compound MgB_2 [1] contains very interesting aspects both related to its record T_c for non-oxide inorganic superconductors (40K), for anisotropic superconducting properties and for an intriguing two-band electronic structure [2].

An impressive number of theoretical and experimental studies have been performed on this new superconductor to determine fundamental properties, like the nature of the pairing mechanism and the origin of superconductivity [3-4].

Its relatively high T_c, long coherence length and fairly high critical current density make this compound a candidate for microelectronic applications and devices. In this framework, thin films play an important role. The availability of in-situ deposited, large area, high quality films with relatively simple techniques is of great importance for such applications.

As far as applications are concerned, the wide availability of a new compound exhibiting a superconducting phase within the easily reached temperature of light, compact, fast cryocoolers has also prompted a discussion on whether MgB_2 might have an impact on the future viability of superconducting electronics [5]. Key advantages of the diboride family over the cuprate family include a larger coherence length, which renders the first compound less sensitive to structural and surface defects and grain boundaries, reduced anisotropy, and of course the presence of a fully gapped Fermi surface, which in principle implies extremely low power dissipation since the number of quasiparticles exponentially vanishes at low temperature. Moreover, its high metallic nature as well as the strongly linked character of grain boundaries in polycrystalline samples [6] makes MgB_2 a promising candidate for the development of microwave passive devices for wireless communications [7] and superconducting cavities for particle accelerators [8]. One should also mention in this context that there is an increasing number of reports indicating that films of good quality can be realized on a variety of substrates, including cheap silicon and sapphire, metals, and even plastic thin sheets [9].

Unfortunately the high vapor pressure of Mg, even at low temperatures, has made difficult the realization of high quality thin films, extremely desirable for a large number of studies and applications, in a single step, without a Mg high pressure postanneal [10-11].

As a second possibility, two-step deposition processes can be developed.

For this reason, most of the first attempts at films fabrication were performed by two-step processes, the second one being an ex-situ post-annealing in Mg saturated vapor [10-11]. Nevertheless, in-situ processes can be desirable for a large number of studies and application. In order to reach this goal, many groups have realized reasonable quality in-situ films by PLD deposition techniques and a subsequent high temperature annealing procedure [12-14], or by a single step procedure [15]. The results have been encouraging, although at the beginning the film quality turned out to be inferior in respect to the best films obtained with ex-situ annealing treatments at much higher Mg partial pressures [10-15].

We developed a simple, innovative method to produce high quality films by a two-step, in-situ technique starting with a precursor film obtained by magnetron sputtering. Among other advantages, the proposed procedure can be easily scaled to obtain large area films for practical applications.

This work is organized as follows.

In the Section 2 a very short summary of MgB_2 main properties is reviewed. In Section 3 we describe our deposition system and technique; this section also concerns the first structural and transport characterizations, showing the main superconducting features. Section 4 is devoted to the temperature and magnetic field dependencies of the critical current density Jc, and to a related analysis of experimental data in terms of pinning forces. In Section 5 we report on microwave measurements, as concerns surface resistance and penetration depth measurements. Finally, in Section 6 we briefly discuss the conclusion of our work and its perspectives.

2. MgB_2 properties

In this section we briefly review the most important properties and features of magnesium diboride. A comprehensive description starting from first principles and theories is beyond the purposes of this section. We will limit ourselves to a rapid review of the basic knowledge of this compound in order to better understand the framework in which our work has been realized.

The crystal lattice of MgB_2 is an honeycomb graphite-like structure, formed by layers containing B atoms in an hexagonal disposition. The B atoms constitute an hexagonal prism [16]. A Mg atom is placed inside this prism. Mg is also located in layers, forming centered hexagons. Mg and B layers are alternated in the crystal lattice. The lattice parameters, identified by the prism, are a = b = 3.086 Å and c = 3.524 Å.

The electronic structure is strongly related to the graphite-like lattice. As concerns the energy bands, MgB_2 exhibits three (bonding) σ bands and two (bonding and anti-bonding) π bands, the former corresponding to the sp^2 hybridization in the boron layer, the latter corresponding to the aromatically hybridized out-of-plane p_z boron orbitals [4, 17-19]. Qualitatively, the two kinds of structures are quite different. Two of the σ bands are only partially filled. The holes at the top of these bands have peculiar two-dimensional properties, and are localized within the boron sheets (corresponding to strongly covalent bonding); in contrast, the π holes and electrons manifest a three-dimensional behavior and are delocalized over the whole lattice structure (being metallic-like states).

The covalent σ bands and the metallic π bands contribute more or less in equal amounts to the density of states at the Fermi level.

The Fermi surface has cylindrical two-dimensional sheets corresponding to the σ bands, while the π bands form two honeycomb tubular three-dimensional networks [4].

It is widely accepted that the superconductivity in this compound arises from electron-phonon coupling (EPC), although its physics presents very unique features compared to the other known electron-phonon superconductors. It is well described by the Migdal Eliashberg theory, which is a standard description of EPC in metals. So an EPC spectral function $\alpha^2F(\omega)$ is introduced in order to determine the superconducting properties.

In the spectral function, all electron bands and all phonon modes have to be considered. The calculations show that the coupling with the boron phonons substantially causes the superconductivity in MgB_2. It has been established that the relevant phonon modes in the EPC coupling are two optical E_{2g} modes [20].

Isotope shift was predicted for both B and Mg, although this effect should be small for Mg [21]. Theory predictions were qualitatively and quantitatively confirmed by experiments [22-23].

The first experiments, especially concerning specific heat and tunneling measurements, showed that the properties of this compound were not consistent with a conventional strong coupling scenario [24-26]. Starting from the electronic band structure and from EPC calculations, a two gaps model was proposed to describe the experimental results. The two gaps are associated with the Fermi surfaces of σ and π band respectively, and the phonon calculation must be performed separately for the two sets of bands. Some tunneling experiments clearly proved the existence of two gaps, and the two band model is now practically universally accepted. From the data, values of $\Delta_\pi = 2.5 - 3$ meV and $\Delta_\sigma = 6.5 - 7.5$ meV have been estimated.

The presence of two gaps makes it difficult to measure some properties separately for each one, such as the temperature dependence. Because of this, some interesting questions about MgB_2 are still debated; for instance, it has been proposed but not yet established that superconductivity in the π band could not be "independent" from the σ band, but rather it may come from a proximity effect induced by the latter.

Impurity scattering has to be considered separately for the two bands, and for the interband scattering. In single crystals, the scattering rates estimated by experimental data [27-28] suggest that the s band is in the clean limit, while the p band is in the dirty limit.

Theoretic arguments show that non-magnetic impurities suppress superconductivity, but only the interband scattering acts as a pair-breaking [29].

In the strong interband scattering limit, a merging of the two gaps has been predicted, together with a critical temperature suppression [29]. This occurrence should be observed in disordered samples, and it is important from our point of view, since from our characterization and from some preliminary measurements we have found an indication of disorder in our samples.

From the point of view of practical applications, upper critical field, critical current and microwave surface impedance measurements are of great importance.

MgB_2 "clean" samples, such as single crystals, appear to be not really competitive in terms of Hc_2 values. However, the unique feature of two-gaps superconductivity of this compound allows in principle a great enhancement of Hc_2 by tuning the non-magnetic impurity scattering, without strong effects on the critical temperature. Some recent reports confirm this prediction [31]. Furthermore, critical currents are not strongly dependent on the field in these samples, so that MgB_2 turns out to be an extremely interesting material for magnet applications, also considering its low weight and cost.

Another possible field of application for MgB_2 is the realization of microwave devices. Results in terms of absolute values of the surface resistance Z_s, obtained on wires, polycrystalline samples and films, but not yet on crystals, are encouraging if compared to state-of-the-art samples of HTS [32-36]. The s-wave character of the order parameter of MgB_2, however, should ensure an exponentially vanishing R_s at the lowest temperatures, whereas most results show that the level of microwave losses is still high, well above BCS expectation and dominated by extrinsic effects. Besides that, in spite of previous reports claiming the absence of weak link behavior in this superconductor, preliminary data of power dependence show that granularity governs the performance of MgB_2 films in the microwave region [33-34].

This scenario is rather disappointing, precluding at present the possibility of applications at temperatures attainable with low-power cryocoolers.

A careful study of Z_s is therefore important to analyze in detail whether this material might be in the near future a valid alternative to Nb and its alloys for cavity applications and to HTS in passive microwave electronics for telecommunications.

3 Thin film fabrication and preliminary transport and structural measurements

MgB_2 thin films were grown at INFM - University of Naples by a planar d.c. magnetron sputtering technique in a UHV system. The vacuum chamber has a rough (rotary) pump, a turbomolecular pump and an ionic pump. We were able to reach a base pressure in the low 10^{-7} Pa range.

The sputtering system is equipped with 3 focused 2" magnetron sources (a stoichiometric MgB_2 target and metallic Mg and B targets by Superconducting Components Inc.).

Sputtering magnetrons are used for sputter etching and thin film deposition. In these devices a magnetic field is used to trap electrons above the cathode, allowing operation at lower Argon pressure than similar discharges not sustained by magnetic fields. These trapped electrons create ions that are accelerated into the cathode by the plasma sheath, giving rise to the desired sputter etching. To balance the flux of ions to the cathode there must be an equal flux of electrons to the anode.

However, the system we built is very flexible: it can be switched from balanced to unbalanced regime simply changing the magnetic core. For the fabrication of MgB_2 films, we used the system in the balanced configuration.

Moreover, the availability, meantime, of three different sputtering sources allows us to perform deposition attempts using different procedures without losing the best vacuum condition and change optimized geometric parameters. The vacuum conditions are also preserved after each deposition thanks to a manipulation device made by a load-lock plus a wobble stick (tweezers) arms. This device allows the operator to load substrates and take out samples through a pre-chamber, so the main vacuum chamber is never exposed to air.

The substrates were placed "on axis" on a molybdenum (Mo) heater. The distance between the heater and the sputtering sources can be changed depending on the heater height. This operation can be performed without losing vacuum conditions too.

We used MgO and sapphire (Al_2O_3) substrates.

The system is also equipped with a Joule Mo evaporator. Once the film has been fabricated, it can be placed in the evaporation chamber, where Pb can be deposited on the surface. Our goal is to realize planar tunnel junction through an in-situ process (both as concerns film oxidation and the Pb counterelectrode evaporation) using appropriate masks.

We tried several deposition procedures. The main problem in MgB_2 sample fabrication is the high volatility of Mg even at low temperatures. In order to obtain films with the correct stoichiometry, a process at very high heater temperatures cannot be realized. On the other hand, to make possible an epitaxial film growth, high substrate temperatures during the deposition are desirable. In the first attempts we tried to reach a compromise between these two competitive effects, trying different deposition temperatures, and sputtering at the same time from a MgB_2 and a Mg target (cosputtering). As the best result, we obtained films with a critical temperature of about 22 K, much lower than the single crystal T_c (39-40 K). In addition, we never were able to obtain the epitaxial growth and the correct stoichiometry, as shown by our X-Rays Diffraction (XRD) measurements, even in the case of cosputtering at room temperature.

As a consequence, we realized that a two-step process was needed: a precursor deposition step by sputtering, and an annealing step in Mg atmosphere. The two step procedure had been previously realized by several groups [10-14], with ex-situ annealing.

In order to achieve an entirely in-situ process, we designed and built a cylindrical Nb box (height = 4 mm) to perform the film post-annealing. The Nb box (Fig. 1) could be closed by a properly designed Nb cap. Both the box and the cap were loaded and placed on the heater together with the substrate.

During the deposition of the precursor film, the substrate was placed over a thin Mg disk, on the bottom of the box (h = 4mm). The deposition was performed at the room temperature (i.e., without turning on the heater).

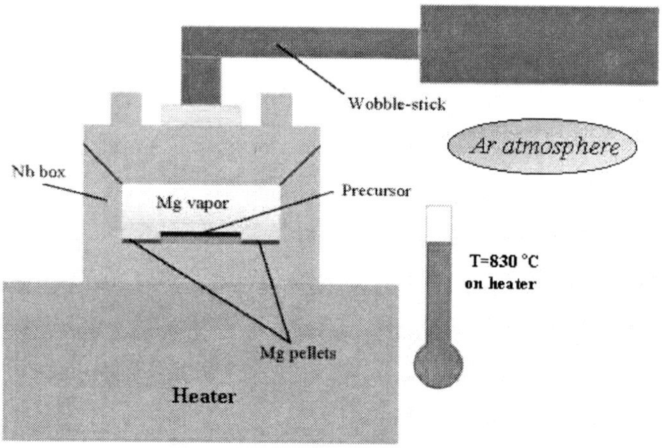

Fig. 1: The annealing step scheme.

After deposition, using the tweezers mounted on the wobble stick, the box was well closed by the cap. An indium wire gasket was inserted between the box and the cap. At this point the heater was switched on and ramped up to the desired temperature. The melting of the In gasket guaranteed a perfect sealing of the box. The box design and the internal Mg overpressure (due to the presence of the Mg disk) prevented any In diffusion in the film. The process was therefore conducted in saturated Mg-vapor as in ex-situ processes, giving high level film quality and reproducibility [37].

Best results were obtained codepositing MgB_2 and Mg for 10min on R-cut sapphire, at room temperature, resulting in a Mg rich Mg-B precursor film. The target voltages and current were 460 V (MgB_2 target), 400 V (Mg target) and 1 A respectively (resulting in target powers slightly lower than 500W). The argon pressure during sputtering was $9x10^{-1}$ Pa. The distance between the substrate and the targets surfaces was 7 cm.

Actually, the cosputtering procedure seemed not to be critical and films with similar properties were obtained starting from precursors obtained sputtering only from the MgB_2 target. The advantage in using only the MgB_2 target is given by the much lower consumption rate compared to the Mg one. Besides economic reasons, avoiding a fast target consumption prevents frequent target replacement and consequent exposure to the air of the vacuum chamber.

Typical post-annealing processes were made at a substrate temperature Ts = 830°C for 10 min (about 30 minutes were required to reach the equilibrium temperature).

After deposition the films could be removed from the system in the sealed Nb box for transfer in a UHV environment for surface studies (Scanning Tunneling Microscope (STM) or others). Recently we have developed a new design for the post-annealing step. At present, a dedicated Nb furnace is being used. The furnace is mounted onto an Inconel heater, and is closed by a Boron Nitride (BN) cap. Because of the different thermal expansion coefficients of the two materials, a tight seal between the BN cover and the Nb furnace is obtained. The advantages of this new annealing technique is the increasing and a more accurate control of the substrate temperature due to the better thermal contact between the heater and the furnace. Furthermore, because of the In seal, the box used so far could not be opened in-situ after the annealing; instead, from the new one the sample can be taken in-situ, allowing junction fabrication avoiding the air exposure of the film surface.

No attempts have been made so far starting from B or B-rich Mg-B precursors.

The process is highly reproducible and similar results were obtained on both sapphire and MgO substrates [37-38]. The film thickness, measured with a standard stylus profilometer, was in the range (depending on deposition time and precursor composition) 0.5 - 1.0 μm.

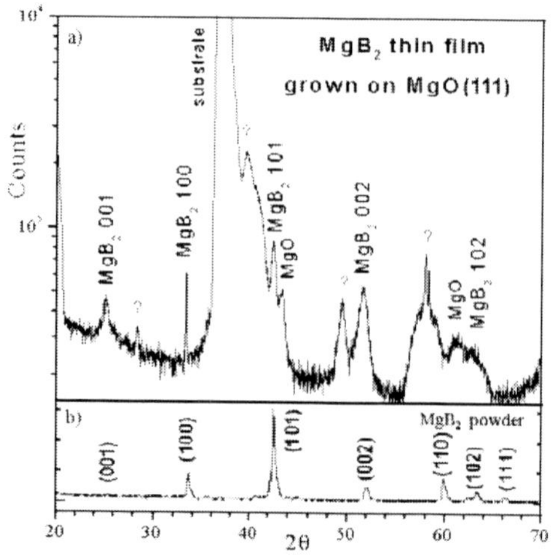

Fig. 2: a) X-ray diffraction (θ-2θ) spectrum for a MgB_2 film on MgO(111) substrate; b) comparison with a θ-2θ spectrum obtained on MgB_2 powders (from [10]).

XRD pattern (Cu Kα line), reported in Fig. 2 for a film deposited on crystalline MgO(111), showed the MgB_2 phase with small amounts of MgO (due to the oxidation of excess Mg) and some unidentified spurious phases. By comparing the experimental spectra with the ones obtained on powders [10], the relative height of the peaks indicates a wide c-axis orientation of our films. From peak positions, we can estimate the lattice parameters: $a = b = 0.310 \pm 0.002$ nm, $c = 0.353 \pm 0.005$ nm. XRD patterns on optimized films on R-cut sapphire are not reported because of the overlapping of the (00n) film reflections with the Al_2O_3 substrate reflections.

Film surface morphology was investigated by Scanning Electron Microscopy (SEM) and Atomic Force Microscopy (AFM). In Fig. 3 an AFM image of a film is reported, showing granular features on the surface. The roughness on a single grain (columnar nature, few microns wide) is about 50nm. The granular structure of the film is probably the source of the quite high estimated resistivity, as reported below. Indeed, this irregular structure affects the estimation of the "effective thickness", due to the limited contact area between the grains.

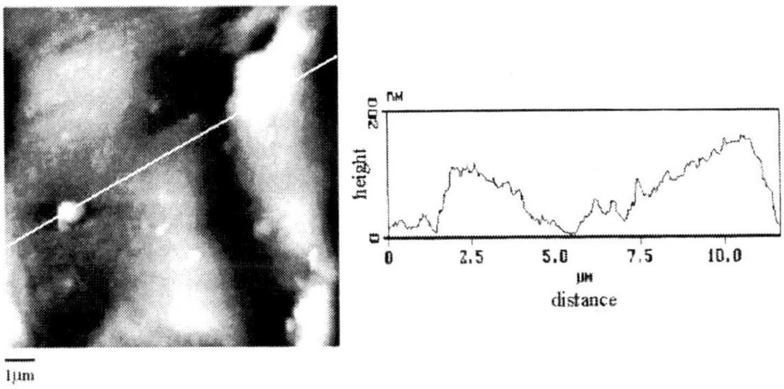

Fig. 3: AFM image of a MgB_2 thin film surface, showing a granular structure. The height profile along the line reported in the image is also shown.

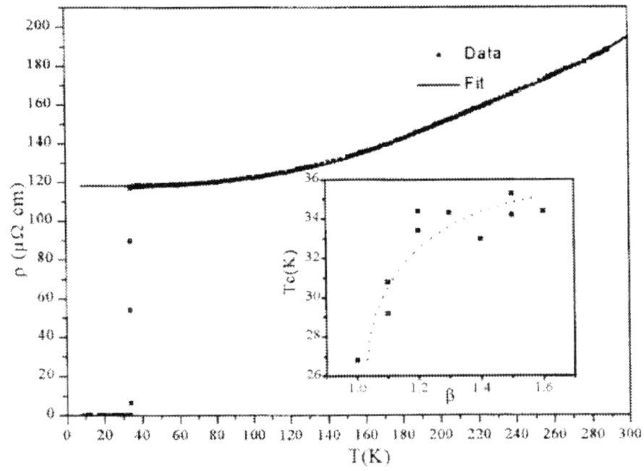

Fig. 4: Resistivity vs. temperature for a MgB_2 film. The continuous line represents the fit made using the generalized Bloch-Gruneisen formula. In the inset the correlation between the residual resistivity ratio and Tc is shown.

In Fig. 4 the resistivity as a function of the temperature is reported for a typical film grown on a sapphire substrate in the standard conditions described above. The absolute value of resistivity was determined using a commercial linear four probe station, the main error being associated with effective thickness overestimation due to the strong granular nature of the samples surface. In such a way, we evaluated the resistivity at room temperature. Then, measuring the resistance as a temperature function in a standard four contact configuration, resistance data have been normalized to room temperature value in order to yield resistivity ρ. The estimated room temperature resistivity is about 200µΩcm, much higher in respect to single crystals. However, this value should only to be considered as an upper limit, since the probably weak connection between the grains as discussed above. Similar or higher values have been reported in literature for films [3, 38], possibly due to similar effective thickness problems.

We do not have a clear explanation for the reduced onset critical temperature (35 K). It is possibly due to the somewhat low maximum annealing temperature that can be reached inside our Nb box. The reduced value of Tc is probably related to a kind of disorder inside our films, on a scale lower than the grain one. Future effort based on STM measurement, already in progress, could help us to clarify this point.

The transition width for the best samples was $\Delta Tc = 0.5$ K (10%-90% criterion).

Equivalent results were obtained for films grown on MgO substrates. In the temperature range explored, the resisitivity closely follows a Bloch-Gruneisen law. The continuous line in Fig. 4 represents the best-fitting data. From the best fit procedure, we obtained a Debye temperature $\Theta_D = 1100 \pm 50$K. At low temperatures a clear T^3 dependence is observed as generally reported in the literature [3].

Our best films exhibited a residual resistivity ratio (RRR) $\beta = \rho$ (300K) / ρ (40K) = 1.6 A clear Tc-β correlation has been observed in film of different quality, as reported in the inset of Fig. 4. The observed relation strongly resembles the behavior of many intermetallic classic superconducting compounds (Nb, A15) [3] as well as borocarbides [39].

We measured the critical current density Jc of our optimized films both inductively [13] and resistively. In Fig. 5 is plotted Jc vs. T in absence of magnetic field, resistively measured on a film deposited on a R-cut sapphire substrate. As shown, $J_c = 2.5$ MA/cm^2 at T = 11.8 K. Details on J_c resistive measurements at several values of temperature and magnetic field, together with a full discussion of the experimental data, are reported in the next session.

T_c and J_c of our films were also evaluated inductively by measuring the third harmonic component voltage V_3 across a small sensor coil mounted very close to the film surface, as a function of temperature or driving current respectively [40]. The temperature dependence of the critical current performed by this method on our standard films is reported in Fig. 6. The extrapolated value for the zero field, zero temperature critical current is $J_c(0) = 1.6$ MA/cm^2. In the inset the Tc evaluation using a plot of V_3 vs T is also shown (as generally observed by this method the onset of the V_3 signal roughly corresponds to the zero resistance value temperature in resistive measurements). The width of the curve is related to the uniformity of the superconducting transition (roughly, it represents a statistical distribution of the "local" critical temperatures of the samples).

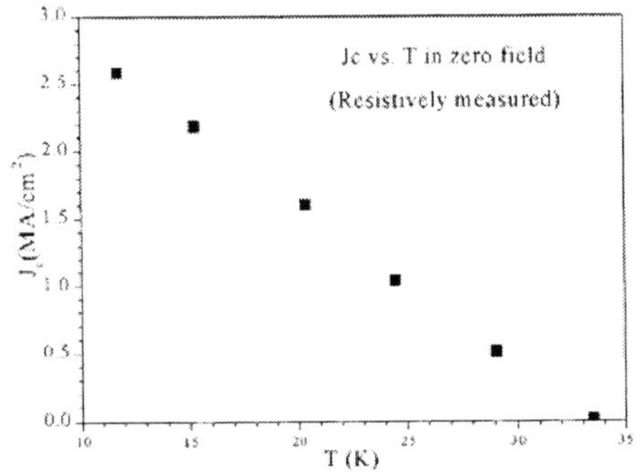

Fig. 5: Critical current density vs. temperature, resistively measured, for a MgB_2 thin film.

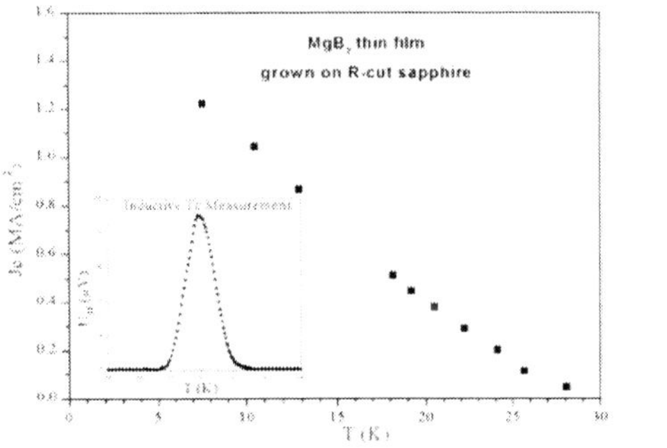

Fig. 6: Critical current density vs. temperature for a MgB_2 film grown on Al_2O_3 substrate. The inset shows an inductive measurement of Tc.

In Fig. 7 the temperature dependence of the upper critical field both in the parallel (||) and perpendicular direction (⊥) with respect to the film plane are reported up to a maximum field of 8 Tesla.

As typically reported [3] both curves show a slight upward curvature close to Tc. From the critical field slope we can estimate the coherence length. We used the following formulas [41-42]:

$$H_{C2}(0) = 0.691 \times T_C \times (dH_{C2}/dT) \quad \text{(for both directions)} \tag{1}$$

$$\xi_{||} = [\Phi_0 / (2\pi H_{C2\perp})]^{1/2} \quad \text{and} \quad \xi_{\perp} = \Phi_0 / (2\pi\, \xi_{||}\, H_{C2||}) \tag{2}$$

where the slope dH_{C2}/dT was numerically determined from the linear region of the experimental data.

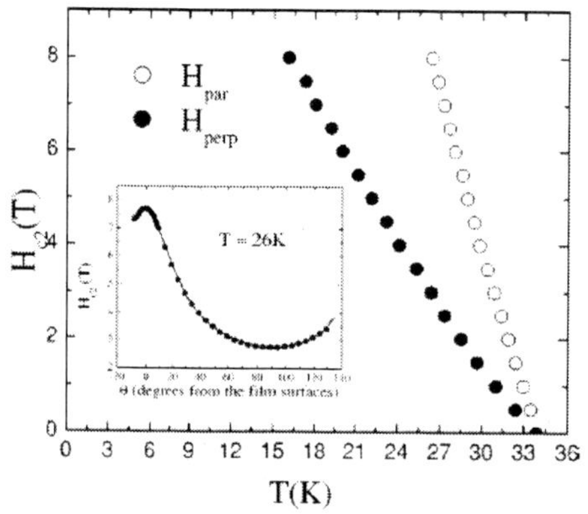

Fig. 7: Temperature dependence of the parallel and perpendicular upper critical fields for our best sample (sample A). In the inset, the angular dependence of the upper critical field H(θ) at T = 26K is shown. The solid line represents the Ginzburg-Landau formula for H(θ) obtained with $\gamma = 2.7$.

For optimized films at T = 0K, $\xi_\perp = 2.3 \pm 0.1$ nm and $\xi_{||} = 5.7 \pm 0.2$ nm, and the anisotropy ratio is $\gamma = 2.5$ (slightly temperature-dependent). This value agrees fairly well with some estimations on single crystals [43-44], indirectly proving the high quality and c-axis orientation of our films. Non-optimized films presented a somewhat lower γ.

A perfect fitting of the angular dependence of the critical field with the Ginzbug-Landau formula [45]:

$$H_{C2}(\theta) = H_{C2\perp} (\cos^2\theta + \gamma^{-2} \sin^2\theta)^{-1/2} \tag{3}$$

was possible at all temperatures. In this formula, θ represents the angle respect to the c-axis.

In the inset in Fig. 7, we report the angular dependence of the upper critical field for an optimized film at T = 26 K, together with the corresponding fit (continuos line). From the fit procedure, we got $\gamma = 2.8$ and $H_{c2\perp} = 2.75$ T. The values of γ determined with the two methods are slightly different, because of the different procedures and temperatures (the first method evaluates γ at T = 0).

It is important to point out the fact that for the experimental data in the inset of Fig. 7, θ is the angle respect to the normal to surface film. The surprisingly accord between the experimental data and the fit curve (in which θ is the angle between the applied field and the c-axis of the film) is another proof of the orientation of our films [46].

Critical fields measurements for a lower show a lower anisotropy (γ = 1.6), possibly corresponding to partial c-axis orientation, and point out as the value of the anisotropy parameter γ in MgB_2 thin films can also be used to indicate the crystallinity of the samples.

Finally, in Table 1 the main properties of our films are summarized.

Table 1. main properties of the best films

Tc (K)	35
ΔTc (K)	0.5
β	1.6
ρ (μΩ cm)	200
Jc (MA/cm^2, 0 Field)	2 (at 11K)
Hc_2 par (T) at T = 25.7K	8.0
Hc_2 perp (T) at T = 25.7K	2.9

4. Critical current density and pinning forces

The discovery of MgB_2 has led to intensive experimental and theoretical activities to understand the basic phenomena of superconductivity and to investigate the pinning dynamics governing dissipative effects. Bulk MgB_2 samples have been largely analyzed, showing well linked grains resulting in large critical current density even in the presence of high external magnetic fields [47].

In type II superconductors with high values of the Ginzburg-Landau parameter κ, the most important elementary interaction between vortices and pinning centers is the so-called core interaction, arising from the influence of the parts of materials with the worse superconducting properties on the spatial variation of the superconducting order parameter. The core interaction is generally prevalent on the magnetic one, related to the presence of superconducting and non-superconducting interfaces parallel to the external field, which is very small in high κ type II superconductors.

MgB_2 bulk samples, with $\kappa \approx 20$ [3], have shown dissipative properties due to core pinning related to randomly distributed spatial variations of the transition temperature (ΔT_c pinning) [48] in contrast with the case of high temperature superconductors where the core interaction is associated to charge carrier mean free path fluctuations (δl pinning) mostly due to crystalline lattice defects [49].

Due to the particular microstructures of thin films, the pinning mechanisms in these samples can be quite different from the bulk and the study of their dissipative properties is interesting from the point of view of both the involved fundamental aspects and the future possible applications. In situ thin films of MgB_2 have been so far fabricated using different deposition techniques and have shown critical current density values higher than 10^{11} A/m^2.

In this section we report on measurements of the J_c dependencies on magnetic field and temperature. Reported measurements are carried out on samples deposited on sapphire R-cut substrates.

Samples with different superconducting properties have been analyzed. In the following, we will refer to the two different samples reported as sample A and sample B. Both of them were deposited on R-cut sapphire substrates.

Our results indicate the presence of a three-dimensional (3D) core pinning mechanism and give evidence of ΔT_c pinning in agreement with that already observed in MgB_2 bulk samples.

For J_c measurements, after the deposition, a microbridge configuration was obtained using a scribing method [50]. Typical widths of the microbridges were around 350 μm. J_c was measured using a standard four-probe technique along with a dc current source generator and adopting a threshold criterion of 1 μV. The magnetic field was applied perpendicular to the film surface.

In Fig. 8 are shown the $J_c(H)$ curves for sample A, our best sample (T_c = 35K, ΔT_c = 0.5K, 10%-90% criterion), at six different temperatures. At low temperatures, the J_c values exceed 10^{10} A/m^2 up to fields equal to 3.5 T, confirming high intergranular current flow in MgB_2 thin films [47, 51]. The inset in Fig. 8 presents the temperature dependence of the irreversibility field $H_{irr}(T)$, defined as the field at which the J_c values become lower than 10^6 A/m^2. The solid line in the inset,

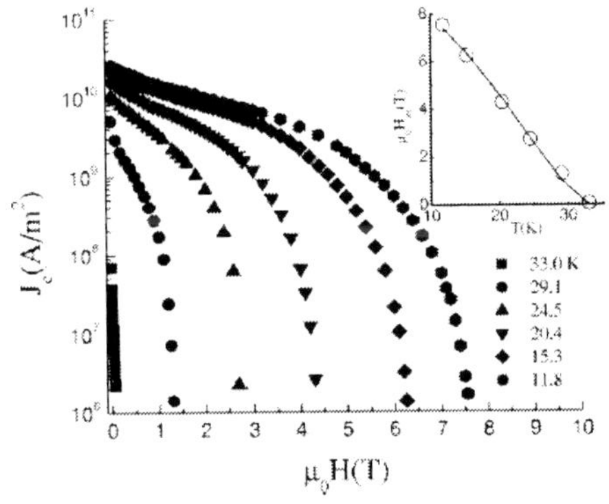

Fig. 8: $J_c(H)$ at several temperatures for sample A. The inset shows the temperature dependence of the irreversibility field for this sample. The solid line is obtained from the $[1-(T/T_c)^2]^{3/2}$.

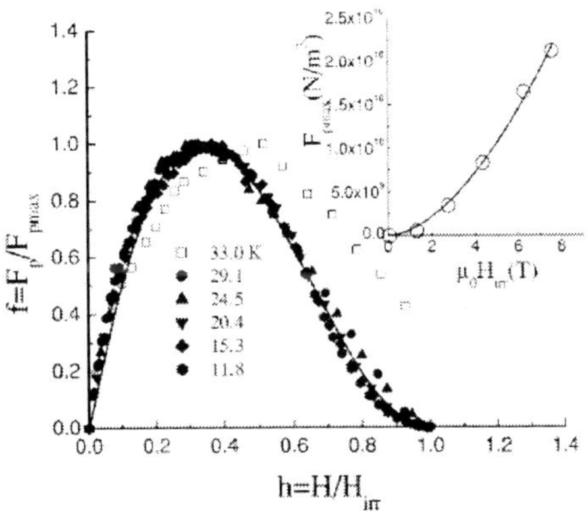

Fig. 9: Magnetic field dependence of the reduced pinning force $f(h)$, for sample A. The solid line represents the $f(h) \sim h^{1.1}(1-h)^{2.1}$ dependence. In the inset the behavior of the maximum pinning force F_{pmax} vs. the irreversibility field H_{irr} is shown. The solid line is the law $F_{pmax} \sim H_{irr}^{\alpha}$ with $\alpha = 1.8$.

in close agreement with the data, is the law $(1-(T/T_c)^2)^{3/2}$, which is the typical behavior expected in the case of 3D flux creep [13]. Pinning forces, defined as $F_p = \mu_0 H \times J_c$, can be calculated from the results of Fig. 8.

In Fig. 9 we plot the reduced pinning force f versus the reduced magnetic field h ($f = F_p/F_{pmax}$, $h = H/H_{irr}$) at the same temperatures of Fig. 8. H_{irr} is the field at which J_c vanishes; it replaces H_{c2} when the value of the critical current is not determined by depairing effects [51]. The curves exhibit a scaling behavior at $T < 30$ K, indicating, in this range of temperature, the presence of a single dominant pinning mechanism. In particular, the best fit of the curves (solid line in Fig. 9) is obtained with a $f(h)$ dependence given by $h^{1.1}(1-h)^{2.1}$, which is very close to the $h(1-h)^2$ one, expected in the case of point like normal core pinning centers [53]. The presence of such a pinning mechanism is confirmed by the dependence of the maximum pinning force at a certain temperature F_{pmax} versus the irreversibility field H_{irr}, shown in the inset in Fig. 9, which obeys the law $F_{pmax} \sim H_{irr}^{\alpha}$ with $\alpha = 1.8$, (solid line in the inset) close to $\alpha=2$ derived by Dew-Hughes for the case of core normal point pinning [53].

Similar results have been obtained also for other MgB_2 thin films with different superconducting properties. As an example, in Fig. 10, are reported the *f(h,T)* curves measured on sample B ($T_c = 28K$) and showing again a scaling behavior at temperatures below the critical one, well described by the dependence $h^{0.97}(1-h)^{1.77}$ (solid line in Fig. 10) close to that expected for core normal point-like pinning.

Given the presence of 3D core pinning in our MgB_2 thin films independently of their particular superconducting properties, it is important to distinguish between the case of ΔT_c and Δl pinning. The three-dimensionality of the pinning phenomena in our samples, which shows relatively low values of the anisotropy ratio [46], has been confirmed by the analysis on the reduced pinning forces. In the frame of the collective pinning theory [54], valid for randomly distributed weak pinning centers, the elasticity or the plasticity of the flux-line lattice strongly influences the dissipative behavior. For the 3D elastic vortex lattice, it has been shown [52] that the critical current density J_c is field independent in the presence of single vortex pinning, i.e. for applied magnetic fields lower than a crossover field H_{sv} defined as

$$H_{sv} = \beta_{sv} \frac{J_{sv}}{J_0} H_{c2}, \tag{4}$$

where $\beta_{sv} \approx 5$, J_0 is the GL depairing current density, J_{sv} is the critical current density in the single vortex-pinning regime and H_{c2} is the upper critical field. At higher fields, for $H > H_{sv}$, the pinning of small vortex bundles starts to be predominant and $J_c(H)$ follows an exponential law [52]

$$J_c(H) \approx J_c(0) \exp\left\{ -\left(\frac{H}{H_0} \right)^{3/2} \right\} \tag{5}$$

with $H_{sv} \approx H_0$.

The experimental behavior shown in Fig. 8 for the $J_c(H)$ dependence of sample A, with an almost constant value of J_c at $H < 4T$ and a fast decrease at higher fields, can be described in terms of Eq. (5). As an example, in Fig. 11 we present the $-log[J_c(H)/J_c(0)]$ versus H dependencies in double logarithmic plot at $T < 30K$ for sample A. It is clear that Eq. (5), as expected, well describes the data for intermediate fields. The deviation at low fields is associated with the crossover from the single vortex pinning regime to the small bundle pinning regime and allows to estimate the field H_{sv}. The determination of H_{sv} is clear from the inset in Fig. 11, where we present the results at T = 24.5 K.

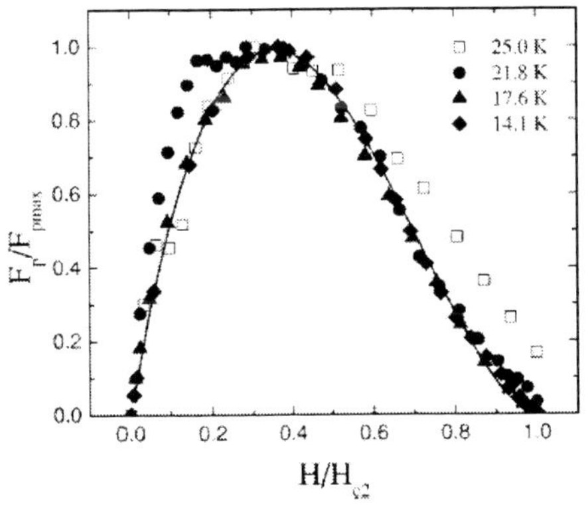

Fig. 10: Magnetic field dependence of the reduced pinning force *f(h)* for the sample with lower T_c (sample B). The solid line represents the $f(h) \sim h(1-h)^{1.8}$ dependence.

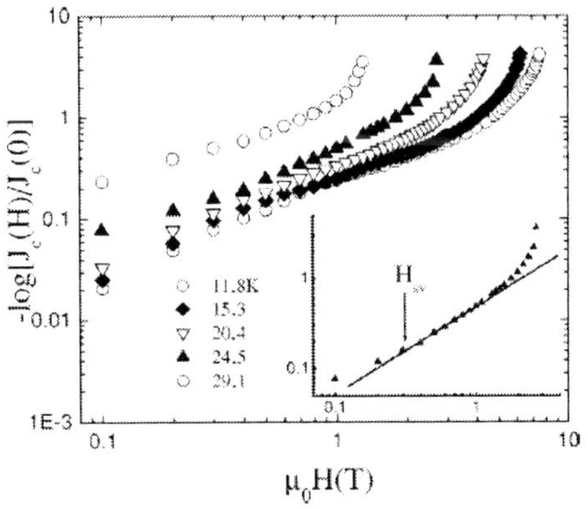

Fig. 11: Double logarithmic plot of $-\log[Jc(H)/Jc(0)]$ vs. H for sample A at several temperatures. In the inset are pointed out the data at T = 24.5K and the determination of the crossover field H_{sv} at this temperature.

A discussion of the nature of the high field deviation from Eq. (2) is beyond the purposes of the present work. We point out that it could be probably related to large thermal fluctuations, as suggested by the 3D flux creep dependence observed for the $H_{irr}(T)$ curves in the inset to Fig. 8. Future works will concern this issue.

The crossover fields H_{sv} as a function of temperature, obtained using Eq. (5) and the afore-mentioned procedure are shown in Fig. 12. As was pointed out by *Griessen et al.* [49], the ΔT_c and Δl pinning mechanisms result in different temperature dependencies of the critical current density J_{sv} in the single vortex pinning regime. In particular, for the case of Δl pinning one obtains a $J_{sv}(T)$ behavior given by $J_{sv} \propto (1-t^2)^{5/2}(1+t^2)^{-1/2}$, with $t = T/T_c$, while for ΔT_c pinning the expected dependence is $J_{sv} \propto (1-t^2)^{7/6}(1+t^2)^{5/6}$. Inserting these two $J_{sv}(T)$ behaviors in Eq. (4), we get for the temperature dependence of the cross over field $H_{sv}(T)$ the following expression

$$H_{sv} = H_{sv}(0)\left(\frac{1-t^2}{1+t^2}\right)^{\nu} \tag{6}$$

where $\nu = 2/3$ characterizes the case of ΔT_c pinning and $\nu = 2$ that of Δl pinning.

Close to the critical temperature, the curvature associated to the ΔT_c case is positive while that of the Δl pinning is negative. As it is clear from the data in Fig. 12, the $H_{sv}(T)$ behavior shows a positive curvature at T < 30 K, strongly indicating the predominance of the ΔT_c pinning mechanism in our thin film samples. Moreover, the agreement among our experimental points and Eq. (6) with $\nu = 2/3$ is very good, as indicated by the solid line in Fig. 12 obtained from Eq. (6) using only one free fitting parameter, $H_{sv}(0)$.

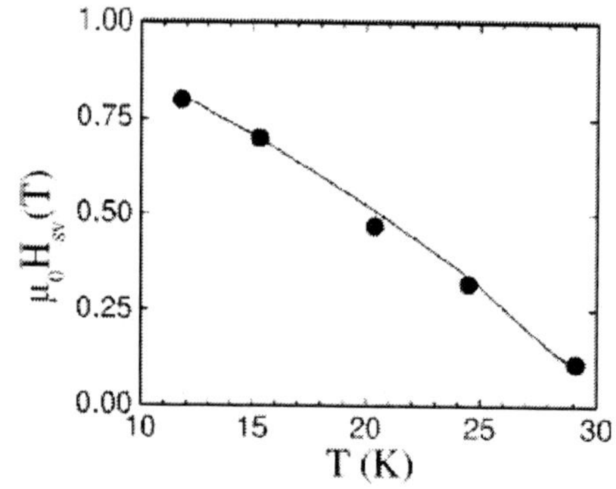

Fig. 12: Temperature dependence of the crossover field $H_{sv}(T)$ for sample A. The solid line is obtained from Eq. (6) with $\nu = 2/3$.

5. Microwave characterizations

The electrodynamic response at 20 GHz of c-axis oriented MgB_2 superconducting thin films is reported in this section, focusing on the temperature T and magnetic field H dependence of the microwave surface impedance $Z_s = R_s + iX_s$.

The microwave surface impedance $Z_s = R_s + iX_s$ is well known to be a relevant quantity for the study of the superconducting state. The surface resistance R_s describes the amount of dissipation at the sample surface, being proportional to the conductivity of thermally excited quasiparticles. The surface reactance X_s can be used to determine the temperature dependence of the magnetic penetration depth, which in turn provides direct information on the existence of a finite gap on the Fermi surface and on its value. In a s-wave superconductor, this is in principle possible looking also at the low temperature behavior of R_s, if the level of extrinsic, defect and/or impurity related, surface losses is low enough.

The study of the electrodynamic response of thin films of MgB_2 in the microwave region therefore offers a twofold interest:

- since it probes the low-lying quasi-particle excitations, the microwave surface impedance can be a useful spectroscopic tool for shedding light on the nature of superconductivity in diborides;
- the investigation of microwave losses is directly related to technological issues of outmost importance for the future of this novel superconducting material, like the quality factor of closed resonant structures, the power handling capability of passive devices and the accelerating field dependence of particle cavities.

Measurements of the surface impedance $Z_s(T, H) = R_s(T, H) + iX_s(T, H) = R_s(T, H) + i\omega\mu_0\lambda(T, H)$ in the microwave region (ω is the angular frequency) were carried out by using a dielectric resonant cavity technique. The resonator (Fig. 13) consists of a cylindrical cavity of diameter 9.5 mm short-circuited at both ends by two plates. A cylindrical dielectric sapphire rod of diameter 7 mm and height 3.5 mm is placed and centered between the two parallel plates. The TE_{011} mode of the resonator is excited and detected by two semi-rigid coaxial cables, each having a small loop at the end, and the resonant frequency f and Q-factor are measured in the transmission configuration. The cavity operates at 20 GHz and at low temperatures down to 4 K.

For the measurements of the surface impedance as a function of temperature, an OFHC (Oxygen Free High Conductivity) copper cylindrical cavity is employed. In this technique, usually the upper and lower plates are substituted by two samples having nominally the same structural, transport and superconducting properties. It is evident that this "symmetric" configuration, where the films under test are rather inhomogeneous, tests only the average electrodynamic response of the material. For this reason, measurements were performed using a calibrated sample ($YBa_2Cu_3O_{7-\delta}$ for temperature measurements or high purity Nb for field measurements) of known properties as a reference.

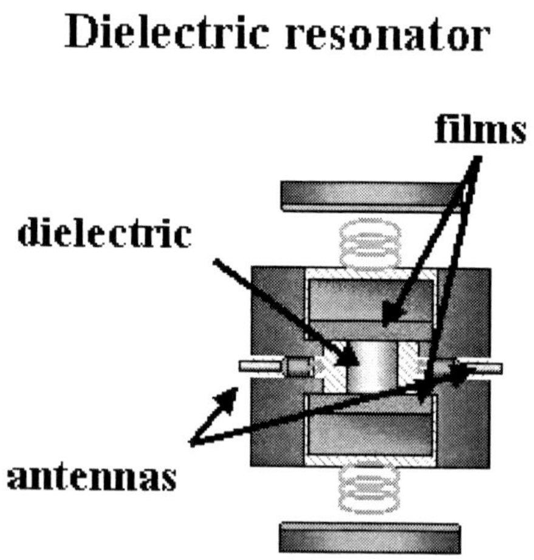

Fig. 13: The dielectric resonator scheme.

For thin films, what is measured is the effective surface impedance $Z_{seff} = R_{seff} + j\mu_0\omega\lambda_{eff}$, which includes the enhancement in both the surface resistance and magnetic penetration depth due to the sample thickness t being of the order of λ. Effective values can be corrected to give the surface impedance Z_s of the "bulk" material in the full temperature range but very close to T_c using the relation [55]:

$$Z_{S_{eff}} = R_S\left[\coth(t/\lambda) + \frac{t}{\lambda}\frac{1}{sinh^2(t/\lambda)}\right] + j\mu_0\omega\lambda\coth(t/\lambda) \qquad (7)$$

The effective surface resistance R_{seff} is obtained measuring the quality factor of the resonator in unloaded condition, neglecting radiation and dielectric contribution, and subtracting the conductive losses due to the reference sample and to the copper lateral walls. For T measurements, at 20 GHz the surface impedance of copper is well described by the anomalous skin effect regime below 50 K, therefore its contribution can be considered as independent of temperature. Z_s(T) for the HTS film has been previously and accurately determined.

The same procedure is used to evaluate the effective change in penetration depth $\Delta\lambda_{eff}$. Here one has to carefully subtract, besides the contribution related to the reference sample, the frequency shifts caused by the thermal expansion of the cavity walls and by the temperature variation of the copper skin depth δ_{Cu} and the single-crystal sapphire dielectric constant ε_r. The analysis is somehow simplified by the fact that the anomalous skin effect behavior implies $\Delta\delta_{Cu}(T) \approx 0$ at all temperatures of interest.

Varying the microwave power feeding the cavity, one can increase the maximum microwave magnetic field on the sample surface, H_{max}. This quantity determines the maximum surface current density on the superconducting plate. In a resonator of infinite diameter, H_{max} is given by the formula [56]:

$$H_{\max} = J_{1,\max}\left\{\frac{2\pi R_s}{P_0}\int_0^d J_1^2(\xi_1 r)r dr\left[1+\varepsilon_r R+\frac{240\pi^2\varepsilon_r \tan\delta}{R_s}\left(\frac{h}{\lambda_0}\right)^3\right]\right\}^{-1/2} \tag{8}$$

where $J_{1,max}$ is the maximum value of the Bessel function of the first kind $J_1(\xi_1 r)$, P_0 is the total power dissipated in the dielectric resonator, R is the ratio of the electrical energy stored outside and inside the dielectric rod, λ_0 is the wavelength in free space, and $\tan\delta$ is the sapphire loss tangent.

The maximum in the radial component of the magnetic field is reached in the cavity around a circle of radius of about 2 mm. The application of this analytical formula to our case ($D/d < 1.5$) gives a relative error in the evaluation of H_{max} below 5% [57].

In an effective two band picture where superconductivity in MgB_2 originates from the σ and π sheets on the Fermi surface and their mutual coupling, a rigorous evaluation of the temperature dependence of the penetration depth should make use of the Eliashberg formalism, taking also into account the effect of the intraband and interband scattering [58].

A reasonable assumption, based *a posteriori* on the results of our analysis and on previous observations [59-60], is to describe the magnetic screening as due to two different isotropic s-wave energy gaps, associated with the 2D and 3D bands respectively.

In this simplified model, a full calculation of the temperature dependence of λ can be carried out within a conventional BCS framework, weighting the contribution from the different sheets according to the relation:

$$\frac{1}{\lambda^2(T)} = \frac{c_\sigma}{\lambda^2_{L,\sigma}(T)} + \frac{c_\pi}{\lambda^2_{L,\pi}(T)} \tag{9}$$

Here the penetration depth in the London, clean limit is assumed for each band:

$$\frac{\lambda^2_{L,i}(0)}{\lambda^2_{L,i}(T)} = 1 - 2\int_{\Delta_i(T)}^{\infty}\left(-\frac{\partial f(E)}{\partial E}\right)\frac{E}{\sqrt{E^2 - \Delta_i^2(T)^2}}dE \tag{10}$$

and

$$c_i = \frac{a_i \lambda_i^2(0)}{\lambda^2(0)} \tag{11}$$

$(i = \sigma, \pi)$

where $\lambda(0)$ represents the effective penetration depth at zero temperature, and $a_\sigma + a_\pi = 1$.

In this picture, the low temperature dependence of λ is primarily determined by the band with the smaller gap, whereas the high temperature behavior should be dominated by the band with the larger gap. However, this is very much dependent on the relative weights the two bands effectively have in the magnetic screening. In our case, the coefficients c_σ and c_π measure the contribution of the respective bands to the screening for an orientation of the magnetic field perpendicular to the sample surface (because the TE_{011} mode is excited in the dielectric cavity).

Using this model, the interaction between the two gaps is taken into account only by assuming they have the same critical temperature. The presence of intraband scattering affects the absolute value of the penetration depth, however it does not change the gap values, according to Anderson's theorem. Moreover, the assumption of gap isotropy contrasts with recent results from first principle calculations, showing that the size of both gaps changes greatly on the different directions of the Fermi surface [61]. Therefore, the results of this simplified analysis will yield information only on the averaged gap values. It has been recently shown, however, that the assumption of a gap-size distribution in the calculation doesn't change significantly $\lambda(T)$ [60].

We applied eqs. (9), (10), and (11) to the penetration depth measurements carried out on one of the two MgB_2 films under study (named sample B). In the data fit, $\lambda(0)$, a_π and a_σ were allowed as free parameters, whereas Δ_π and Δ_σ could vary within the energy windows 1.2 - 3.7 meV and 6.4 - 7.2 meV respectively [61]. Results show that the contribution to the screening from the σ band is absolutely negligible ($a_\pi \approx 0.98$) and that the experimental λ dependence can be very well fitted in the whole temperature range below T_c simply assuming a single s-wave gap originating from the π sheets, with the following parameters: $\Delta_\pi(0) = 3.1$ meV and $\lambda_\pi(0) \approx \lambda(0) = 108$ nm. The estimated error on the fitting parameters is about 20%. In Fig. 14, data are displayed in terms of the normalized superfluid density $n_s(T)/n_s(0) = [\lambda(0)/\lambda(T)]^2$ together with the best fit results (continuous line). In Fig. 15 the low temperature behavior of the magnetic penetration depth is displayed, clearly showing the thermally activated exponential behavior that represents the signature of s-wave superconductivity. The dashed line represents the expected BCS behavior according to the formula:

$$\Delta\lambda(T) = \lambda_\pi(0)\sqrt{\frac{\pi\Delta_\pi(0)}{2k_BT}}e^{-\Delta_\pi(0)/k_BT} \tag{12}$$

The gap value for the π band is slightly larger than the one determined by tunneling measurements [25-26], but it is in line with previous observations based on microwave measurements. It is worth to emphasizing that in the case of a thin film with thickness comparable to the magnetic penetration depth, microwave surface impedance measurements, differently from tunneling experiments which are sensitive to disorder on the scale of the coherence length, probes almost the entire sample volume. Therefore, surface degradation, that might affect the determination of the energy gap value in other spectroscopic techniques, plays a minor role here.

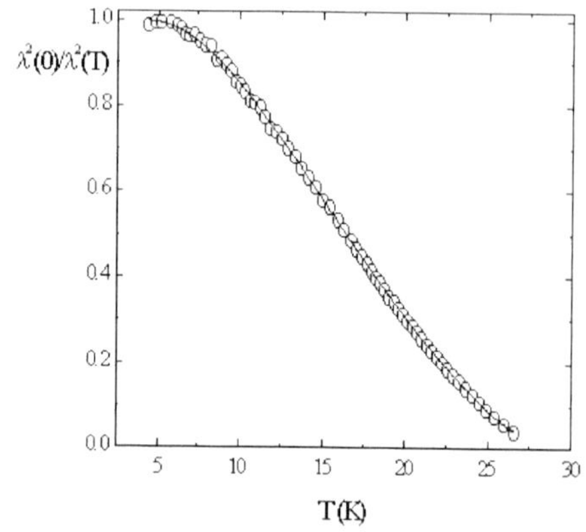

Fig. 14: $[\lambda(0)/\lambda(T)]^2$ dependence for sample B. The continuous line represents the BCS fit using a simplified two gap model.

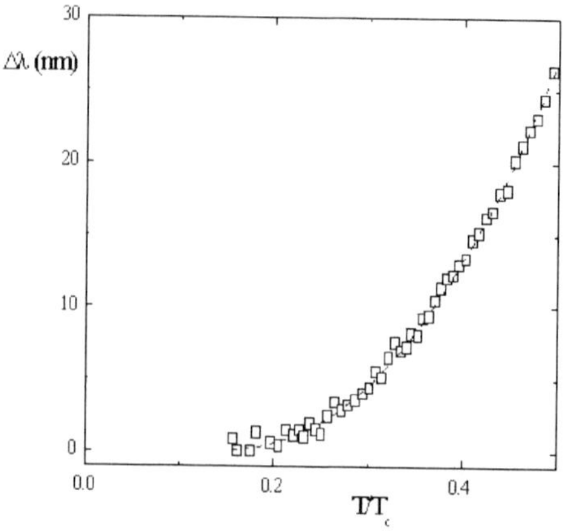

Fig. 15: Low temperature behavior of the penetration depth for sample B, and the expected BCS behavior (dashed line) according to eq. (6) and using $\Delta_\pi(0) = 3.1$ meV.

The averaged $\Delta_\pi(0)$ extracted from $\lambda(T)$ is also higher than the value predicted by first principle calculations (1.8 meV) [61]. A possible explanation is to invoke the presence of a large amount of impurity interband scattering, which mixes together and forces the two gaps to converge to the same value at a reduced T_c [62]. This would explain also the absence of any sign of the larger gap in the temperature dependence of λ. However, such an argument contrasts with the observation that films having T_c values in the range 36-39 K show similar [59] or even higher [60] values for the π band energy gap. It has been recently hypothesized, in order to explain the anomalous normal transport properties, that interband impurity scattering instead must be small, even in low-quality (low-T_c) samples [63].

Recent theoretical calculations [58] pointed out that the σ band cannot contribute to the screening currents unless the angle between the orientation of magnetic field and the c-axis approaches zero. Therefore, in polycrystalline samples the penetration depth is mostly determined by the 3D band. According to this study, we will have to wait until truly epitaxial films are available for detecting the larger 2D gap in $\lambda(T)$ measurements. $\lambda(0)$ is of the same order of magnitude of previous results reported on both single crystals [64] and thin films [59]. Its value points to a picture where conductivity in the π band is limited by impurity scattering, giving a screening response which is more in the intermediate than in the clean case. This is consistent with the high values of the residual resistivity measured in the samples under study.

In Fig. 16 the behavior of the surface resistance as a function of temperature for two *in situ* films (#A and #B) grown in the same nominal conditions is shown in the overall range. In both cases $R_s(T)$ rapidly approaches a large residual term decreasing T below $T_c/2$, even if saturation occurs at quite different R_s values. This difference is nevertheless a clear indication that the surface properties of MgB_2 in the microwave region are far from being optimized, with plenty of room for improvement increasing the quality of the samples.

Assuming the usual f^2 frequency law to scale the data at 10GHz, one can compare the measured microwave losses with results on thin films from other groups: present values are in line [65] or even lower [33, 35]. In spite of this, data cannot be consistently fitted in the overall temperature range within a BCS framework, since the level of losses is still too high. Surface impurities and other structural imperfections may of course affect the surface resistance in various ways.

For T less than $T_c/2$, in conventional superconductors the surface resistance behavior can be described using the standard BCS exponential dependence:

$$R_s - R_{res} \approx A\sqrt{\Delta / k_B T}\, e^{-\Delta / k_B T} \tag{13}$$

where R_{res} is the residual surface resistance and A is a phenomenological parameter. Because of the large scattering of data at the lowest temperatures, the value found for the ratio $2\Delta(0)/k_BT_c$ lies between 1.5 and 2.5, depending mainly on the value chosen for the constant term R_{res}.

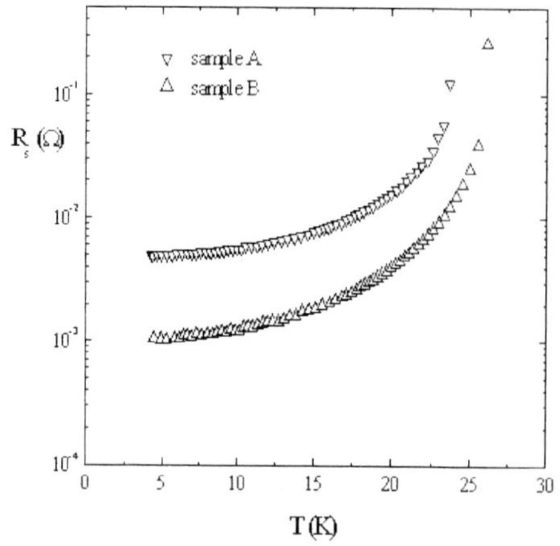

Fig. 16: Surface resistance versus temperature for samples A and B.

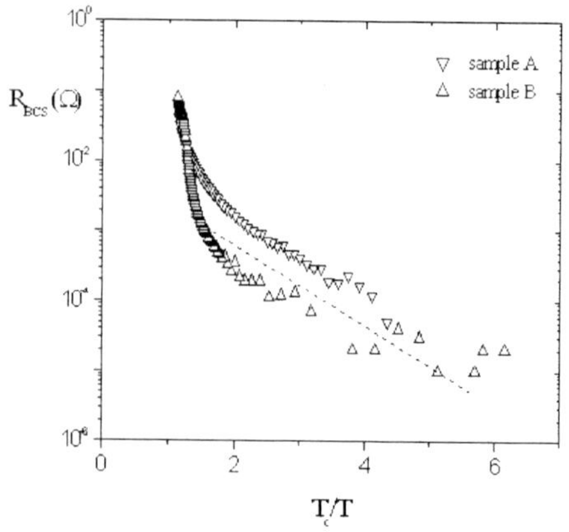

Fig. 17: The B.C.S. contribution to the surface resistance for samples A and B. The dashed line represents the low temperature B.C.S. slope with a reduced value of the $2\Delta(0)/k_BT_c$ ratio (see text for details).

In Fig. 17 the quantity R_s - R_{res} is displayed for both samples, together with the low temperature BCS slope (setting $2\Delta(0)/k_BT_c = 2.0$). Here $R_{res} = R_s(T_{min})$ is chosen. Of course, due to the high degree of arbitrariness in such a procedure, the only thing one can confidently say is that the observed temperature dependence, cleared of extrinsic effects, is *consistent* with the low value of the energy gap observed in the penetration depth data.

Using a high power amplifier, we have increased the microwave signal feeding the cavity to study the surface impedance as a function of the maximum microwave magnetic field on the sample surface, $H_{r.f.,max}$. In Fig. 18 the $R_s(H_{r.f.max})$ change at liquid helium temperature is displayed on a semi-log scale for samples A and B. In spite of the fact that films have similar superconducting and transport properties, and there is not much difference between the surface resistance values in the low field regime, a striking difference in their field behavior is observed.

A useful parameter that is often used to identify the source of non-linearity of superconducting materials in the microwave region is the differential loss [66]:

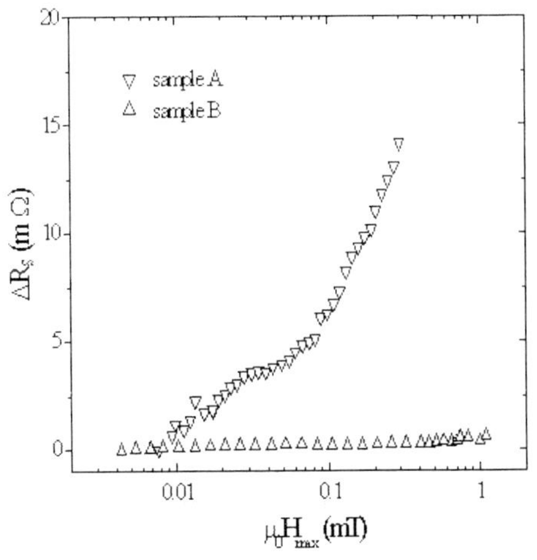

Fig. 18: The change in the surface resistance as a function of the peak r.f. magnetic field is reported at 4 K for both film A and B.

$$r = \frac{\partial R_s / \partial H_{max}}{\partial X_s / \partial H_{max}} \tag{14}$$

Film A showed a pronounced linear or sublinear dependence (on a linear scale), with a very rapid increase of the surface losses and a value of r close to unity. These distinctive features indicate that the most likely cause of dissipation is penetration of vortices in weakly coupled grains [67].

Film B, on the contrary, showed an almost flat dependence up to the maximum input power available (1 W), with $r \approx 10^{-2}$. Granularity doesn't seem to play a detrimental role for this sample, at least in the low-to-intermediate field region. We believe that the slight increase in R_s observed at the highest magnetic fields has likely to be related to global microwave heating of the dielectric cavity.

6. Conclusions and perspectives

In conclusion we have presented a new method to produce high quality films by a two-step, in-situ technique starting by a precursor film obtained by magnetron sputtering. The process is performed completely in-situ, which is strongly desirable in order to obtain samples suitable for applications. The fabrication process can be further optimized, as showed by the T_c value lower than single crystals, but the overall film quality well compares to the best films obtained by two-step, ex-situ processes, as concerns both transport and structural properties. The proposed preparation technique can be easily scaled to produce large area "in-situ" films for different applications.

Moreover, the structural microscopic disorder in our films strongly enhanced the upper critical field value when compared with single crystals and even with most of the films in the current scientific literature. This happened even for our best samples with $T_c = 35$ K, showing that the pinning mechanism does not dramatically decrease the superconducting properties.

Our measurements of J_c (H,T) and pinning forces gave us important information about this topic. Independently from the superconducting and structural quality of the investigated films, the measurements of the magnetic dependence of the pinning forces have pointed out the presence of 3D point like normal core pinning in the studied samples. Moreover, the analysis of the experimental data in terms of the collective pinning model has allowed determination of a crossover magnetic field from a single vortex to a small vortex bundle pinning regime. The temperature dependence of this crossover field gives strong evidence for a pinning mechanism associated to spatial fluctuations of the transition temperature, the so-called δT_c pinning. These experimental findings are in agreement with previous observations performed on MgB_2 bulk materials and indicate that in the analyzed samples pinning mechanisms typically present in thin film, such as for example surface or edge pinning, do not influence the dissipative phenomena.

As concerns the electrodynamic response of MgB_2 in the microwave region, further indications in view of applications can be extracted. The analysis of the penetration depth confirms the s-wave nature of the superconducting state. Surface resistance data show that this material should be considered as a promising alternative to both HTS and LTS for microwave applications, even if its performance is still far below expectations. In particular, one of the investigated samples displayed fairly low values of R_s and a very weak sensitivity to the r.f. magnetic field level.

Our future efforts will be spent to achieve full control on the effect of the disorder and impurities on the film properties. We are still working on possible improvements of our deposition technique: as described above, we built a new annealing environment for better control of the growth parameters and for a completely in-situ manipulation, and we are also considering new solutions, such as starting from a B or B-rich Mg-B precursor.

The new annealing apparatus also allows us to perform planar tunnel junction fabrication completely in-situ. Spectroscopic information that can be achieved by tunnel measurements (as long as STM measurements) will be very helpful for an understanding of the transport mechanism in our samples.

If the control of the quality of the films and their availability on low cost and/or high thermal conductivity substrates improves, MgB_2 might become more and more of interest for wireless communications and even for particle accelerators.

Acknowledgements

The authors wish to thank C. Ferdeghini, M. Putti and V. Palmieri for discussions and suggestions, and G. Ausanio for the AFM measurements. The technical support of A. Maggio and S. Marrazzo is also warmly acknowledged.

This work has been partially supported by the INFN-MABO Project and the INFN Eloisatron Special Project.

References

[1] J. Nagamatsu, N. Nakagawa, T. Muranaka, Y. Zenitani and J. Akimitsu, *Nature* **410**, 63 (2001).

[2] A. Y. Liu, I.I. Mazin, and J. Kortus, *Phys. Rev. Lett.* **87**, 087005 (2001).

[3] For a review, see C. Buzea and T. Yamashita, *Supercond. Sci. Technol.* **14**, R115 (2001).

[4] For a review, see I.I. Mazin and V.P. Antropov, *Physica C* **385**, 49 (2003).

[5] M. Nisenoff, "An assessment of superconducting digital technology: the possible impact of the discovery of Magnesium Diboride", unpublished. Available on: http://www.iitap.iastate.edu/htcu/nisenoffcomment.html

[6] D. C. Larbalestier, L. D. Cooley, M. O. Rikel, A. A. Polyanskii, J. Jiang, S. Patnaik, X. Y. Cai, D. M. Feldmann, A. Gurevich, A. A. Squitieri, M. T. Naus, C. B. Eom, E. E. Hellstrom, R. J. Cava, K. A. Regan, N. Rogado, M. A. Hayward, T. He, J. S. Slusky, P. Khalifah, K. Inumaru and M. Haas, *Nature* **410**, 186 (2001).

[7] M. Hein, "High-temperature superconductor thin films at microwave frequencies", *Springer Tracts in Modern Physics* **155**, Berlin: Springer-Verlag (1999).

[8] R. Vaglio, "RF superconducting cavities for accelerators", in Microwave Superconductivity, *NATO Science Series* vol. **375**, H. Weinstock and M. Nisenoff, Eds. Dordrecht: Kluwer Academic Publ., 2001, pp. 447-471.

[9] P. Kus, A. Plecenik, L. Satrapinsky, Y. Xu and R. Sobolewski, cond-mat/0206442 (2002).

[10] M. Paranthaman, C. Cantoni, H.Y. Zhai, H.M. Christen, T. Aytug, S. Sathyamurthy, E.D. Specht, J.R. Thompson, D.H. Lowndes, H.R. Kerchner and D.K. Christen, *Appl. Phys. Lett.* **78**, 3669 (2001).

[11] W.N. Kang, H.J. Kim, E.M. Choi, C.U. Jung and S.I. Lee, *Science* **292**, 1521 (2001).

[12] Zhai H. Y., Christen H. M., Zhang L., Cantoni C., Paranthaman M., Sales B. C., Christen D. K. and Lowndes D. H., *Appl. Phys. Lett.* **79**, 2603 (2001).

[13] Shinde S. R., Ogale S. B., Greene R. L., Venkatesan T., Canfield P.C., Bud'ko S. L., Lapertot G. and Petrovic C., *Appl. Phys. Lett.* **79**, 227 (2001).

[14] Zeng X. H., Sukiasyan A., Xi X. X., Hu Y. F., Wertz E., Qi Li., Tian W., Sun H. P., Pan X. Q., Lettieri J., Schlom D. G., Brubaker C. O., Liu Z. K. and Q. Li, *Appl. Phys. Lett.* **79**, 1840 (2001).

[15] Ueda K. and Naito M., *Appl. Phys. Lett.* **79**, 2046 (2001).

[16] S. Lee, H. Mori, T. Masui, Y. Eltsev, A. Yamamoto, and S. Tajima, *J. Phys. Soc. Jap.* **70**, 2255 (2001).

[17] I.I. Tupitsyn, *Sov. Phys. Solid State* **18**, 1688 (1976).

[18] D.R. Armstrong and P.G. Perkins, *J.C.S. Faraday II* **75**, 12 (1979).

[19] A.I. Ivanovskii and N.I. Medvedeva, *Russ. J. Inorg. Chem.* **45**, 1234 (2000).

[20] J. An and W.E. Pickett, *Phys. Rev. Lett.* **86**, 4366 (2001).

[21] J. Kortus, I.I. Mazin, K.D. Belashchenko, V.P. Antropov and L.L. Boyer, *Phys. Rev. Lett.* **86**, 4656 (2001).

[22] S. Bud'ko, G. Lapertot, C. Petrovic, C.E. Cunningham, N. Anderson and P.C. Canfield, *Phys. Rev. Lett.* **86**, 1877 (2001).

[23] D.G. Hinks, H. Claus and J.D. Jorgensen, *Nature* **411**, 6836 (2001).

[24] F. Bouquet, Y. Wang, R.A. Fisher, D.G. Hinks, J.D. Jorgensen, A. Junod and N.E. Phillips, *Europhys. Lett.* **56**, 856 (2001).

[25] F. Giubileo, D. Roditchev, W. Sacks, R. Lamy, D.X. Thanh, J. Klein, S. Miraglia, D. Fruchart, J. Marcus and P. Monod, *Phys. Rev. Lett.* **87**, 177008 (2001).

[26] M. Iavarone, G. Karapetrov, A.E. Koshelev, W.K. Kwok, G.W. Crabtree and D.G. Hinks, *Phys. Rev. Lett.* **89**, 187002 (2002).

[27] E. A. Yelland, J. R. Cooper, . Carrington, N. E. Hussey, P. J. Meeson, S. Lee, A. Yamamoto and S. Tajima, *Phys. Rev. Lett.* **88**, 217002 (2002);

[28] J. R. Cooper, A. Carrington, P.J. Meeson, E.A. Yelland, N.E. Hussey, L. Balicas, S. Tajima, S. Lee, S.M. Kazakov and J. Karpinski, *Physica C* **385**, 75 (2003).

[29] I.I. Mazin, O.K. Andersen, O. Jepsen, O.V. Dolgov, J. Kortus, A.A. Golubov, A.B. Kuz'menko and D. van der Marel, *Phys. Rev. Lett.* **89**, 107002 (2002).

[30] P. Canfield and G.W. Crabtree, *Physics Today* **56**, 34 (2003).

[31] A. Gurevich, S. Patnaik, V. Braccini, K.H. Kim, C. Mielke, X. Song, L.D. Cooley, S.D. Bu, D.M. Kim, J.H. Choi, L.J. Belenky, J. Giencke, M.K. Lee, W. Tian, X.Q. Pan, A. Siri, E.E. Hellstrom, C.B. Eom and D.C. Larbalestier, submitted to *Nature.*

[32] N. Hakim, P.V. Parimi, C. Kusko, S. Sridhar, P.C. Canfield, S. L. Bud'ko and D.K. Finnemore, *Appl. Phys. Lett.* **78**, 4160 (2001).

[33] A. Zhukov, A. Purnell, Y. Miyoshi, Y. Bugoslavsky, Z. Lockman, A. Berenov, H.Y. Zhai, H.M Christen, M. P. Paranthaman, D.H. Lowndes, M.H. Jo, M.G. Blamire, L. Hao, J. Gallop, J.L. MacManus-Driscoll and L.F. Cohen, *Appl. Phys. Lett.* **80**, 2347 (2002)

[34] A. Andreone, A. Cassinese, C. Cantoni, E. Di Gennaro, G. Lamura, M. G. Maglione, M. Paranthaman, M. Salluzzo, and R. Vaglio, *Physica C* **372-376**, 1287 (2002).

[35] S.Y. Lee, J.H. Lee, J.S. Ryu, J. Lim, S.H. Moon, H.N. Lee, H.G. Kim and B. Ohh, *Appl. Phys. Lett.* **79**, 3299 (2001).

[36] A. Andreone, A. Cassinese, F. Chiarella, R. Di Capua, E. Di Gennaro, G. Lamura, M.G. Maglione, M. Salluzzo and R. Vaglio, in press on *IEEE Trans. on Appl. Supercond.*

[37] R. Vaglio, M.G. Maglione and R. Di Capua, *Supercond. Sci. Technol.* **15**, 1236 (2002).

[38] C.B. Eom, M.K. Lee, J.H. Choi, L. Belenky, X. Song, L.D. Cooley, M.T. Naus, S. Patnaik, J. Jiang, M. Rikel, A. Polyanskii, A. Gurevich, X.Y. Cai, S.D. Bu, S.E. Babcock, E.E. Hellstrom, D.C. Larbalestier, N. Rogado, K.A. Regan, M.A. Hayward, T. He, J.S. Slusky, K. Inumaru, M.K. Haas and R.J. Cava, *Nature* **411**, 558 (2001).

[39] R. Vaglio, A. Andreone, C. Aruta, A. Cassinese, F. Fontana, G.W. Crabtree, M. Iavarone, Y. De Wilde, L. Maritato, C. Attanasio, C. Coccorese, M. Salluzzo and M. Salvato, *Phys. Rev. B.* **56**, 934 (1997).

[40] J.H. Classen, M.E. Reeves and J.R. Soulen jr, *Rev. Sci. Instrum.* **62**, 996 (1991).

[41] N.R. Werthamer, E. Helfand and P.C. Hohemberg, *Phys. Rev.* **147**, 295 (1966).

[42] K. Maki, *Phys. Rev.* **148**, 362 (1966).

[43] K.H.P. Kim, J.H. Choi, C.U. Jung, P. Chowdhury, H.S. Lee, M.S. Park, H.J. Kim, J.Y. Kim, Z. Du, E.M. Choi, M.S. Kim, W.N. Kang, S.I. Lee, G.Y. Sung and J.Y. Lee, *Phys. Rev. B.* **65**, 100510 (2002).

[44] M. Xu, H. Kitazawa, Y. Takano, J. Ye, K. Nishida, H. Abe, A. Matsushita, N. Tsujii and G. Kido, *Appl. Phys. Lett.* **79**, 2779 (2001).

[45] D.R. Tilley, *Proc. Phys. Soc. London* **86**, 289 (1965).

[46] M.G. Maglione, F. Chiarella, R. Di Capua, R. Vaglio, M. Salvato, L. Maritato and S.L. Prischepa, *Int. J. of Mod. Phys. B* **17**, 779 (2003).

[47] K. Kawano, J.S. Abell, M. Kambara, N. Hari Babu and D.A. Cardwell, *Appl. Phys. Lett.* **79**, 2216 (2001).

[48] M.J. Qin, X.L. Wang, H.K. Lin and S.X. Don, *Phys. Rev. B* **65**, 132508 (2002).

[49] R. Griessen, Wen Hai-hu, A.J.J. van Dalen, B. Dam, J. Rector and H.G. Schnack, *Phys. Rev. Lett.* **72**, 1910 (1994).

[50] R.I. Chiao, M.J. Feldman, H. Ohta and P.T. Parris, *Rev. Phys. Appl.* **9**, 183 (1974).

[51] S.L. Prischepa, M.L. Della Rocca, L. Maritato, M. Salvato, R. Di Capua, M.G. Maglione, R. Vaglio, *Phys. Rev. B.* **67**, 024512 (2003).

[52] G. Blatter, M.V. Feigel'man, V.B. Geshkenbein, A.I. Larkin and V.M. Vinokur, *Rev. Mod. Phys.* **66**, 1125 (1994).

[53] D. Dew-Hughes, *Philos. Mag.* **30**, 293 (1974).

[54] A.I. Larkin and Yu.N. Ovchinnikov, *J. Low Temp. Phys.* **34**, 409 (1979).

[55] N. Klein, H. Chaloupka, G. Müller, S. Orbach, H. Piel, B. Roas, L. Schultz, U. Klein and M. Peiniger, *J. Appl. Phys.* **67**, 6940 (1990).

[56] Z.-Y. Shen, C. Wilker, P. Pang, W. L. Holstein, D. Face and D. J. Kountz, *IEEE Trans. Microwave Theory Techn.* **40**, 2424 (1992).

[57] J. Mazierska and R. Grabovickic, *IEEE Trans. Applied Supercond.* **8**, 178 (1998).

[58] A.A. Golubov, A. Brinkman, O.V. Dolgov, J. Kortus and O. Jepsen, cond-mat/0205154.

[59] G. Lamura, E. Di Gennaro, M. Salluzzo, A. Andreone, J. Le Cochec, A. Gauzzi, C. Cantoni, M. Paranthaman, D.K. Christen, H..M. Christen, G. Giunchi and S. Ceresara, *Phys. Rev. B* **65**, 020506 (2002).

[60] M.S. Kim, J.A. Skinta, T.R. Lemberger, W.N. Kang, H.J. Kim, E.M. Choi and S.I. Lee, *Phys. Rev. B* **66**, 064511 (2002).

[61] H.J. Choi, D. Roundy, H. Sun, M.L. Cohen, and S.G. Louie, *Nature* **418**, 758 (2002).

[62] A. Brinkman, A.A. Golubov, H.Rogalla, O.V. Dolgov, J. Kortus, Y. Kong, O. Jepsen, and O.K. Andersen, *Phys. Rev. B* **65**, 180517 (2002).

[63] I.I. Mazin, O.K. Andersen, O. Jepsen, O.V. Dolgov, J. Kortus, A.A. Golubov, A.B. Kuz'menko and D. van der Marel, cond-mat/0204013.

[64] F. Manzano, A. Carrington, N.E. Hussey, S. Lee, A. Yamamoto and S. Tajima, *Phys. Rev. Lett.* **88**, 047002 (2002).

[65] B.B. Jin, N. Klein, W.N. Kang, H.J. Kim, E.M. Choi, S.I. Lee, T. Dahm and K. Maki, in press on *Phys. Rev. B*.

[66] J. Halbritter, *Phys. Rev. B* **48**, 9735 (1993).

[67] M.A. Golosovsky, H.J. Snortland and M.R. Beasley, *Phys. Rev. B* **51**, 6462 (1995).

The Role of Nonlocality in the Pinning Properties of Borocarbide Materials

A. V. Silhanek,* J. R. Thompson,† L. Civale,‡ S. L. Bud'ko,§ and P. Canfield¶

An experimental review on the influence of nonlocal electrodynamics in the vortex pinning properties of non-magnetic borocarbide superconductors is presented. We show that the pinning force density F_p exhibits a rich and complex anisotropic behavior that sharply contrast with the small mass anisotropy of these compounds. For magnetic fields $\mathbf{H}$ applied parallel to the crystallographic c-axis, the first order reorientation transition between two rhombic lattices manifests itself as a kink in $F_p(H)$. For $\mathbf{H}\perp$c-axis, a much larger $F_p(H)$ and a slower relaxation rate is observed. In this field configuration, nonlocality induces a fourfold periodicity in F_p when $\mathbf{H}$ is rotated within the square basal plane. Unlike the out-of-plane anisotropy, which persists for increasing impurity levels, the in-plane fourfold anisotropy can be strongly suppressed by reducing the electronic mean free path. This result unambiguously demonstrate that the in-plane anisotropy is a consequence of nonlocal effects.

1 Introduction

The large attention that the borocarbide family of intermetallics (RNi_2B_2C, where R = rare earth) has received during the last years is in part due to the wide variety of interesting phenomena that these materials exhibit. Special attention has been devoted to R = Tm, Er, Ho and Dy, where superconductivity and antiferromagnetism coexist in a large portion of the phase diagram. The high superconducting transition temperatures T_c and the broad variation of the ratio T_N/T_c (where T_N is the Neel temperature, ranging from 1.5 K to 10 K) make this family particularly appropriate to explore that coexistence[1, 2, 3, 4, 5].

Even in the simplest case of non-magnetic borocarbides (R = Y, Lu), many remarkable properties have been reported. For example, in the superconducting mixed state the vortex lattice symmetry exhibits a strong field dependence with structural phase transitions separating a variety of exotic rhombic and square flux line lattices (FLL)[6, 7, 8, 9, 10, 11, 12, 13]. In addition, the equilibrium magnetization M deviates from the local London prediction[14] and exhibits a fourfold anisotropy when the field is rotated within the basal plane of these tetragonal materials[15, 16].

*Laboratorium voor Vaste-Stoffysica en Magnetisme, K. U. Leuven, Celestijnenlaan 200 D, B-3001 Leuven, Belgium.

†Oak Ridge National Laboratory, Oak Ridge, Tennessee 37831-6061 and Department of Physics, University of Tennessee, Knoxville, Tennessee 37996-1200.

‡Superconductivity Technology Center, MS K763; Los Alamos National Laboratory, Los Alamos, NM 87545, USA

§Ames Laboratory, U.S. DoE and Department of Physics and Astronomy, Ames, Iowa, USA

¶Ames Laboratory, U.S. DoE and Department of Physics and Astronomy, Ames, Iowa, USA

The presence of these non-hexagonal lattices has been attributed to the effects of nonlocal electrodynamics, which arise when the electronic mean free path ℓ is larger than the BCS zero temperature superconducting coherence length ξ_0. Nonlocal electrodynamics in superconductors had been traditionally associated with very low values of the Ginzburg-Landau parameter, $\kappa \sim 1$. Borocarbide superconductors have κ values in the range of 10 to 20, which allows one to avoid cumbersome core treatments by using the very simple London approach and simultaneously introduce the nonlocal effects as a perturbative term.

This approach was first developed by Kogan et al.[17] to analyze the case of a superconductor with an isotropic gap and an isotropic cylindrical Fermi surface. In this scenario, the authors successfully explained the observed deviations of the reversible magnetization $M(H)$ of Bi:2212 in the mixed state from the logarithmic dependence, $M \propto ln(H_{c2}/H)$, predicted by the London model[18]. Later on, Song et al.[14] found similar deviations in YNi_2B_2C when $\mathbf{H} \parallel c$-axis, that could also be quantitatively accounted for by this model. More recently we have extended that study to all field orientations and showed that this generalization of the London theory provides a satisfactory complete description of the anisotropic $M(H)$ with a self-consistent set of parameters[19].

In general, the additional nonlocal corrections introduced in the London equation give rise to a coupling of the microscopic supercurrents in a vortex to the underlying crystal symmetry. As a consequence, nonlocality induces an anisotropic response even in cubic materials[20], which according to the local London theory, should behave isotropically.

How actually the superconducting currents are connected to the crystal symmetry is still a matter of debate. First, Kogan et al.[7, 17] developed a model considering a superconductor with an anisotropic Fermi surface and an order parameter with s-wave symmetry. Later on, Franz and co-workers[21] analyzed the opposite case of an isotropic cylindrical Fermi surface in a d-wave superconductor. The applicability of each one of these models depends eventually on the material studied.

In the particular case of non-magnetic borocarbides compounds, there is growing evidence that both an anisotropic Fermi surface[22, 23] and a non conventional pairing mechanism[23, 24, 25, 26, 27, 28, 29, 30, 31] are present. In the last years, the lack of any corroborative evidence for a non conventional pairing mechanism in these materials meant that most of the experimental results were interpreted within the Kogan et al.'s model. However, the proven existence of a pronounced anisotropy in the gap symmetry challenges the original view and strongly encourages one to critically re-examine several previous interpretations.

As we pointed out above, none of the introduced models has to be necessarily invoked in order to explain the deviation in the reversible magnetization from $M \propto ln(H_{c2}/H)$, whereas both of them correctly account for the anisotropic in-plane magnetization. However, still some differences appear between these approaches, when analyzing the field and temperature evolution of the vortex lattice.

The model of Kogan et al. predicts[7] that two structural transitions in the FLL should occur in borocarbides for $\mathbf{H} \parallel c$: a first order reorientation transition between two rhombic lattices at a field H_1 and a second order transition from rhombic-to-square at $H_2 > H_1$. According to this model, both transition fields shift up as temperature is increased. Recent small angle neutron scattering (SANS) studies[11, 32, 33] confirmed the existence of these transitions in YNi_2B_2C and $LuNi_2B_2C$. A jump in the apical angle β of the rhombic lattice, discontinuous within the resolution, occurs at $H_1 \sim 1$ to 1.5 kOe, and the lattice becomes square ($\beta = 90°$) at $H_2 \sim 2$ to 2.5 kOe[33].

Franz et al.[21] showed that similar FLL rearrangements should appear in the case of a d-wave superconductor. However, two distinctive predictions emerge from this model. First, an additional first order transition should take place at very low temperatures. Second, in sharp contrast to the Kogan et al.'s model, the H_1 boundary should decrease as temperature is increased. In a recent work, Nakai et al.[34] showed that when both anisotropic gap and Fermi surface are considered simultaneously, the intrinsic competition between these two effects leads to a much richer $H - T$ phase diagram.

Although the role of nonlocality on the *equilibrium* properties of the FLL has been convincingly established, much less attention has been paid to the effects on the dynamic or *nonequilibrium* vortex response. The very low critical current density J_c observed in non magnetic borocarbides for $\mathbf{H} \parallel c$, associated with large pinning correlation volumes[8], indicates that the elastic properties of the FLL must play a key role in the pinning. Since the shear modulus C_{66} depends on the vortex lattice symmetry[35], and the apex angle β undergoes a discontinuous jump at H_1, it is expected that C_{66} and hence the pinning properties change abruptly at this field[8]. In other words, vortex pinning, which involves distortions from equilibrium vortex configurations, should be affected by the symmetry changes in the vortex lattice. Indeed, as we will show throughout this work, nonlocal effects influence the vortex pinning in several ways.

First, in both non-magnetic compounds YNi_2B_2C and $LuNi_2B_2C$, and for $\mathbf{H} \parallel c$, the reorientation transition at H_1 induces a kink in the pinning force density $F_p(H)$. We find that $H_1(T)$ slightly decreases as T increases, in contrast to $H_2(T)$. We also study the effect of Co-doping in $Lu(Ni_{1-x}Co_x)_2B_2C$. We observe that H_1 decreases as the nonlocal effects progressively fade out when x increases. These results are in agreement with the expected evolution of H_1 within a non conventional superconducting gap scenario.

Second, we observe a fourfold oscillation in $F_p(H)$ when $\mathbf{H}$ is rotated within the *ab*-plane (in-plane anisotropy). We show that this effect is strongly suppressed as the amount of impurities is increased, i.e. as the nonlocal effects are reduced. This clearly demonstrates that the in-plane anisotropy is a consequence of nonlocal effects.

Strikingly, we also observe a large anisotropy in F_p between the c-axis and the basal plane (out-of-plane anisotropy). We found that F_p for $\mathbf{H} \perp c$ is about one order of magnitude larger than for $\mathbf{H} \parallel c$ and has a quite different field dependence. Accordingly, a much faster normalized relaxation rate S is detected for $\mathbf{H} \parallel c$. This effect persists for all the explored impurity concentrations, demonstrating that the out-of-plane anisotropy is not related with nonlocal effects. We also rule out the presence of surface barriers for $\mathbf{H} \perp c$ by performing minor hysterisis loops.

This work is organized as follows. In the next section we briefly introduce the experimental details and the samples studied. In section 3 we discuss the reorientational structural transition and how it influences the dynamic response. In section 4 we focus on the in-plane anisotropy of the pinning force density and in section 5 we discuss the out-of-plane anisotropy. Finally, in section 6 we state our conclusions.

2 Experimental Aspects

The composition, dimensions, critical temperature and estimated electronic mean free path for each of the studied single crystals is summarized in Table I. Normal state magnetization measurements in the Y-0 sample reflect the presence of a very diluted distribution of localized magnetic moments. The paramagnetic signal follows a Curie law which corresponds to a rare-earth impurity content of 0.1 at. % relative to yttrium, probably due to contaminants in the yttrium starting material[19]. Similar measurements in the Lu-x single crystals show a much weaker Curie tail at low temperatures, $T < 100$ K, which might be due to a 0.001% magnetic impurities of Gd in the Lu crystallographic site[36].

Table 1: sample name, composition, volume, thickness, superconducting critical temperature and electronic mean free path for the investigated samples.

sample	composition	$V(\text{mm}^3)$	$t(\text{mm})$	$T_c(\text{K})$	$l(\text{Å})$
Y-0	YNi_2B_2C	2.8	0.5	15.1	300
Lu-0	$LuNi_2B_2C$	2.5	0.3	15.7	270
Lu-1.5	$Lu(Ni_{1-x}Co_x)_2B_2C$ (x=1.5%)	1.2	0.4	14.9	100
Lu-3	$Lu(Ni_{1-x}Co_x)_2B_2C$ (x=3%)	0.44	0.2	14.1	70

Magnetization measurements were conducted on commercial Quantum Design SQUID magnetometers. Part of the relaxation measurements were taken in a MPMS-7 ($H \leq 7$ T) and the angular studies were performed in a MPMS-5S ($H \leq 5$ T) equipped with a home-made rotating system[38, 39]. In the superconducting mixed state, isothermal magnetization $M(H)$ loops were recorded. For the angular studies, both components of $\mathbf{M}(H)$ were measured using the two sets of pick up coils (longitudinal and transverse). The critical current density J_c was determined from the width of the hysteresis loops according to the Bean critical state model, as previously described[38]. Relaxation measurements $M(t)$ were performed on both branches (increasing and decreasing) of the hysteresis loop over periods of 1 hour.

3 Reorientational Transition

According to the existing models,[7, 21] two types of structural transitions in the vortex lattice should occur in borocarbides materials, namely a first order reorientation transition between two rhombic lattices at a field H_1 and a second order transition from the rhombic to a square lattice at a higher field H_2. These predictions were recently confirmed by small angle neutron scattering (SANS) experiments[11, 32, 33] *on a sister crystal to the Y-0 sample studied here.* For $\mathbf{H} \parallel c$ and at $T = 4.5$ K, a jump in the apical angle β of the rhombic vortex lattice occurs at $H_1 \sim 1$ to 1.5 kOe, and the lattice becomes square ($\beta = 90°$) at $H_2 \sim 2$ to 2.5 kOe.

As we pointed out above, it is expected that the discontinuous jump of the apex angle β at H_1 induces an abrupt change in the pinning properties through the shear modulus $C_{66}(\beta)$[8, 35]. In order to check this prediction, we measured the pinning force density $F_p = |\mathbf{J_c} \times \mathbf{B}|$ for the Y-0 sample as a function of the applied field for $\mathbf{H} \parallel$ **c**-axis at several T (see Figure 1(a)).

We observe that at low fields $F_p(H)$ strongly decreases with increasing H, up to a certain field $H^* \sim 1.2$ kOe, above which the field dependence is much less pronounced. Several facts indicate that this jump in dF_p/dH is a signature of the reorientation phase transition H_1 in the FLL[40]. First, the position of the kink for $\mathbf{H} \parallel \mathbf{c}$ coincides with the value of H_1 reported in the literature[33]. Second, as shown in Figure 2, where $F_p(H)$ for sample Y-0 is plotted at several field orientations, H^* is rather insensitive to the field orientation, in agreement with the behavior of H_1 determined from SANS experiments[11].

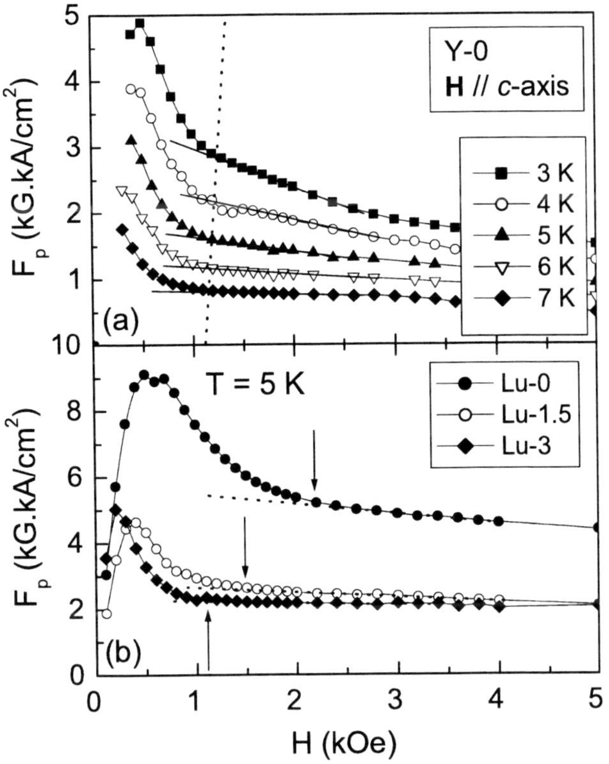

Figure 1: Field dependence of the pinning force density for **H** || **c**-axis for (a) Y-0 sample at several temperatures and (b) Lu-0, Lu-1.5 and Lu-3 samples at $T = 5$ K.

In Figure 1(a), it can be also observed that the transition field $H^*(T)$ remains almost constant at low T and, unlike the rhombic-to-square second order transition $H_2(T)$, it slightly decreases with T at higher temperatures. This behavior is in agreement with recent neutron scattering experiments[33] and with theoretical predictions for a d-wave superconducting gap[21]. In contrast, it follows from the model of Kogan et al. that both transitions, H_1 and H_2, should *increase* as nonlocality vanishes. In Figure 3 we show the temperature evolution of H^* together with the upper critical field H_{c2}.

Further evidence that the observed feature at the field H^* arises from nonlocal effects come from the dependency of this transition field with the electronic mean free path. Indeed, the strength of the nonlocal perturbations is parametrized by a new characteristic distance, the nonlocality radius $\rho(T, \ell)$: smaller $\rho(T, \ell)$ corresponds to weaker nonlocality effects. This means that $\rho(T, \ell)$ decreases with increasing T or decreasing ℓ. Thus, if the position of the kink is related with nonlocal effects, an increase in T or a decrease in ℓ should produce qualitatively similar effects[7, 17].

It has been shown that the Co substitutes on the Ni site in borocarbides compounds as a nonmagnetic impurity[36] that suppresses T_c[37], but does not modify significantly the critical current J_c[4]. This Co doping procedure allows one to accurately control the

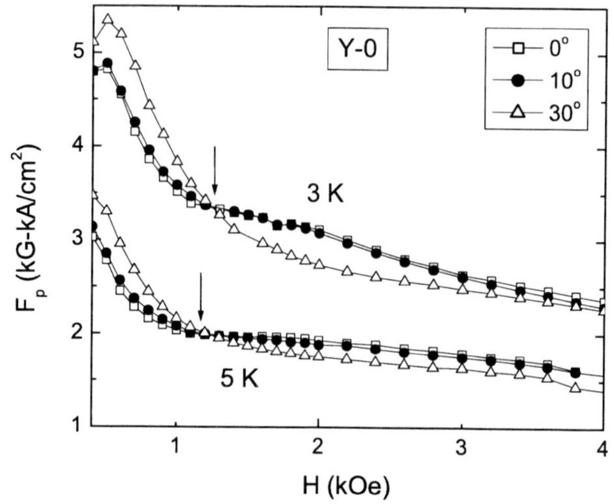

Figure 2: Field dependence of the pinning force density for three different angles of **H** with respect to the c-axis at $T = 3$ and 5 K.

electronic mean free path by tuning the amount x of impurities.

To determine the ℓ dependence of H^*, we performed measurements on the Lu-0, Lu-1.5 and Lu-3 samples for $\mathbf{H} \parallel \mathbf{c}$ (estimates of ℓ are given in Table I). The results are shown in Figure 1(b), where we plotted $F_p(H)$ at $T = 5$ K. We observe that the kink in F_p (indicated by the arrows) is still visible in the field range where the transition H_1 should appear, and that it shifts to lower fields with increasing x, in agreement with the T dependence. In other words, the analogy between x and T is satisfied for H^*, thus confirming that the kink arises from nonlocality.

From Figure 1(b) we also confirmed the fact that the introduction of Co does not affect the pinning properties. Another interesting fact is that the Lu-0 sample has a larger F_p than the Y-0 sample at the same T, even though it has a lower density of magnetic impurities. This indicates that the magnetic moments in the Y-0 are not relevant pinning centers for the flux lines when $\mathbf{H} \parallel c$.

4 In-Plane Anisotropy

Let us now analyze the pinning properties for $\mathbf{H} \perp c$. Figure 4 shows $F_p(H)$ for $\mathbf{H}$ applied along the symmetry axes [001], [100] and [110], at $T = 5$ K for the Y-0 sample. We observe that for the in-plane orientations, $F_p(H)$ exhibits a very different behavior than for $\mathbf{H} \parallel c$. First, over most of the field range $F_p(\mathbf{H} \perp c) \gg F_p(\mathbf{H} \parallel c)$. Second, the pinning force density exhibits a clear and systematic in-plane anisotropy, $F_p[100] > F_p[110]$. We now focus on the origin of this in-plane anisotropy and defer the discussion of the large out-of-plane anisotropy to the next section.

The fourfold nature of the in-plane anisotropy becomes evident in the lower panel of Figure 5, where we show the angular dependence of the pinning force density, $F_p(\varphi)$, at

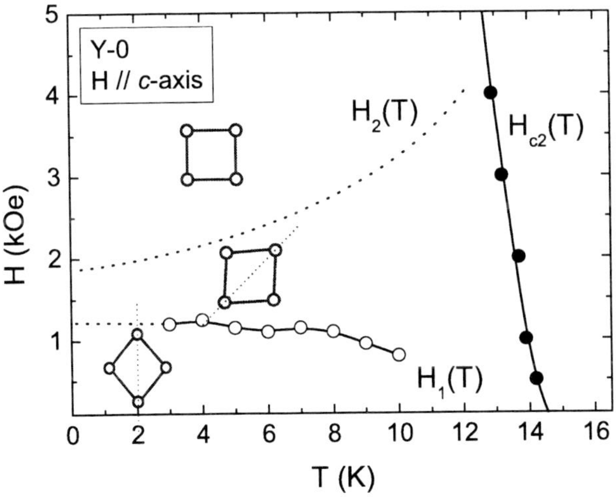

Figure 3: Temperature dependence of the upper critical field and the structural reorientation transition fields for the Y-0 sample when $\mathbf{H} \parallel c$.

$T = 7$ K for several H. This figure shows that for all $H > 2$ kOe, $F_p(\varphi)$ exhibits a rather complex behavior: in addition to the main peaks at [100] and [010], secondary maxima are visible at [110] and [1$\bar{1}$0].

For comparison, in the upper panel we show the in-plane angular dependence of the Meissner slope $-4\pi(dM/dH)$ for $H = 30$ Oe at $T = 7$ K. As $H = 30$ Oe is well below the lower critical field H_{c1} for all φ, this curve represents the total flux exclusion of the Meissner state. The oscillatory behavior with periodicity π (two-fold symmetry) originates from purely geometrical effects. Indeed, a field applied at any orientation within the basal plane can be decomposed in $H_x = Hcos(\varphi + 45°)$ and $H_y = Hsin(\varphi + 45°)$. If we approximate the crystal shape by the ellipse, the Meissner response associated with each component is $4\pi M_i = -H_i/(1 - \nu_i)$, where $i = x; y$ and $\nu_i = t/L_i$ are the demagnetizing factors, thus $4\pi M = -H[cos^2(\varphi + 45°)/(1 - \nu_x) + sin^2(\varphi + 45°)/(1 - \nu_y)]$.

While it is very unlikely that any type of crystallographic defects could account for the complex in-plane variations in F_p, nonlocal effects can provide a natural explanation for them. Due to nonlocality, the geometry of the vortex lattice depends on the orientation within the plane. We can again argue (as in the $\mathbf{H} \parallel c$ case) that C_{66} depends on the lattice geometry, and that such dependence must be reflected in F_p. Interestingly, F_p has local maxima at the high symmetry crystallographic orientations [100] and [110], where C_{66} is expected to exhibit local minima. In agreement with a nonlocal scenario, we have also observed that the in-plane anisotropy progessively decreases as T approaches T_c[40].

Conclusive evidence that the in-plane fourfold anisotropy arises from nonlocal effects is provided by similar measurements conducted in the doped samples Lu-1.5 and Lu-3. As we pointed out above, by tuning the impurity content in the sample, we are able to control the electronic mean free path and so the nonlocal effects. Figure 6(b) shows the irreversible magnetization M_i (proportional to the pinning force density) as a function of φ for several

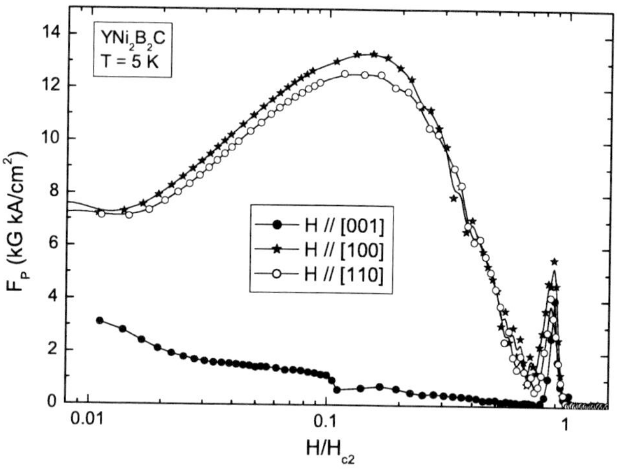

Figure 4: Pinning force density F_p vs H with **H** applied along the principal axes [100], [110] and [001] at $T = 5$ K.

fields at $T = 5$ K. Even though in this sample ℓ is about three times smaller than in the Y-0 crystal, the fourfold anisotropy is still observed. For comparison, in Fig. 6(a) we show the Meissner slope $-4\pi(dM/dH) = (1-\nu)^{-1}$ which reflects the sample geometry effects. The smallness of the amplitude of this twofold oscillation indicates that the sample shape is closer to a disk.

Interestingly, further decreasing the mean free path down to $\ell = 70\AA$ by increasing the impurity concentration level to $x = 3\%$, converts the oscillatory response from a fourfold to a twofold anisotropy (see Figure 7). Surprisingly, the irreversible magnetization does not maximize at the same angular position as the Meissner curve, but there is a shift of nearly 45° between them. This is an unexpected misalignment that cannot be accounted for by a bianisotropic current distribution, but may be related to the irregular shape of the crystal (viewed along the c-axis).

5 OUT-OF-PLANE ANISOTROPY

In the previous section we showed that the pinning force density in the Y-0 sample is much larger for $\mathbf{H} \perp c$ than for $\mathbf{H} \parallel c$. This out-of-plane F_p anisotropy sharply contrasts with the very small ($< 10\%$) mass anisotropy[15, 16, 19], therefore, explanations based on the anisotropic scaling frequently used in high T_c superconductors[42, 43] can be ruled out.

In the same way, this effect is too large to be ascribed to nonlocality, which should appear as a perturbatively small effect. This conclusion is confirmed by the presence of similar anisotropy values in the doped samples Lu-1.5 and Lu-3, where nonlocal effects are strongly reduced. Indeed, in the main panel of Figure 8 we show $F_p(\theta)$, where θ is the angle between the applied field and the c-axis, for the Lu-1.5 and Lu-3 at $T = 5$ K and $H = 3$ kOe. As the field is progressively tilted off from the c-axis, we first observe an almost angle independent pinning force F_p up to $\theta \sim 60°$. Beyond this angle, F_p increases very fast up to

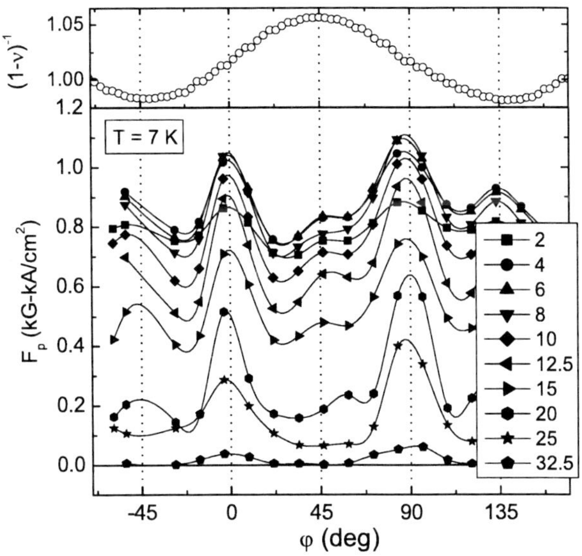

Figure 5: In-plane angular dependence of (a) Meissner slope $-4\pi dM/dH = (1-\nu)^{-1}$ at $T = 7$ K (upper panel) and (b) pinning force density $F_p(\varphi)$ at $T = 7$ K and several fields (lower panel), for the Y-0 single crystal. The labels indicate the applied field in kOe.

nearly one order of magnitud larger than for $\theta = 0°$, when **H** appoaches the basal plane. As we have previously demonstrated, this out-of-plane anisotropy is field dependent and drops to almost isotropic behavior near the peak effect (see Fig. 4).

One possible reason for the sharp increase of $F_p(\theta)$ as $\theta \to 90°$ could be the presence of significant surface barriers for $\mathbf{H}\perp c$. One way to check whether the surface barriers play a relevant role in the measured pinning force is to perform minor hysteresis loops with $\mathbf{H} \parallel ab$ at several T and H. In the larger inset of Figure 8 we show an examples for the Y-0 sample at $T = 5$ K. If surface barriers were the main source of hysteresis, no flux changes would occur in the bulk while H is changing from one branch of the main loop to the other one, hence the data of the minor loop connecting the lower and upper branches would be Meissner-like straight lines[44]. In contrast, in the case of bulk pinning, the lines connecting both branches are curved (parabolic in the simplest Bean model for an infinite slab) just as we observe in the smaller inset of Figure 8. Moreover, in a recent work[41] we have demonstrated that F_p calculated from these minor loops assuming only bulk pinning are in good agreement with those obtained from the main loops. Thus, a significant contribution to magnetic hysteresis arising from surface barriers can be ruled out. Furhermore, it is worth noting that the peak effect (near H_{c2}) which is a bulk phenomena, is observed in the whole field orientation, clearly indicating that bulk pinning dominates the magnetic response[45].

A fact that we have not considered up to now is that, due to the significantly large time relaxation rates of the persistent currents in these materials, the current density J determined through magnetization measurements in the typical time scale of the SQUID-magnetometers (~ 20 sec) is smaller than the "true" critical current density J_c. This suggests that the ob-

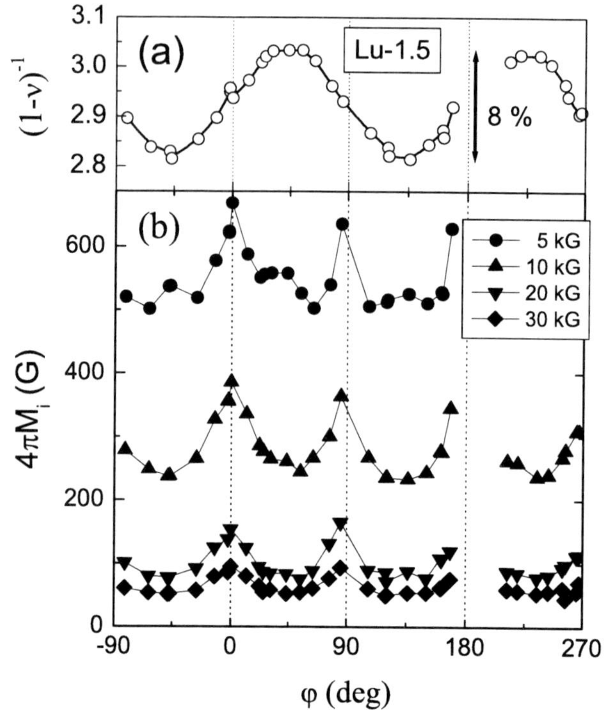

Figure 6: In-plane angular dependence of (a) Meissner slope $-4\pi dM/dH = (1-\nu)^{-1}$ at $T = 5$ K (upper panel) and (b) irreversible magnetization $M_i(\varphi)$ at $T = 5$ K and several fields (lower panel), for the Lu-1.5 single crystal.

served large out-of-plane anisotropy may be related to an angular dependence of the time relaxation of J.

To explore this possibility, we have measured the normalized time relaxation rate of the irreversible magnetization $S = -d\ln J/d\ln t$ for the Y-0 and Lu-1.5 samples for $\mathbf{H} \parallel c$ and $\mathbf{H} \perp c$ at several fields. These measurements are shown in Figure 9. Surprisingly, in both samples the creep rate S for $\mathbf{H} \parallel c$ is comparable or even larger than the values obtained in HTSC at the same temperature (5 K). In the simplest Anderson-Kim scenario, disregarding the possible influence of both quantum creep and glassy relaxation (see below), the pinning energy U_p is given by $U_p \approx T/S$. For instance, in the particular case of the Lu-1.5 sample at $H = 6$ kOe and $T = 5$ K, we obtain $U_p \sim 85$ K, which is low even for HTSC standards. With regards to these values, it is worth keeping in mind that the scale of the *elementary* pinning energy u_p is $\left(H_c^2/8\pi\right)\epsilon\xi^3$, where H_c is the thermodynamic critical field and ϵ is the mass anisotropy. In the HTSC, the low pinning energy is associated to the small u_p, which in turn is due to the very small coherence length. In contrast, in the borocarbide crystals the small value of U_p is a consequence of the very low density of defects.

A remarkable fact observed in Fig. 9 is the large difference (almost one order of magnitude) of the creep rate between the two field orientations studied for the Lu-1.5 sample. We additionally find that for both orientations, and also for sample Y-0 (in the $H \parallel c$ ori-

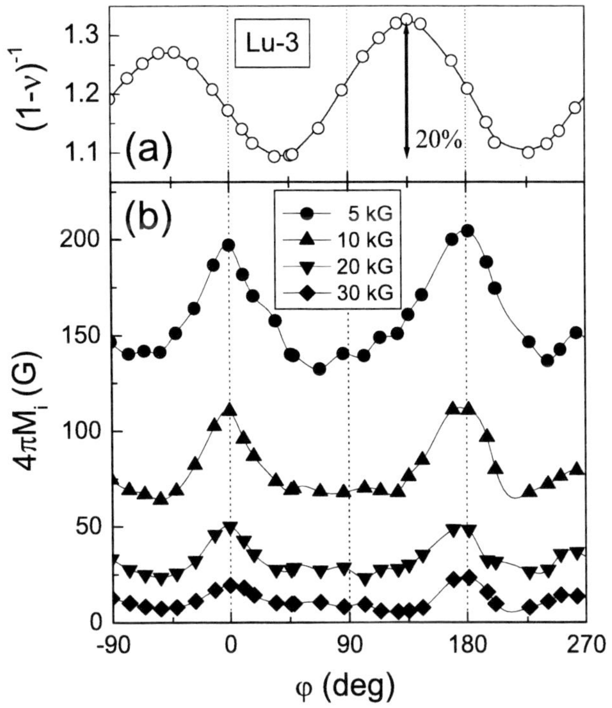

Figure 7: In-plane angular dependence of (a) Meissner slope $-4\pi dM/dH = (1-\nu)^{-1}$ at $T = 5$ K (upper panel) and (b) irreversible magnetization $M_i(\varphi)$ at $T = 5$ K and several fields (lower panel), for the Lu-3 single crystal.

entation) $S \propto H^n$ with an exponent $n = 1.28(2)$. Considering again the simplest scenario, U_p and F_p are related by $U_p \approx F_p V_c \xi$ where V_c is the flux line lattice correlation volume. By combining this expression with $S \approx T/U_p$, we obtain $S \approx T/F_p V_c \xi$, so the creep rate anisotropy should be approximately the inverse of the F_p anisotropy, as indeed observed. This result confirms that the source of the observed anisotropies is the anisotropic pinning energy U_p. So, to complete the solution of this issue an explanation for the anisotropy in U_p must be found.

In brief, the origin of the large out-of-plane pinning anisotropy is unclear. A simple explanation for it could be the presence of some still unidentified anisotropic pinning centers, such as planar defects. Clearly, the complexity of the angular dependence of F_p deserves further investigation.

Another puzzling result comes from the study of the temperature dependence of the creep rate $S(T)$ for fixed fields. In the inset of Figure 9 we show $S(T)$, for the Lu-1.5 sample at $H = 4$ kOe and $\mathbf{H} \parallel c$. We observe that S decreases monotonically as T decreases and it seems to saturate at low temperatures ($T < 4$ K) in a value $S \sim 0.02$. Both the finite value of S as temperature approaches to zero and its temperature independent behavior are typical indications of a quantum creep process. However, an estimation of normalized creep rate (near j_c) is given by $S_Q = \hbar/(\eta \xi^2 L_c)$,[47] where η is the friction coefficient for

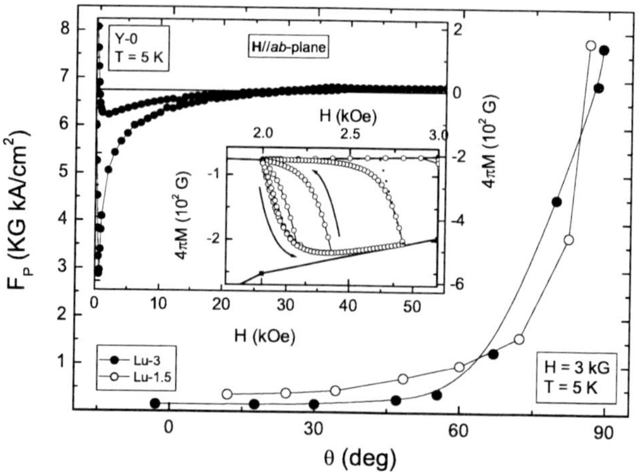

Figure 8: Main panel: pinning force density F_p as a function of the angle θ between $\mathbf{H}$ and the c-axis, for the Lu-1.5 and Lu-3 samples at $T = 5$ K and $H = 3$ kG. The outer inset shows an hysterisis loop for $\mathbf{H}\perp c$ for the Y-0 sample at $T = 5$ K. A zoom in of the minor hysterisis loops corresponding to the full loop showed in the outer inset is shown in the inner inset. The dotted line shows the behavior expected for surface barriers.

a vortex line and L_c is the length of the tunneling vortex segment. This relation can be written as $S_Q \sim Q_u\sqrt{j_c/j_0}$ where $Q_u = e^2\rho_n/\hbar\epsilon\xi$, ρ_n is normal-state resistivity and ϵ the mass anisotropy. For the Lu-1.5 sample, $\rho_n \approx 4.2 \times 10^{-6}\Omega$ cm, $\epsilon \sim 1.1$ and $j_c/j_0 \sim 10^{-5}$, therefore $S_Q \sim 4 \times 10^{-6}$, four orders of magnitude smaller than the measured value. The preceding analysis assumes that the dynamics of the quantum relaxation is dissipative. However, in our borocarbide crystals the electronic mean free path ℓ is considerably larger than ξ_0. This raises the possibility that the quantum relaxation may be more accurately described by a Hall-type vortex dynamics, which is supposed to dominate in the super-clean limit. In that case, an analogous expression for S_Q should apply, with η replaced by a Hall coefficient $\alpha \gg \eta$[47]. Thus, if that were the case, the numerical discrepancy with the experimental result would be even larger.

An alternative interpretation could be that the observed T-independent behavior corresponds to the well known plateau range predicted by the glassy relaxation and widely observed in HTSC. If that were the case, further reducing the temperature (to $T < 1$ K) should result in a decreasing creep rate that tends to zero as T approaches zero. In this scenario, in the plateau range $S^{-1} \sim \mu \ln(1 + t/t_0)$, and hence $S \sim 0.02$ implies that the glassy exponent $\mu \approx 2$ (assuming, as is usually done, that $\ln(1 + t/t_0) \sim 25$). However, the μ value obtained from the Maley analysis[48] is only around 0.3. Moreover, a $\mu \approx 2$ should produce very clear deviations from logarithmic relaxation, which we have failed to observe. A natural way to define this issue would be to perform a set of long term relaxation measurements ($\sim$ 12 to 24 hours). Another problem with this interpretation is that it implies an extremely small pinning energy, $U_p \ll T\mu\ln(1 + t/t_0)$ for $T > 2$ K, that is, $U_p \ll 100$ K.

In summary, although the observed $S(T)$ is suggestive of quantum creep, a quantitative description remains elusive at this point. The alternative explanation in terms of a glassy

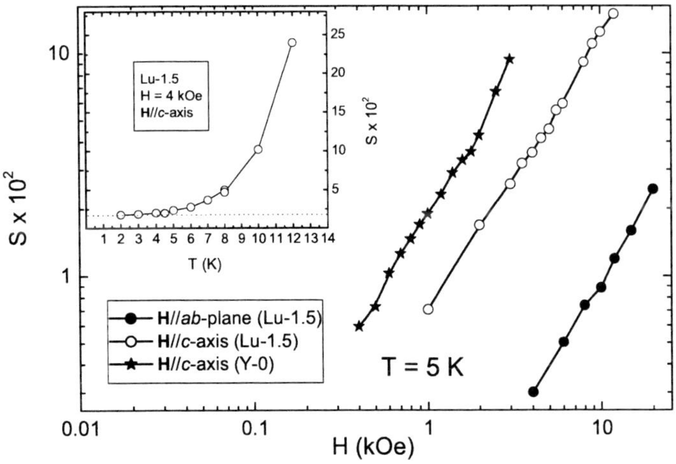

Figure 9: Main panel: normalized time relaxation rate $S(H)$ for different samples and field orientations. Inset: S vs. T for the Lu-1.5 sample at $H = 4$ KOe and $\mathbf{H} \parallel c$.

plateau also has serious difficulties. This complex situation highligths the relevance of the measurements of the normalized relaxation rate S. Indeed, S is a fundamental variable of the dynamics of the vortex system, whereas the persistent current density J is measured at a particular time, and thus it is a more derived variable that depends on both the "initial" critical current J_c and the relaxation rate. Clearly, more detailed studies of the flux creep phenomena in borocarbide superconductors are desirable.

As a final application of the creep results, let us use them to estimate the dimensions of the correlation volume. As mentioned above, at $H = 6$ kOe and $T = 5$ K, we have $U_p \sim 85$ K. At this field value $F_p \sim 2.12$ kG.kA/cm^2, which results in a correlation volume $V_c \approx 10^{10} \mathring{A}^3$. Because of the diluted distribution of pinning centers of these compounds, the Larkin-Ovchinnikov(LO) theory should apply without restrictions. According to this model $V_c = R_c^2 L_c$, where R_c and L_c are the dimensions of the vortex bundle perpendicular and parallel to the field direction and $L_c/R_c \sim \sqrt{2C_{44}/C_{66}}$, with C_{44} the tilt modulus and C_{66} the shear modulus of the FLL. Within this description $C_{44} \approx H^2/4\pi$ and in the simplest case of a triangular FLL in an isotropic medium with $\kappa \gg 1$ in the intermediate field regime $C_{66} \approx H_{c1}H(1-h^2)/16\pi$[46], where $h = H/H_{c2}$. From this we can easily compute the size of the LO correlation length in the field direction $L_c \sim 10R_c \sim 10^4 \mathring{A}$, which in units of the intervortex distance a_0 gives $L_c/a_0 \sim 20$ for $H = 6$ kOe. This value turns out to be one order of magnitude smaller than that obtained by SANS measurements[8] at $T = 2.2$ K in Lu-0 and Y-0 crystals. However, we have naively assumed that $C_{66} \sim H_{c1}H/16\pi$ which according to the recent work of Knigavko et al.[49] is a overestimation of the total shear modulus. Indeed, in that work the authors demonstrate that the squash component C_{66} decreases as H increases, vanishes at the transition field H_1 and then grows slowly. In addition, Eskildsen et al.[8] showed that for fields above 10 kOe the size of the correlation volume is dominated by the properties of the shear modulus. Moreover, using the expression $F_p \propto C_{44}^{-1}C_{66}^{-2}$ corresponding to the LO scenario and the experimental $F_p(H)$, we computed

$C_{66}(H)$, and surprisingly obtained that C_{66} decreases monotonically with H both below and *above* H_1, in contradiction with the standard behavior[40]. This reinforce the idea that C_{66} values derived from LO theory are larger than the "real" shear modulus and therefore the obtained L_c tends to be somewhat smaller than those observed by SANS experiments.

6 Conclusions

The high quality of the borocarbides single crystals have the double benefit of producing large mean free paths and a very dilute distribution of vortex pinning centers. The combination of these factors favours the observation of the influence of nonlocality on vortex pinning. In this work, we have shown that nonlocality significantly affects the irreversible properties of these materials. With the magnetic field directed along the c-axis, the pinning force density $F_p(H)$ changes abruptly at the vortex reorientation field H_1, which is controlled by nonlocal effects. In addition, its dependence on temperature and electron scattering (mean free path) further ties the observed structure in F_p to nonlocal electrodynamics. With the magnetic field in the square ab-basal plane, the four-fold periodicity in F_p and M_{irr} (which is reminiscent of the four-fold periodicity in the *equilibrium* magnetization) again shows a coupling of the vortex lattice to the crystalline lattice; this higher order coupling (greater than a second rank mass-anisotropy tensor) arises from nonlocal effects, which again are washed out by thermal or electron-scattering disorder. These experimental observations demonstrate that nonlocality has a surprisingly profound influence on vortices, the flux line lattice, and vortex pinning in these remarkable materials.

However, the rather complex angular dependence of the pinning force density clearly suggests that other mechanisms besides nonlocality are involved as well. In particular, the origin of the large out-of-plane anisotropy remains unclear. We have conclusively ruled out explanations based on the mass anisotropy, pinning by magnetic impurities, non-local effects and surface barriers. On the other hand, we have observed that this effect is also present in the time relaxation rate S, thus confirming that the source of the observed out-of-plane anisotropy is the anisotropic pinning energy U_p. On top of this, the creep rate S for $\mathbf{H} \parallel c$ exhibits two additional remarkable properties. First, the observed S values are comparable or even larger than the values obtained in HTSC at the same temperature. Second, it is shown that S saturate at low temperatures in a finite value, likely owing to a quantum creep process. These unexpected behaviors cannot be quantitatively accounted for by the usual creep models for HTSC. Clearly, further experimental and theoretical studies are necessary to gain insight into this rather unexplored and fascinating field of the influence of nonlocality on the vortex pinning.

7 Acknowledgments

We are pleased to thank the Atomic Energy Commission of Argentina and Oak Ridge National Laboratory, where the measurements presented in this review have been performed. We also want to thank the CONICET of Argentina for financial support. The experimental results described in this review were obtained in collaboration with C.V. Tomy and D. McK. Paul. We acknowledge many valuable discussions with H.R. Kerchner, Hyun Jeong Kim, D.K. Christen, M. Yethiraj. A.V.S. is supported by the Fund for Scientific Research, Belgium. Oak Ridge National Laboratory is managed by UT-Batelle, LLC for the United States Department of Energy under contract No. DE-AC05-00OR22725.

References

[1] U. Yaron, P. L. Gammel, A. P. Ramirez, D. A. Huse, D. J. Bishop, A. I. Goldman, C. Stassis, P. C. Canfield, K. Mortensen, and M. R. Eskildsen, *Nature* **382**, 236 (1996).

[2] H. Eisaki, H. Takagi, R. J. Cava, B. Batlogg, J. J. Krajewski, W. F. Peck, Jr., K. Mizuhashi, J. O. Lee, and S. Uchida, *Phys. Rev. B* **50**, 647 (1994).

[3] M. R. Eskildsen; K. Harada; P. L. Gammel; A. B. Abrahamsen; N. H. Andersen; G. Ernst; A. P. Ramirez; D. J. Bishop, K. Mortensen, D. G. Naugle, K. D. D. Rathnayaka, and P. C. Canfield, *Nature* **393**, 242 (1998).

[4] P. L. Gammel, B. P. Barber, A. P. Ramirez, C. M. Varma, D. J. Bishop, P. C. Canfield V. G. Kogan, M. R. Eskildsen, N. H. Andersen, K. Mortensen, and K. Harada, *Phys. Rev. Lett.* **82**, 1756 (1999).

[5] K. Nørgaard, M. R. Eskildsen, and N. H. Andersen, J. Jensen, P. Hedegård, and S. N. Klausen, and P. C. Canfield, *Phys. Rev. Lett.* **84**, 4982 (2000).

[6] M. Yethiraj, D.McK. Paul, C.V. Tomy and E.M. Forgan, *Phys. Rev. Lett.* **78**, 4849 (1997).

[7] V.G. Kogan, M. Bullock, B. Harmon, P. Miranović, Lj. Dobrosavljević-Grujić, P. L. Gammel, and D. J. Bishop, *Phys. Rev. B* **55**, R8693 (1997).

[8] M. R. Eskildsen, P. L. Gammel, B. P. Barber, U. Yaron, A. P. Ramirez, D. A. Huse, D. J. Bishop, C. Bolle, C. M. Lieber, S. Oxx, S. Sridhar, N. H. Andersen, K. Mortensen, and P. C. Canfield, *Phys. Rev. Lett.* **78**, 1968 (1997).

[9] Y. De Wilde, M. Iavarone, U. Welp, V. Metlushko, A. E. Koshelev, I. Aranson, G. W. Crabtree, and P. C. Canfield, *Phys. Rev. Lett.* **78**, 4273 (1997).

[10] M. Yethiraj, D. McK. Paul, C. V. Tomy and J. R. Thompson. *Phys. Rev. B* **58**, R14767 (1998).

[11] D.McK. Paul, C.V. Tomy, C. M. Aegerter, R. Cubitt, S. H. Lloyd, E.M. Forgan, S. L. Lee, and M. Yethiraj, *Phys. Rev. Lett.* **80**, 1517 (1998).

[12] P. L. Gammel, D. J. Bishop, M. R. Eskildsen, K. Mortensen, N. H. Andersen, I.R. Fisher, K.O. Cheon, P. C. Canfield, and V. G. Kogan, *Phys. Rev. Lett.* **82**, 4082 (1999).

[13] Hideaki Sakata, Morimi Oosawa, Ken Matsuba, Nobuhiko Nishida, Hiroyuki Takeya, and Kazuto Hirata, *Phys. Rev. Lett.* **84**, 1583 (2000).

[14] K. J. Song, J.R. Thompson, M.Yethiraj, D.K. Christen, C.V. Tomy and D. McK. Paul, *Phys. Rev. B* **59**, R6620 (1999).

[15] L. Civale, A. V. Silhanek, J. R. Thompson, K. J. Song, C. V. Tomy and D. McK. Paul, *Phys. Rev. Lett.* **83**, 3920 (1999).

[16] V. G. Kogan, S. L. Bud′ko, P. C. Canfield and P. Miranović, *Phys. Rev. B* **60**, R12577 (1999).

[17] V. G. Kogan, A. Gurevich, J. H. Cho, D. C. Johnston, Ming Xu, J. R. Thompson and A. Martynovich, *Phys. Rev. B* **54**, 12386 (1996).

[18] V. G. Kogan, M. M. Fang, and S. Mitra, *Phys. Rev. B* **38**, 11958 (1988).

[19] J. R. Thompson, A. V. Silhanek, L. Civale, K. J. Song, D. McK Paul and C. V. Tomy. *Phys. Rev. B* **64**, 24510 (2001).

[20] V. G. Kogan, P. Miranović, Lj. Dobrosavljević-Grujić, W. E. Pickett, and D. K. Christen. *Phys. Rev. Lett.* **79**, 741 (1997).

[21] M. Franz, I. Affleck, and M. H. S. Amin, *Phys. Rev. Lett.* **79**, 1555 (1997).

[22] S. B. Dugdale, M. A. Alam, I. Wilkinson, R. J. Hughes, I. R. Fisher, P. C. Canfield, T. Jarlborg, and G. Santi, *Phys. Rev. Lett.* **83**, 4824 (1999).

[23] Martinez-Samper P, Suderow H, Vieira S, Brison JP, Luchier N, Lejay P, Canfield PC, *Phys. Rev. B* **67**, 014526 (2003).

[24] T. Kohara, T. Oda, K. Ueda, Y. Yamada, A. Mahajan, K. Elankumaran, Zakir Hossian, L. C. Gupta, R. Nagarajan, R. Vijayaraghavan, and Chandan Mazumdar, *Phys. Rev. B* **51**, 3985 (1995).

[25] T. Jacobs, Balam A. Willemsen, S. Sridhar, R. Nagarajan, L. C. Gupta, Z. Hossain, Chandan Mazumdar, P. C. Canfield, and B. K. Cho, *Phys. Rev. B* **52**, R7022 (1995).

[26] Zheng GQ, Wada Y, Hashimoto K, Kitaoka Y, Asayama K, Takeya H, Kadowaki K, *J. Phys. Chem. Solids* **59**, 2169 (1998).

[27] M. Nohara et al., *J. Phys. Soc. Jpn.* **68**, 1078 (1999).

[28] T. Yokoya, T. Kiss, T. Watanabe, S. Shin, M. Nohara, H. Takagi, and T. Oguchi, *Phys. Rev. Lett.* **85**, 4952 (2000).

[29] In-Sang Yang, M. V. Klein, S. L. Cooper, P. C. Canfield, B. K. Cho, and Sung-Ik Lee, *Phys. Rev. B* **62**, 1291 (2000).

[30] Etienne Boaknin, R. W. Hill, Cyril Proust, C. Lupien, Louis Taillefer, and P. C. Canfield, *Phys. Rev. Lett.* **87**, 237001 (2001).

[31] K. Izawa, K. Kamata, Y. Nakajima, Y. Matsuda, T. Watanabe, M. Nohara, H. Takagi, P. Thalmeier, and K. Maki, *Phys. Rev. Lett.* **89**, 137006 (2002)

[32] M. R. Eskildsen, A. B. Abrahamsen, V. G. Kogan, P. L. Gammel, K. Mortensen, N. H. Andersen, and P. C. Canfield, *Phys. Rev. Lett.* **86**, 5148 (2001).

[33] S. J. Levett, C. D. Dewhurst, and D. McK. Paul, *Phys. Rev. B* **66**, 014515 (2002).

[34] N. Nakai, P. Miranović, M. Ichioka, and K. Machida, *Phys. Rev. Lett.* **89**, 237004 (2002).

[35] B. Rosenstein and A. Knigavko, *Phys. Rev. Lett.* **83**, 844 (1999).

[36] K.O. Cheon, I.R. Fisher, V.G. Kogan, P.C. Canfield, P. Miranovic, and P.L. Gammel *Phys. Rev. B* **58**, 6463 (1998).

[37] H. Schmidt and H. F. Braun, *Phys. Rev. B* **55**, 8497 (1997).

[38] A.V. Silhanek, L. Civale, S. Candia, G. Nieva, G. Pasquini, H. Lanza, *Phys. Rev. B* **59**, 13620 (1999).

[39] A.V. Silhanek, D. Niebieskikwiat, L. Civale, M. A. Avila, O. Billoni and D. Casa, *Phys. Rev. B* **60**, 13189 (1999).

[40] A.V. Silhanek, J. R. Thompson, L. Civale, D. McK Paul and C.V. Tomy. *Phys. Rev. B* **64**, 12512 (2001).

[41] A.V. Silhanek, L. Civale, J.R. Thompson, K.J. Song, D.McK Paul, C.V. Tomy, S. Bud'ko, and P.C. Canfield, NATO conference New Trends in Superconductivity, Yalta (Ukraine), September 2001. Kluwer Series **67**, 255 (2002).

[42] G. Blatter, V.B. Geshkenbein and A.I. Larkin. *Phys. Rev. Lett.* **68**, 875 (1992)

[43] A.V. Silhanek and L. Civale. *Physica C*, Vol. **341-348** (1-4) pp.1227-1228 (2000).

[44] H. Ullmaier, *Irreversible Properties of Type II Superconductors* (Springer-Verlag, Berlin-Heidelberg-New York, 1975), p. 124.

[45] Z.L. Xiao, E.Y. Andrei, Paltiel Y, E. Zeldov, P. Shuk, and M. Greenblatt, *Phys. Rev. B* **65** (9): 094511 (2002)

[46] E.H. Brandt, *J. Low Temp. Phys.* **26**, 709 (1977).

[47] G. Blatter, M. V. Feigel'man, V. B. Geshkenbein, A. I. Larkin and V. M. Vinokur, *Rev. Mod. Phys.* **66**, 1125 (1994).

[48] M. P. Maley, J. O. Willis, H. Lessure, and M. E. McHenry, *Phys. Rev. B* **42**, 2639 (1990).

[49] A. Knigavko, V.G. Kogan, B. Rosenstein and T.J. Yang, *Phys. Rev. B* **62**, 111 (2000).

Vortices in low-T_c layered Ta_xGe_{1-x}/Ge superconductors

Andreas Engel*and Benjamin J. Ruck†

Abstract

The unique combination of superconducting and material parameters of the cuprate high-temperature superconductors gives rise to tremendously rich vortex phase diagrams and raises many fundamentally and technologically important questions. Complex structured low-temperature superconductors may exhibit similarly intricate phase diagrams and can offer alternative and sometimes advantageous ways of addressing some of the unsolved problems.

Amorphous films of alternating Ta_xGe_{1-x} superconducting and Ge insulating layers provide such a system with arbitrary layer thicknesses and thus full control over anisotropy and coupling between adjacent superconducting layers. Extensive dc-conductance measurements over a large part of the H-T phase diagram were performed on a number of films, where in some cases the layering was augmented with a columnar microstructure. This columnar structure results in a network of extended strong pinning sites comparable to twin boundaries in twinned $YBa_2Cu_3O_{7-\delta}$. For the films presented $T_c(0)$ values were in the range from 1.7 to 2.8 K. They are strongly type-II superconductors with $\kappa \equiv \lambda/\xi \approx 90$ or higher and the full range from weak to strong anisotropy.

The current-voltage (I-V) curves measured from non-columnar samples can be collapsed according to the vortex glass scaling laws. However, a lack of universality in the critical exponents indicates that the scaling analysis may simply be highlighting a continuous crossover between strong pinning at low T and H and much weaker pinning at high T and H, with no actual phase transition separating the two regimes. For the most anisotropic samples, with essentially two-dimensional decoupled layers, the strongly pinned phase is absent, and the low T and H regime is characterized by thermally activated plastic vortex flow.

The micro-structured columnar films show strongly enhanced vortex pinning for magnetic fields co-aligned with the extended pinning sites. The T and H range for which dissipation-free current transport was observed was considerably expanded relative to non-columnar films. For these films a critical scaling analysis clearly identified the pinned vortex phase as a Bose-glass, lending support to the notion that the Bose-glass is a universal phase exhibited by superconductors containing extended defects. It was noted, however, that for the most anisotropic of the micro-structured samples Bose-glass scaling was successful only at relatively low magnetic fields. The high-field vortex phase in this sample was instead best described as a very viscous vortex liquid, with no phase transition to a glass upon lowering the temperature.

Further analysis of the I-V characteristics taken in the Bose-glass phase allowed for the extraction of the field, temperature and current dependent glass exponent μ. A

*Corresponding author: Physics Institute of the University of Zurich,Winterthurerstr. 190, 8057 Zurich, Switzerland, Tel.: +41 1 635 5721, Fax : +41 1 635 5704, e-mail:dr.engel@arcor.de

†School of Chemical and Physical Sciences, Victoria University of Wellington, P.O. Box 600, Wellington, New Zealand, email: Ben.Ruck@vuw.ac.nz

markedly different T and H dependence of μ for films with different anisotropy suggests different mechanisms for vortex creep within the pinned vortex phases. Variable-range hopping of vortices and collective flux creep are considered as models to describe the experimental data.

1 Introduction

Vortices are encountered in many areas of physics and in everyday life [1]. A prominent example of a classical vortex that everyone is familiar with is the rotating water flowing out of a bath tub. Vortices may also form in frictionless liquids such as superfluid ^{4}He or ^{3}He [2], Bose-Einstein condensates [3] and superconductors [4]. It has long been known that superconductors can be divided into two types, conventionally termed type-I and type-II. The distinction lies in the ratio of two of the characteristic superconducting length scales, namely the coherence length ξ and the magnetic penetration depth λ [5, 4]. Type-II superconductors, for which $\kappa \equiv \lambda/\xi$ is greater than $1/\sqrt{2}$, exhibit the remarkable property that an applied magnetic field penetrates the superconductor in the form of quantised magnetic flux vortices, each carrying one quanta of flux $\Phi_0 \equiv h/(2e) = 2 \times 10^{-15}$ Wb $= 2 \times 10^{-7}$ G cm^2. The characteristic spacing a_0 between flux lines is field dependent, given by $a_0 \approx (\Phi_0/B)^{1/2}$. This so-called vortex state has attracted an enormous amount of attention because an applied current exerts a Lorentz force on the vortices that tends to cause them to move. The moving flux lines generate an electric field that causes the current to flow through the non-superconducting vortex cores, and the superconductor no longer displays zero resistivity. In a perfect crystalline sample the vortex motion is opposed by a finite viscosity, but this cannot absolutely prevent flux motion, and a finite free-flux-flow resistivity results even at the smallest currents. Fortunately, native or induced defects in the material form natural low energy sites for the vortices [4], and can thus suppress vortex motion and restore the true superconducting response.

The discovery of high-temperature superconductors (HTSC) in 1986 triggered an enormous boost in the study of the vortex state. As well as the high transition temperature, HTSCs posses a number of novel characteristics. These include a layered crystal structure with the superconductivity concentrated in nearly two-dimensional CuO_2 planes, large penetration depths and very short coherence lengths, and a wide range of defects ranging from point impurities and vacancies to extended twin planes and grain boundaries. It was quickly realised that these unusual parameters made accessible a vast array of vortex states, with consequent effects on the ability of defects to pin the vortices. Although the study of these vortex states is extremely interesting from both a fundamental and applied perspective, it is also extremely difficult due to the very large number of relevant length scales and parameters associated with the various types of HTSC. Furthermore, these parameters are generally fixed for a given material, so a systematic study of the dependence of the vortex properties on any given parameter is generally not possible.

For example, the two most widely studied HTSCs are at almost opposite ends in terms of the degree of coupling between the CuO_2 layers. $YBa_2Cu_3O_{7-\delta}$ (Y123) shows moderate anisotropy and strong interlayer coupling, whereas vortices in adjacent layers in $Bi_2Sr_2CaCu_2O_{8+\delta}$ (Bi2212) are much less coupled due to the higher anisotropy. The preparation of artificially layered systems, consisting of alternating superconducting and non-superconducting layers, offers an option to overcome this situation. The individual layer thicknesses can be varied continuously, allowing a systematic investigation of the role of anisotropy and reduced dimensionality. Indeed, there have been a number of significant studies on systems such as Nb/Ge [6, 7, 8], Mo/Ge [9], and Y123/$PrBa_2Cu_3O_7$ [10, 11, 12, 13].

In this paper we review results obtained from an extensive study of Ta_xGe_{1-x}/Ge thin film superconductors. An oblique deposition technique allowed us to prepare some of the films with an intrinsic columnar microstructure that introduces correlated pinning defects. Three important aspects make this system attractive: (i) the constituents form a consistent amorphous structure across the entire range of thicknesses required for the study, and (ii) most of the important measurements are at temperatures below 2.17 K, and (iii) the oblique deposition technique allows a continuous tuning of the strength and orientation of the correlated disorder. The first of these assures that the layers do not change their properties as their thickness is varied, and furthermore encourages the formation of smooth layers. The second allows measurements to be performed while the films are immersed in superfluid He; the excellent heat extraction ensures a temperature very close to the bath temperature even at the high currents required to drive the material into the normal state. The electron tunneling length in amorphous Ge is approximately 8 Å [14, 15], so the degree of coupling between the superconducting layers can easily be varied over a wide range by changing the Ge layer thickness. It will be shown that the key length scales describing the system lead to phase diagrams in these low temperature superconductors that are very similar to those in HTSCs, despite the temperature scale being at least one order of magnitude lower.

Magnetic vortices are elastic objects, with individual vortices characterised by a line tension, and vortex aggregates characterised by a series of elastic modulii [16]. There are many length scales relevant for describing the vortex phase. Intrinsic parameters, such as the coherence length and penetration depth, are determined by the material system[1]. The individual layer thicknesses, the total thickness, and the spacing between defects are also characteristic of a given sample. The intervortex spacing can be varied by changing the externally applied magnetic field. Finally, there are many derived length scales, such as the distance over which vortices are able to bend, that are determined by a combination of intrinsic and extrinsic parameters. These length scales combine to affect the dimensionality and are responsible for the many complex thermodynamic vortex phases, both observed and predicted, in these materials. In an abstract way this complexity is highly desirable, because vortices in superconductors allow one to study interacting, one(zero)-dimensional, elastic objects in a random three(two)-dimensional potential[2].

Two aspects of vortex physics will be discussed in greater detail. The first one deals with the question of whether there exists a thermodynamic phase transition from a vortex liquid to a solid vortex phase in superconductors with randomly distributed point-like or extended pinning sites. It is generally accepted that vortices in superconductors essentially free of pinning defects undergo a first-order phase transition from a vortex liquid state to a vortex crystal with long range order [17, 18]. The situation in the presence of randomly distributed pinning sites is much more disputed. Two models predicting a second-order phase transition from the liquid phase into a glass phase have been developed for point-like pinning, [19, 20] and for pinning by extended disorder [21]. There have been numerous publications on a wide variety of systems claiming to have verified these theoretical predictions. However, there continue to be serious doubts as to whether there is a thermodynamic phase transition at

[1] The intrinsic length scales are strongly affected by disorder in amorphous Ta_xGe_{1-x}/Ge multilayers. For example, the zero temperature coherence length is given by $\xi = (\xi_0 \ell)^{1/2}$, where ξ_0 is the coherence length in the crystalline material, and ℓ is the electronic mean free path.

[2] In highly anisotropic uniaxial superconductors vortices are confined to two-dimensional layers and can become effectively point-like, zero dimensional objects.

all in these situations [22, 23] or just a continuous crossover from a weakly pinned to a more strongly pinned vortex configuration.

The second focus will be on vortex creep, focussing especially on low temperatures and magnetic fields. Whether the vortices form a separate phase or not, they are strongly pinned, and vortex motion is strongly current dependent and only possible due to thermally activated vortex jumps over the pinning barrier. Current-voltage characteristics in this regime show an exponential dependence on the applied current which can be characterized by a so called glass exponent. Glass exponents for different films with varying anisotropy will be discussed with regard to two different models: vortex creep by thermally activated motion of vortex bundles[16] and variable-range hopping of vortices[21].

2 Ta_xGe_{1-x}/Ge Superconducting Films

All of the films were deposited onto glass substrates in an oil-free ultra-high vacuum system with a base pressure of less than 10^{-8} mbar. Commercially available high-purity Ge and Ta were used as raw materials. The amorphous superconducting binary alloy Ta_xGe_{1-x} has a maximum critical temperature $T_c(0)$ for a Ta-content of approximately 35% [24]. Therefore, the independently controlled evaporation rates were chosen to obtain roughly this Ta-concentration in the superconducting layers, with the exception of sample D (see Table 1) for which the superconducting layers consist of pure Ta. The layering itself was achieved by periodically placing a shutter across the Ta vapor stream.

Some of the samples (F - H) were grown such that they have an additional columnar microstructure. This columnar structure results in strongly pinning defects [25, 26] comparable, for example, to twin planes in Y123. The columnar structure was obtained during the evaporation process by simply tilting the substrates with respect to the incident vapor flux. By means of a geometrical shadowing effect [27] the films grow in the form of columns, with a degree of separation that depends on the evaporation parameters (deposition angle, substrate temperature, etc.). The orientation of the columns lies somewhere between the direction of the incident vapor flux and the substrate normal. In the case of the Ta_xGe_{1-x}/Ge multilayers the resulting films are still continuous. The columns, with approximately bulk density and typical diameter some 10 to 100 nm, are separated by much thinner areas with reduced mass density; the latter act as the flux pinning sites.

All of the films have been thoroughly characterized with respect to their structure and chemical composition. A range of standard techniques were applied to obtain the required information, such as Rutherford backscattering spectroscopy and x-ray fluorescence for the chemical composition, and multiple beam interferometry and transmission electron microscopy (TEM) for film and layer thicknesses. Full details may be found elsewhere [28, 29]. As an example, Figure 1 shows a TEM image taken from film G. Both the layering and the leaning columnar microstructure are clearly visible.

Electrical conductivity measurements were performed in standard ^{4}He-bath cryostats. The samples were immersed in liquid helium to maximize heat extraction, and to ensure film temperatures very near the bath temperature even at the highest applied currents where the superconductors switched into the normal conducting state. The measured temperature stability below the lambda-point of liquid helium (2.17 K) was about ± 1 mK, and better than ± 5 mK at higher temperatures. Each of the samples was patterned into a bridge approximately 1 to 2 mm wide and 5 mm long for four terminal conductance measurements. The software-controlled current was supplied by a Keithley model 224 precision current source

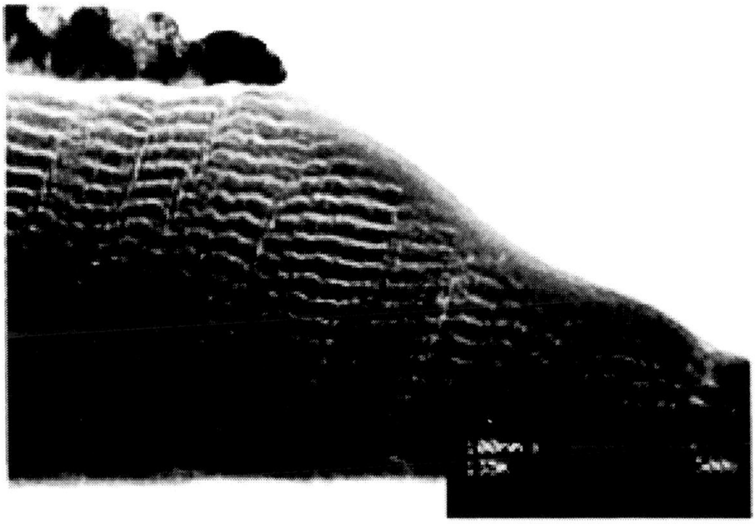

Figure 1: TEM photograph of sample G; the dark layers are superconducting Ta_xGe_{1-x} whereas the thin bright layers are insulating Ge. At the very top a thick protective Au layer separated from the film by a relatively thick Ge layer can be seen. The additional columnar microstructure leaning to the right is also easily visible. In the right half of the Figure the top layers of the film have been ablated during the ion milling process when preparing the specimen for TEM.

and the voltage measured with a Keithley model 182 nanovoltmeter. The magnetic field was applied by either a Varian electromagnet (maximum field ≈ 1 T) or a superconducting solenoid capable of reaching 7 T. The direction of the field could be freely rotated by 180° about the sample (see inset of Figure 2).

Rotating the magnetic field orientation allowed for a verification of flux pinning by the extended defect structure, and thus a determination of the exact columnar growth direction. Figure 2 shows resistance measurements for sample F as a function of magnetic field orientation θ, where $\theta = 0°$ corresponds to the magnetic field oriented perpendicular to the film plane. At high magnetic fields, such that the vortex system is in the free flux flow (FFF) regime (1 T in Figure 2), the effect of the columnar microstructure is negligible and the only anisotropy arises from the thin film itself and the layering, leading to zero resistance for the magnetic field applied parallel to the film ($\theta = \pm 90°$). At somewhat lower magnetic fields the vortices form a pinned vortex fluid (see Section 4.1 below) and the resistance is governed by thermally assisted flux flow (TAFF). In this phase the effects of the columnar structure are most obvious: a second resistance minimum appears near $\theta_{\text{min}} = 24°$. We call this direction the columnar or C-direction. The C-directions for all samples with columnar microstructure have been determined this way. They compare very well with the columnar growth directions determined from TEM images. However, angles for C-directions determined from resistance measurements are consistently 1° to 4° larger, which may be a result of the emergence of vortex staircases [30].

Zero-field and in-field resistance measurements were also performed as a function of temperature to extract the important superconductivity parameters. The zero field resistance data above T_c were analyzed within the fluctuation conductivity framework [31, 32, 33] from which reliable values of $T_c(0)$ were extracted. Similar measurements with applied magnetic fields parallel or perpendicular to the film plane, and where relevant along the

Vortices in low-T_c layered Ta_xGe_{1-x}/Ge superconductors

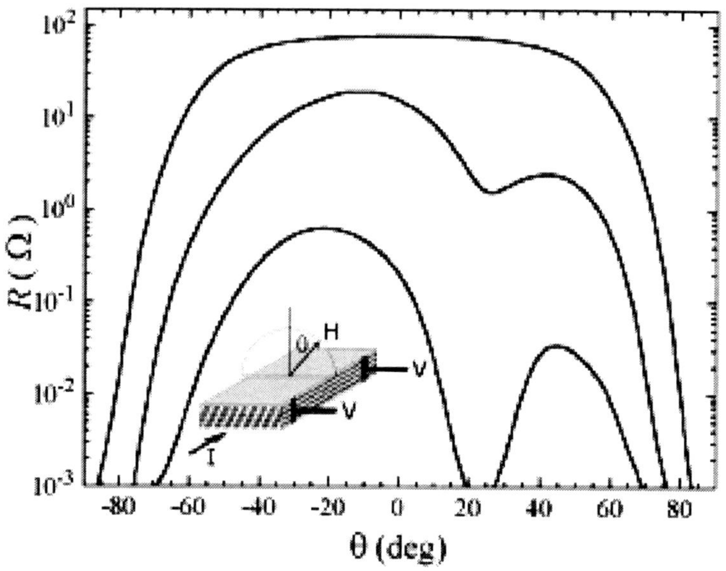

Figure 2: Resistance versus magnetic field orientation for sample F taken at $T = 2$ K and $H = 1.0$, 0.6, 0.4 T from top to bottom. The magnetic field could be rotated by 180° about the sample. The columnar growth direction was also perpendicular to the applied current and lay in the same plane as the magnetic field. See also the inset at the bottom of the graph where a schematic drawing of the measurement geometry is shown. For certain combinations of fields and temperatures distinct resistance minima appeared when the magnetic field was applied parallel to the columnar growth direction.

Table 1: Summary of important parameters for all of the films. From the left the columns are film identifier, layer thickness superconducting(s)/insulating(i) in nm, number of s layers, Ta-concentration in s-layer, C-direction, normal state resistivity extrapolated to $T = 0$ K in $\mu\Omega$ cm, critical temperature in K, critical field in T, coherence length in nm, penetration depth in nm, and GL-parameter.

	s/i	#	Ta	$\theta_{\min}$	$\rho_N(0)$	$T_c(0)$	$H_{c2}(0)$	$\xi_{ab}(0)$	$\lambda_{ab}(0)$	κ
A	21/18	8	45%	–	290	2.66	4.8	8.3	1100	80
B	4/3	13	25%	–	340	1.89	3.6	9.6	1400	90
C	67/0	1	27%	–	310	2.80	5.9	7.5	1100	90
D	2.5/2.4	25	100%	–	220	1.66	3.0	10.0	1200	70
E	6/17	12	38%	–	250	2.27	4.8	8.2	1100	90
F	13.6/3.5	12	32%	23.8°	442	2.40	7.4	6.7	1430	131
G	8.8/3.1	20	35%	29.3°	526	2.21	7.0	6.9	1620	144
H	13.0/7.5	16	37%	26.3°	555	2.27	7.3	6.7	1670	153

columnar direction, allowed us to determine the form of $H_{c2}(T)$ [34, 35]. Using well-known relations between superconducting parameters, the in-plane coherence length $\xi_{ab}(0)$ [4] and the in-plane penetration depth $\lambda_{ab}(0)$ [36] were determined, as well as the GL-parameter[3] $\kappa = \lambda_{ab}(0)/1.63\,\xi_{ab}(0)$. The important structural and superconducting parameters are summarized for all samples in Table 1.

3 Non-columnar samples

We begin our analysis of the vortex state in $Ta_xGe_1 - x$ based multilayers by examining the properties of thin film and multilayer samples grown at normal incidence. These samples are thus free of extended defects, although they still show a wide range of dissipation regimes associated with various vortex structures. In particular, the dimensionality of the samples plays a central role in determining the types of vortex motion that take place in each sample, and we examine the relevant length scales that determine this dimensionality. Despite the extremely rapid decrease in the resistivity that occurs below T_c in the 3D samples, we do not find any unambiguous evidence for a transition to a vortex glass phase. This contrasts with the results for the columnar samples that will be presented in Section 4 below, where the correlated disorder is found to lead to a true phase transition.

3.1 Resistance measurements

The resistive transitions of samples A and B are shown in Figures 3(a) and (b) for various perpendicular ($\perp$) applied magnetic fields. Qualitatively similar behavior is observed in both cases, with the most striking feature being the field induced broadening of the transition due to the motion of magnetic vortices below $H_{c2\perp}$. A more detailed analysis of these data is obtained by applying the scaling functions of Ullah and Dorsey for the fluctuation conductivity above $T_c(H)$ [34, 35]. As $T_c(0)$ has already been determined by fitting the zero-field fluctuation conductivity, the only free parameter required for the scaling is the

[3]The factor 1.63 is due to using the zero temperature values $\lambda_{ab}(0)$ and $\xi_{ab}(0)$ [36].

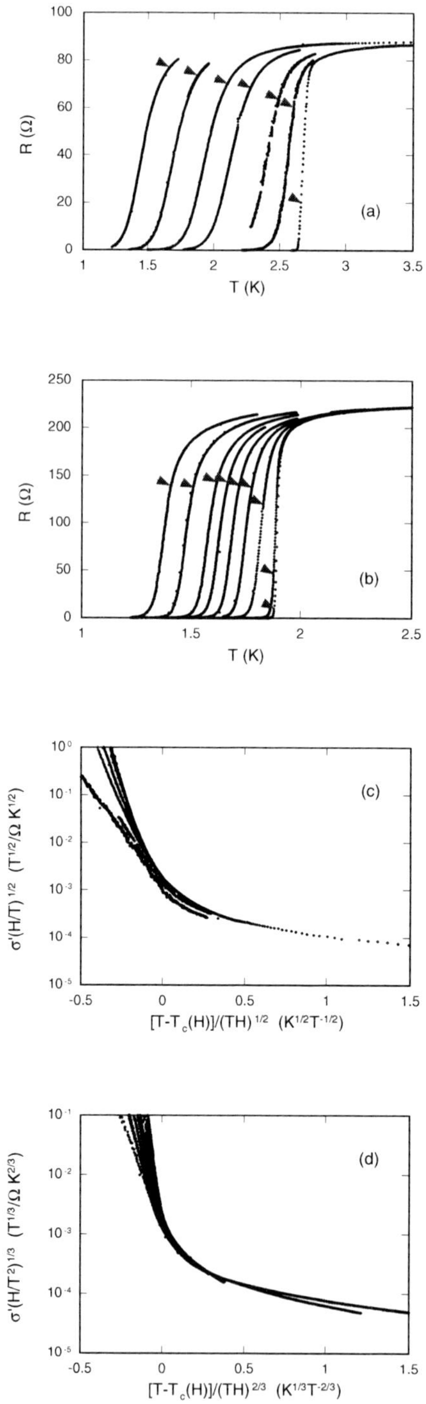

Figure 3: (a) Resistive transitions in a perpendicular applied field for sample A. From right to left the curves correspond to fields of 0, 0.1, 0.3, 0.7, 1.0, 1.4 and 1.8 T. (b) Resistive transitions in a perpendicular applied field for sample B. From right to left the curves correspond to fields of 0, 0.003, 0.1, 0.2, 0.3, 0.4, 0.5, 0.7 and 0.9 T. (c) 2D scaled form of the fluctuation conductivity for sample A. (d) 3D scaled form of the fluctuation conductivity for sample B. The arrows on (a) and (b) indicate the position of $H_{c2\perp}$ determined from the scaling parameters.

slope of the perpendicular critical field at $T = T_c$. For sample A a satisfactory collapse of the data was obtained only with the 2D form of the scaling functions [Fig. 3(c)], whereas sample B required the 3D scaling form [Fig. 3(d)]. Note that in both cases the scaled data deviate from the universal curve at values below zero on the x-axis, where the resistivity is affected more by flux motion than by fluctuation effects. The arrows in Figs. 3(a) and (b) show the locations of $T_c(H)$ determined from the scaling analysis. Clearly, using a simpler criteria for determining $T_c(H)$, such as taking the midpoint of the resistive transition, would lead to a systematic error in the results. This treatment underlines the complexity associated with determining even basic parameters, such as the transition temperature, in the presence of the vortex state.

The 3D nature of sample B is consistent with its thin insulating layers, which allow strong coupling of the order parameter across the whole sample. In contrast, sample A has thick insulating layers, and the superconducting layer thickness of 21 nm is less than the coherence length $\xi_{ab}(T) = 8.3 \times (1 - T/T_c)^{-0.5}$ nm even at temperatures far from T_c, explaining the 2D nature of the transition. Investigation of the resistive transition of these samples in parallel ($\|$) magnetic fields provided results consistent with the perpendicular field case. For sample B $H_{c2\|}$ is linear close to T_c, with a slope about 6 times larger than in the perpendicular field case, thus defining the anisotropy factor $\gamma \equiv H_{c2\perp}/H_{c2\|} = 1/6$. For sample A $H_{c2\|}$ shows a square root dependence on temperature as expected for a 2D film [4].

We turn now to an investigation of the vortex motion below the fluctuation conductivity regime. An Arrhenius plot of the resistance of sample C, measured with a low applied current of 1 μA, is shown in Figure 4(a), where the different curves correspond to different perpendicular fields. A linear portion is clearly evident at low temperatures, indicating a thermally activated resistance $R \propto \exp(-U/k_BT)$. If the activation energy is assumed to be of the form $U(H,T) = U(H) \times (1 - T/T_c)$ then the slope of the linear region gives a measure of $U(H)$ [37]. The activation energy thus determined is plotted as a function of field in Fig. 4(b), together with the corresponding activation energy for sample D. The solid lines show fits of the form $U(H) = U_0H^{-0.5}$, where U_0/k_B takes the values 93 K and 64 K for samples C and D, respectively. The $H^{-0.5}$ field dependence implies that $U(H)$ can be rewritten as

$$U(H) = U_0 \frac{a_0}{\sqrt{\Phi_0}}, \tag{1}$$

with Φ_0 the flux quantum and a_0 the inter-vortex spacing. This form of activation energy is characteristic of plastic vortex motion [16], where the main barrier relates to the energy required for the vortices to hop over a characteristic distance a_0.

The elastic properties of the vortex lattice are expected to strongly inhibit plastic vortex motion in a three-dimensional vortex solid [16, 38]. The same restrictions do not apply to the vortex liquid, where an activation barrier of the form

$$U_{pl} \simeq \frac{\Phi_0^2 a_0}{2\pi\mu_0\gamma\lambda_{ab}^2(t)} \tag{2}$$

has been shown to exist [39, 40, 41]. This plastic activation barrier gives the liquid a viscous nature such that pinning forces are effective in preventing free flux flow[4]. Equation 2 does

[4]At temperatures or fields very close to $T_c(H)$ thermal motion of the vortices averages out the pinning forces, and the resistivity approaches the free flux flow limit $\rho = \rho_N H/H_{c2}$, with ρ_N the normal state resistivity.

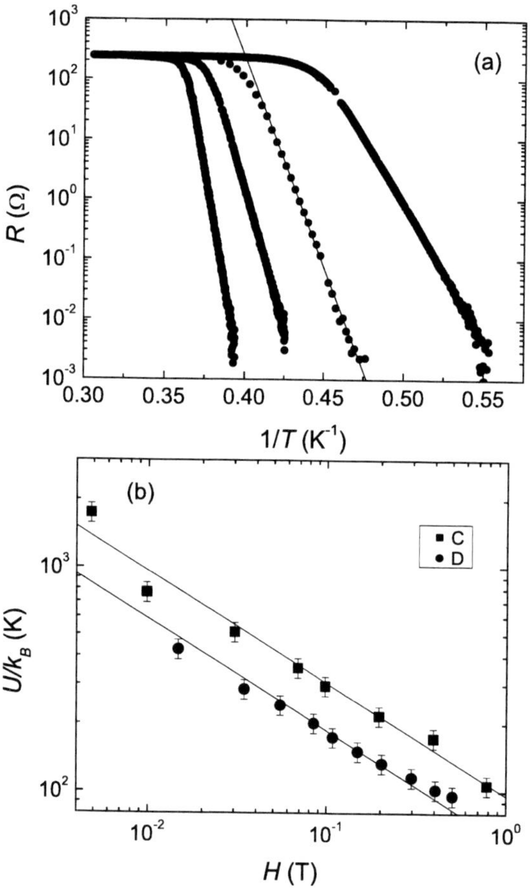

Figure 4: (a) Arrhenius plot for sample C in perpendicular fields of (left to right) 0.07, 0.2, 0.4, and 0.8 T. The solid line through the 0.4 T data indicates the activated portion of the resistive transition. (b) Activation energy for samples C and D. The solid lines are fits showing $U \propto 1/H^{0.5}$, indicative of quasi-3D plastic vortex motion.

indeed agree with the observed field dependence of the activation barrier in samples C and D. However, the measured prefactors U_0 are roughly an order of magnitude less than the values calculated from Equation 2 using the parameters listed in Table 1. We interpret this discrepancy between the measured and predicted prefactors as a feature of the finite thickness of these samples. The barrier described by Equation 2 results from the entangled nature of the vortices. Entanglement requires that the vortices are able to bend appreciably as they traverse the sample, so the total thickness must be greater than a characteristic bending length, the scale of which is given by the penetration depth λ [16]. All of our samples are considerably thinner than this, so we do not expect a fully entangled vortex liquid phase to exist. Nevertheless, the field dependence of the activation barrier implies plastic dissipation by hopping of vortices over a distance of order a_0. This is in clear contrast to the behavior that we show below for 2D layers, so we describe the vortex phase that gives rise to the observed activated behavior as a quasi-3D phase with the properties of a vortex liquid.

The fluctuation conductivity of samples C and D was well described by the 3D scaling theory. The fact that the fluctuation conductivity is fully 3D, while the thermally activated vortex motion behaves only in a quasi-3D fashion, is a result of the fact that two different length scales determine the behavior in the two regimes: these are the coherence length and the vortex bending length, respectively.

The quasi-3D behavior described above may be contrasted with the activated flux motion observed in the samples with highly decoupled 2D layers. A perpendicular field Arrhenius plot for sample E is displayed in Figure 5(a). Thermally activated resistivity is evident at low temperatures, but more strikingly there is a sudden change in the slope of the curves at a field dependent temperature T_x. As the field is increased T_x moves closer to the non-activated region until the change in slope is no longer discernable. A change from one slope to another on the Arrhenius plot implies a change in the dominant dissipation mechanism, with a corresponding change in the activation energy. Similar kinks have been observed in the Arrhenius plots of several different layered systems, with the change in activation energy being attributed either to a dimensional crossover [9] or to 2D vortex lattice melting [8, 42]. It will be shown below that neither of these scenarios is applicable here, and instead the crossover at T_x is due to a change in the dominant contribution to the resistivity from two competing modes of vortex motion.

The activation energies of sample E measured at temperatures below and above T_x (U_1 and U_2, respectively) are shown as a function of field in Figure 5(b). U_1 and U_2 converge at a field of about 0.5 T, above which the activation energy corresponds closely to the extrapolation of U_1. The lower solid line shows a fit of the form $U_1(H) = 8.4 \times \ln(2.5/H)$. A similar field dependence is also seen in the activation energy of sample A [solid triangles in Fig. 5(b)] for which $U(H) = 30 \times \ln(6.3/H)$. The logarithmic field dependence of the activation energy, observed here in samples with thin, highly decoupled superconducting layers, originates from the logarithmic interaction between dislocation-antidislocation pairs separated by a distance r in the 2D vortex lattice [38]. Before discussing this further, we briefly review the role of dislocations in determining the resistivity in 2D samples.

The dislocation-antidislocation pair interaction energy takes the form [38]

$$\epsilon_d(r) \simeq \frac{\Phi_0^2 d_s}{16\pi^2 \mu_0 \lambda_{ab}^2(T)} \ln\left(\frac{r}{a_0}\right), \tag{3}$$

where d_s is the layer thickness. This energy is finite, and the resistivity associated with the motion of thermally created dislocation-antidislocation pairs can be calculated by averaging

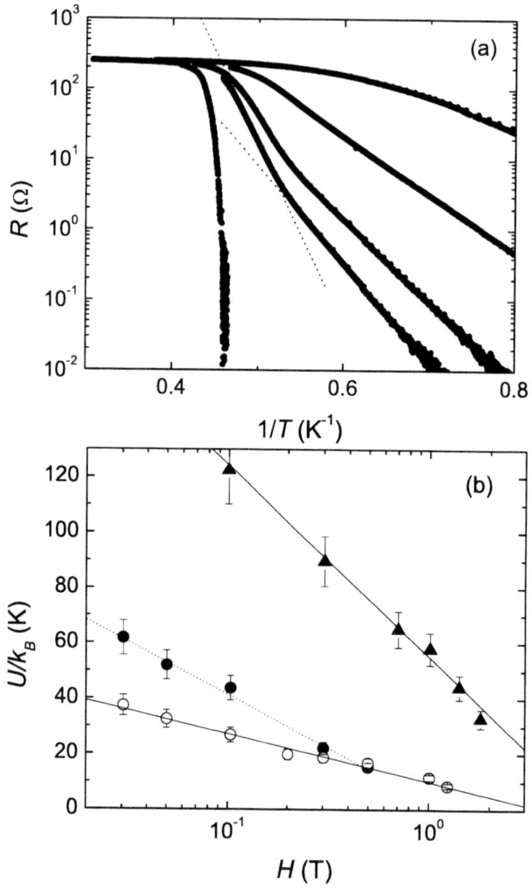

Figure 5: (a) Arrhenius plot for sample E in fields of (left to right) 0.004, 0.05, 0.1, 0.3, and 1.0 T. For low fields two separate activated regions are evident, separated by a characteristic temperature $T_x(H)$. (b) Activation energies U_1 (○) and U_2 (●) corresponding to temperatures below and above T_x, respectively. Fitted curves: $U_1(H) = 7.5 \times \ln(3.8/H)$, $U_2(H) = 16.0 \times \ln(1.4/H)$. Also shown is the activation energy for sample A (▲), with the fitted line $U(H) = 30 \times \ln(6.3/H)$.

over pairs of all sizes. The resulting resistivity is thermally activated, with a field independent activation energy given by the core energy of the dislocations [38, 43]. A correction to this activation energy is introduced by pinning forces, although this is typically relatively small. Additional dislocation-antidislocation pairs can also be introduced into the lattice by the quenched disorder in the samples [44, 43, 45], and at low temperatures the density of disorder induced defects can become equal to the thermally created density.

Because the interaction is logarithmic in the separation r there is a Berezinskii-Kosterlitz-Thouless (BKT) type melting transition at a field dependent temperature

$$T_m^{2D} = \alpha c_{66} a_0^2 d_s/(4\pi k_B),$$

where c_{66} is the vortex lattice shear modulus, and $0.4 < \alpha < 0.75$ [16, 46, 47, 48, 49, 50]. At T_m^{2D} the most widely separated pairs unbind, with successively smaller pairs becoming unbound as the temperature increases above T_m^{2D}.

Finally, in the presence of disorder there is also the possibility of the creation of unbound dislocations even at temperatures where the BKT melting theory would predict them to be bound [38]. A dislocation displaces the vortices around it by an amount which decreases with the distance from the dislocation. Beyond a distance $R_0 \simeq a_0^2/\xi$ the displacement of the vortices becomes less than the scale ξ of the pinning potential, so that the vortex positions are dominated by the quenched disorder rather than the thermally created dislocations. Thus, collectively pinned bundles at distances greater than R_0 from the dislocation are not affected by the dislocation, effectively cutting off the logarithmic interaction between dislocation pairs at a distance $R_0 + R_c^{2D}$, where R_c^{2D} is the two-dimensional collective pinning length. The cutoff means that the energy needed to create a free dislocation is now finite and given by

$$U_{dis} \simeq \frac{\Phi_0^2 d_s}{16\pi^2 \mu_0 \lambda_{ab}^2(T)} \ln\left(\frac{R_c^{2D}}{a_0} + \frac{a_0}{\xi}\right). \tag{4}$$

Dislocations separated by less than $R_0 + R_c^{2D}$ will still interact in the usual manner and remain bound at low temperature, but when the disorder is strong so that $R_c^{2D} \simeq a_0$ most of the dislocations will be unbound. In this case the substitution $(R_c^{2D}/a_0 + a_0/\xi) \approx a_0/\xi \propto \sqrt{(1/H)}$ can be made and the activation energy for the creation of a free dislocation is

$$U_{dis} \simeq \frac{\Phi_0^2 d_s}{32\pi^2 \mu_0 \lambda_{ab}^2(T)} \ln\left(\frac{H_0}{H}\right). \tag{5}$$

where $H_0 \simeq H_{c2}$ is a characteristic field at which U_{dis} goes to zero. An activation energy of this form has been observed in a variety of a-MoGe films with a high degree of disorder in the vortex lattice [51, 52], and also in very anisotropic multilayers of Y123/$PrBa_2Cu_3O_7$ [10].

Equation 5 reproduces the field dependence of the activation energy in sample A, with the measured prefactor $U_0/k_B = 30\,\mathrm{K}$ in good agreement with the predicted value for this sample of 14±4 K. Similarly, the prefactor of 7.5 K for the activation energy U_1 in sample E is reasonably close to the predicted value of 4±1 K. In both samples the characteristic field H_0 is of the order of the critical field, as expected. We thus conclude that the activated resistivity in sample A, and that below T_x in sample E, is due to motion of free dislocations of size $\sim a_0^2/\xi_{ab}$ created due to the disorder in the vortex lattice.

The activation energy at temperatures above T_x is also best fitted by a logarithmic Equation of the form $U_2(H) = 16.0 \times \ln(1.4/H)$, where it should be noted that the coefficient is almost exactly twice that of $U_1(H)$. The model which led to Equation 5 implied that in the limit of strong disorder only dislocations separated by less than a_0^2/ξ remain bound in pairs. The activation energy for creating the bound pairs can be approximated from Equation 3 by making the substitution $r = a_0^2/\xi_{ab}$, leading to [53]

$$U_{pair} \simeq \frac{\Phi_0^2 d_s}{16\pi^2 \mu_0 \lambda_{ab}^2(T)} \ln\left(\frac{H_0}{H}\right) \qquad (6)$$

again with $H_0 \simeq H_{c2}$. Note that this differs from the result obtained in the absence of disorder, where a thermal average is taken over dislocation-antidislocation pairs of all sizes, Equation 3. Because this mode involves two dislocations the activation energy is exactly twice that of the free dislocations which are responsible for $U_1(H)$ (Equation 5), so $U_2(H)$ may be identified with the barrier required to create small dislocation *pairs*.

We also point out that the calculated position of the BKT melting curve lies considerably below T_x, so one might expect there to be sufficient numbers of thermally created free dislocations to make disorder induced free dislocations irrelevant. However, as stated above, T_m^{2D} marks the temperature at which the largest dislocation-antidislocation pairs unbind, with smaller pairs unbinding only at higher temperatures. Since both U_1 and U_2 relate to dislocations or dislocation-antidislocation pairs of very small size, the thermally induced unbinding transition is not significant in these samples.

3.2 Current-voltage characteristics

Thus far we have examined the resistivity only in the limit of low applied currents, where it has been found that plastic vortex motion dominates over the field and temperature range where the resistivity is measurable. As the current is increased the Lorentz force tilts the vortex pinning landscape such that the separation between adjacent metastable pinning sites decreases [16]. Vortex hopping then takes place over shorter and shorter distances, and alternative hopping processes, that contribute little to the resistivity in the low current limit, may become important. To examine this we turn to measurements of the current-voltage (I-V) characteristics of the samples.

A log–log plot of I-V curves taken from sample D at 1.373 K in various perpendicular fields is shown in Figure 6(a). The persistence of superconductivity is limited at the highest currents by the existence of an instability, which will be discussed below. Below the instability the shape of the I-V curves is heavily dependent on the magnetic field. When the field is small the I-V curves are strongly nonlinear over the entire measurable voltage range. At higher fields the nonlinearity is confined to high currents, while at low currents the resistivity is linear. The linear region corresponds to thermally activated plastic flux flow for which the activation energy was described above.

It is of fundamental interest to question whether the linear, low current resistivity extends to low fields, or whether a transition takes place to a glassy state in which the thermal activation barriers become infinite and the resistivity vanishes as the current tends to zero. There are strong theoretical arguments to suggest that the latter possibility may be the case. To understand this, we note firstly that the activation barrier measured above for samples c and D was interpreted as the signature of a vortex liquid-like state. The vortex liquid is expected to freeze at low fields and temperatures, at which point the elastic properties of the vortex solid prevent the plastic vortex flow that occurs in the liquid [16, 38]. The finite film thickness was also found to be important in our films, and it may be that finite size effects give liquid-like properties to what would otherwise be a 3D vortex solid. However, this does not affect the conclusion that in fully three-dimensional samples the $U_{pl} \propto H^{-0.5}$ dependence

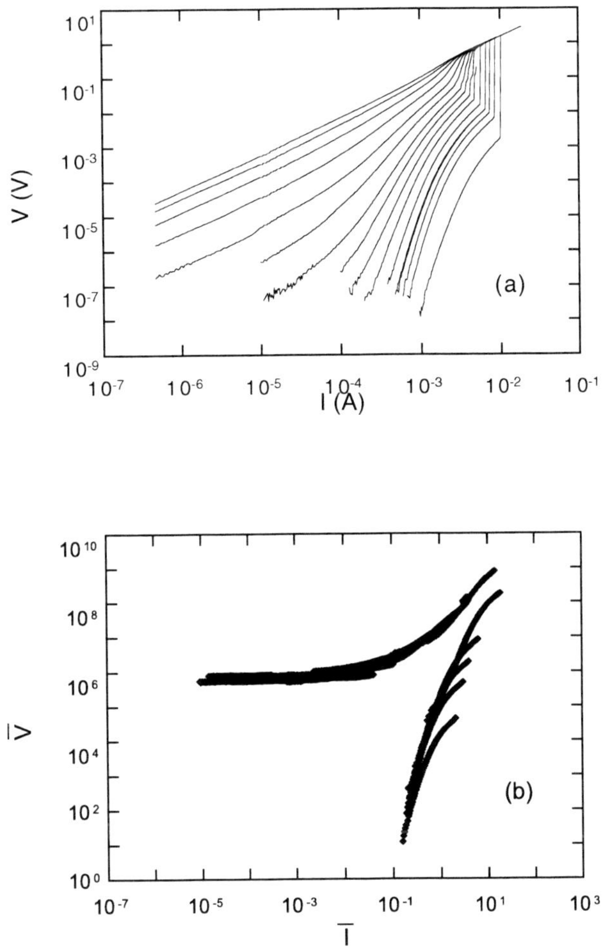

Figure 6: (a) *I-V* curves taken from sample *D* at 1.373 K. From right to left the curves correspond to fields of 0.0035, 0.015, 0.025, 0.035, 0.055, 0.085, 0.11, 0.14, 0.17, 0.2, 0.25, 0.3, 0.35, 0.4, and 0.45 T. (b) Vortex glass scaling of the *I-V* curves in (a). A reasonable scaling collapse is obtained, but as described in the text this does not necessarily imply a true phase transition.

of the activation energy is expected to be terminated when the vortex liquid freezes into a vortex glass, and instead one expects $U_{pl} \to \infty$ as $I \to 0$. Indeed, the qualitative shape of the measured I-V curves is consistent with the predictions of the vortex glass (VG) theory developed by Fisher [19] and by Fisher, Fisher, and Huse [20]. Therefore, we will proceed to carefully compare our data with the predictions of this theory, to determine whether a vortex glass transition takes place in our samples at a well defined temperature $T_g(H)$. The vortex glass also provides the background for the Bose-glass model, which will be shown below to be applicable for describing the samples with columnar defects, so we begin by summarizing the main features of the vortex glass theory in some detail.

It is expected that certain variables show universal behavior in the vicinity of a second order phase transition. Explicitly, as the glass melting temperature T_g is approached the VG correlation length ξ_{VG} is expected to diverge according to

$$\xi_{\mathrm{VG}}(T) \propto |T - T_g|^{-\nu}, \tag{7}$$

with ν being the static glass exponent. The dynamic response of the system is given by the relaxation time τ_{VG}, which also diverges close to the glass phase in a manner characterized by the dynamic critical exponent z, i.e.,

$$\tau_{\mathrm{VG}}(T) \propto \xi_{\mathrm{VG}}^{z}. \tag{8}$$

From these relations one can obtain scaling relations for the dynamic response functions such as the nonlinear current-voltage characteristics. Using simple dimensional arguments based on the scaling behavior of the vector potential $\vec{A}$, the following scaling ansatz is obtained

$$E\xi_{\mathrm{VG}}^{z+1} = \mathcal{E}_{\pm}(J\xi_{\mathrm{VG}}^{D-1}), \tag{9}$$

with D being the dimensionality of the system, $\mathcal{E}_{\pm}$ being universal scaling functions above (+) and below (−) T_g, and E and J are the electric field and current density, respectively. Using some rather general arguments one can extract a number of scaling relations which allow the determination of the critical exponents ν and z, as well as the glass melting temperature T_g.

Right at the melting temperature, the correlation length ξ_{VG} diverges and for the electrical field to remain finite, ξ_{VG} has to cancel out on both sides of Equation 9. Hence $\mathcal{E}_{\pm}(x \to \infty) \propto x^{(z+1)/(D-1)}$, which results in a power-law relation between current density and electric field

$$E \propto J^{(z+1)/(D-1)}, \text{ for } T = T_g. \tag{10}$$

For temperatures $T > T_g$ the system is in the vortex liquid state, showing ohmic resistance for small applied currents. Accordingly, the scaling function is linear in its argument $\mathcal{E}_{+}(x \to 0) \propto x$, which results in the following temperature dependence for the resistance at temperatures above, but close to T_g:

$$\rho \propto \xi_{\mathrm{VG}}^{(D-z-2)} \propto |T - T_g|^{\nu(z+2-D)} \; (T > T_g). \tag{11}$$

Below the transition temperature glassy behavior is expected, $\mathcal{E}_{-}(x \to 0) \propto \exp(-a/x^{\mu})$, leading to an exponential dependence of the electrical field on current density

$$E \propto e^{-c(J_c/J)^{\mu}} \; (T < T_g), \tag{12}$$

with μ being the glass exponent. At high current densities the current-voltage curves above and below the glass temperature are expected to show critical power-law behavior. The critical current density that marks the crossover from the low current to the high current regime scales again with the correlation length

$$J_x^{\pm} \propto \xi_{\rm VG}^{(1-D)} \propto |T - T_g|^{\nu(D-1)}. \tag{13}$$

At small fields when the glass melting temperature $T_g \to T_c(0)$, the following power-law should be observed

$$[T_c(0) - T_g(H)] \propto H^{1/2\nu_0}, \tag{14}$$

with $\nu_0 \simeq 2/3$.

For a second order phase transition critical scaling is expected to be universal, that is, the critical exponents ν and z depend only on dimensionality and symmetry and not on magnetic field or temperature, or even the superconducting material itself. If a plot is made of appropriately scaled E-J, or equivalently I-V, characteristics taken at different temperatures and fields within the critical region near $T_g(H)$, all curves should collapse onto the scaling functions $\mathcal{E}_{\pm}$ for temperatures above and below the melting temperature, respectively. From Equation 9 the following scaling laws for I-V curves are derived:

$$\begin{aligned} \overline{I} &= I\,|1-(T/T_g)|^{\nu(1-D)} \\ \overline{V} &= (V/I)\,|1-(T/T_g)|^{\nu(D-2-z)}. \end{aligned} \tag{15}$$

An attempt has been made to collapse the I-V data of Fig. 6(a) onto two universal curves according to Equations 15. The scaling exponents and the field dependent melting temperature were varied to produce the scaling fit shown in Fig. 6(b), which was achieved using the optimized values $\nu = 2 \pm 0.1$, $z = 6 \pm 0.5$, and a melting line of the form $H_g = 1.6 \times (T_c - T_g)^{2.2}$ or $\nu_0 = 1.1$. The collapse is quite reasonable, apart from a deviation at high currents below T_g where the vortices approach the free flux flow limit. Similar scaling was also observed for data sets taken at other temperatures.

This analysis appears to demonstrate the existence of a vortex glass in sample D. This is in agreement with numerous published results, in which the same scaling analysis has been used to provide evidence for a vortex glass phase in Y123 films [54], single crystals of Y123 [55] and Bi2212 [56], Bi2212 tapes [57], and also a-Mo_3Si films [58]. However, a careful investigation of our data reveals that the optimal scaling exponent z tends to increase at low fields, indicating non-universality. Furthermore, the entire scaling analysis method has been called into question recently by several authors [23, 22], who point out that a nonlinear I-V characteristic very similar to the one described by Equation 12 is obtained in the simple Anderson-Kim flux creep theory [59], which makes no reference to diverging activation barriers. Most notably, Strachan *et al.* [22] have devised a more rigorous criteria for establishing vortex glass scaling, namely that I-V curves at equal temperatures from T_g must have opposite concavities (on the log–log plot) *at the same current.* A close inspection of Fig. 6(a) reveals that our data do not satisfy this criteria.

We conclude then, that the negative concavity seen at low fields in Fig. 6(a) results merely from a saturation of the steeply rising nonlinear activated resistance as the free flux flow regime is approached. All of the I-V curves should then have a linear portion at low currents, although this is below the detection limit at low fields. Nonlinearity sets into the I-V characteristics when the current becomes large enough to significantly tilt the pinning potential landscape experienced by the vortices. It is not possible to experimentally measure the low current behavior of the activation barrier as the field decreases towards zero, and there remains the possibility that changes occur in the dominant mode of flux motion, for example from the measured plastic regime to elastic flux movement. But the significant conclusion is that the absence of convincing vortex glass scaling implies that there is no true vortex glass phase transition. We do make the comment that sample D is what we have described as quasi-3D, and the finite film thickness affects the vortex properties. The Y123 film analyzed by Strachan *et al.*, and used as evidence for the lack of a vortex glass phase transition, was only 2200 Å thick, so it too may have been subject to finite thickness effects. An analysis of a much thicker film with layer dimensions similar to sample D would clearly be of interest.

It is interesting to compare the I-V data for the quasi-3D samples to the data for the 2D samples. A set of perpendicular field I-V curves taken from the 2D sample E at 1.710 K is shown in Figure 7(a). The absence of any strongly nonlinear I-V curves is the result of the dislocation mediated resistivity analyzed above. This type of flux motion, which is only possible in 2D samples, creates a relatively high resistivity at all fields. A similar data set taken from sample D at a temperature close to T_c (1.570 K) is displayed in Fig.7(b). These data are qualitatively different from the quasi-3D lower temperature data from this same sample [Fig. 6(a)], and in fact the data closely resemble the I-V curves shown in Fig. 7(a). Both the superconducting coherence length ξ and the penetration depth λ diverge as T_c is approached, and it appears that this is causing sample D to shift from quasi-3D behavior further towards the 2D limit at temperatures close to T_c.

We finish the discussion of the non-columnar films by considering the very high-current limit. As mentioned above, an instability in the flowing vortex system terminates the superconducting portion of the I-V curves in Fig. 6(a) and causes a transition back to the normal state resistivity. At fields and temperatures well below the superconducting phase boundary the instability manifests itself as a discontinuous jump in the resistance. As the field or temperature are increased the jump first broadens into a series of discontinuous steps, and then smoothes out into a continuous rise from the superconducting to the normal state.

An instability arises when the total retarding force on the vortices, represented by the sum of viscous and pinning forces, becomes a decreasing function of the vortex velocity. In this case any increase in the velocity causes a decrease in the retarding force, leading to a positive feedback situation and an instability. Such behavior has been predicted by Larkin and Ovchinnikov to occur due to the escape of non-equilibrium quasi-particles from the vortex cores into the surrounding superconductor [60, 61, 62]. A somewhat different approach, considering the effects of the inevitable heating of the quasi-particles in the core at high vortex velocities, has been used by Bezuglyj and Shklovskij to predict a similar instability [63].

Both theories predict a broadening in the instability near $T_c(H)$, just as is observed in the data. However, we bring attention to the fact that the field or temperature where the instability changes from a single abrupt jump to a series of smaller transitions also corresponds to the point where a linear low current resistance first becomes discernable. It was shown above that the low current resistance is the result of plastic vortex motion. We conclude that the stepwise transitions at the instability point appear when the vortex lattice becomes susceptible to plastic deformation, so that different parts of the vortex lattice become unstable at slightly different vortex velocities. A more detailed analysis of the instability in non-columnar Ta/Ge films and multilayers, including consideration of the effect of pinning forces, can be found in Refs. [64, 65].

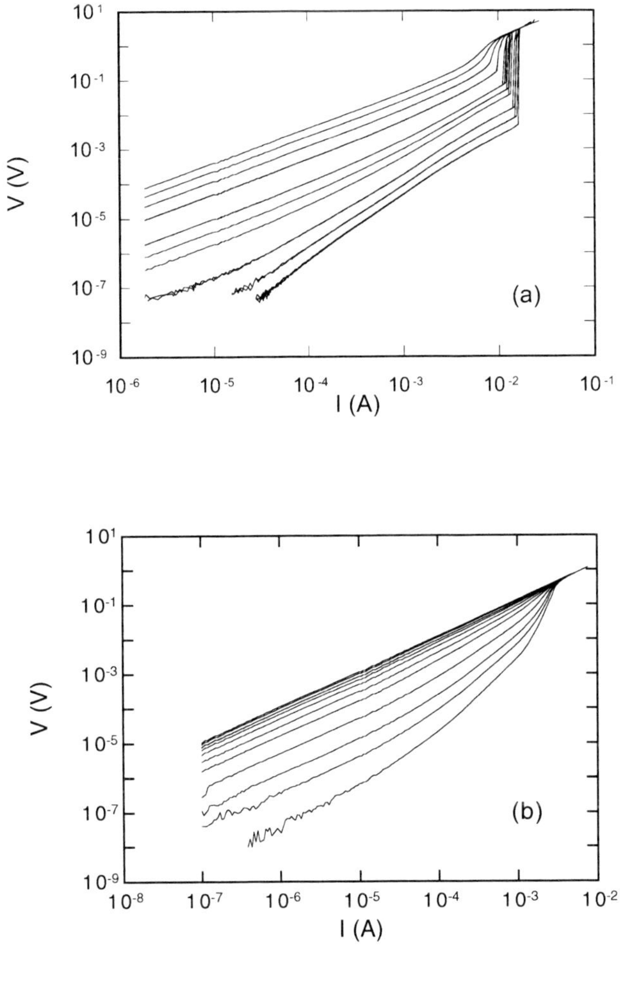

Figure 7: (a) *I-V* curves taken from sample *E* at 1.710 K. From right to left the curves correspond to fields of 0.004, 0.01, 0.02, 0.05, 0.07, 0.1, 0.2, 0.3, 0.4, and 0.5 T. (b) *I-V* curves taken from sample *D* at 1.570 K. From right to left the curves correspond to fields of 0.015, 0.025, 0.035, 0.055, 0.085, 0.11, 0.14, 0.17, 0.2, 0.25 and 0.3 T. Note the absence of downwards sloping *I-V* curves in both data sets, characteristic of 2D behavior.

4 Samples with columnar structure

In this section the superconducting phase diagrams of the multilayered samples with columnar microstructure (F–H) will be discussed in detail and compared to results obtained for the non-columnar films. Similar to samples A–E R-T measurements were performed with low applied currents, typically $I = 1\ \mu$A, and a large range of applied magnetic fields ($0 \le H \le 2.5$ T). From these measurements basic superconducting parameters were extracted, which have already been summarized in Table 1. Additionally, flux flow modes could be determined. Without going into the details of the analysis to the same extent as in section 3.1 the results can be summarized as follows: Just below the upper critical field H_{c2} the vortices are in a narrow FFF mode followed by a TAFF region. In samples F and G, the vortices are assumed to form a three dimensional vortex liquid in this TAFF region, whereas in sample H we have found indications of 2D-3D crossovers depending on temperature, magnetic field and field orientation with respect to the defect structure. Furthermore, I-V curves were measured to complement the R-T measurements and to shed light on the question of the existence of a glass phase at low temperatures.

Special emphasis will be placed on the possible glass transition and how the structure of the films influences the vortex dynamics in the resulting glass phase, if it does exist. In order to extract the role the extended pinning sites of the columnar structure play for the behavior of the vortices in the glass phase, the leaning columns are particularly suited. For once, the external magnetic field can be applied parallel to the extended pinning sites such that their pinning efficiency is maximized. As an example for sample F this is for the field applied at an angle $\theta \approx 24°$ (see Figure 2). On the other hand one can probe the vortex behavior in the same sample with identical geometry but *turned off* pinning by the extended pinning sites when the magnetic field is rotated the same amount towards negative angles, i.e. $\theta \approx -24°$ in the above case.

4.1 Vortex Phase Diagrams

The discussion of the vortex phase diagrams of the samples with columnar microstructure is started with sample F and the magnetic field misaligned with the extended defects. As described above, this turns off the strong pinning by the extended defects and the vortex behavior should be very similar to that observed in the samples discussed in the previous Section 3. Unlike the magnetic field orientation in the previous section, when the field was applied perpendicular to the film surface, the field was applied at negative angles with respect to the film normal. This way, the angle between the strongly pinning defects and the magnetic field was relatively large ($> 45°$ for all samples), minimizing the pinning effects of the defects and the results obtained for this misaligned field configuration could be directly compared to the case when the field was well aligned with the defects. Of course, this brings into play the films' anisotropy caused by their layered structure. However, at tilting angles $\theta < 30°$ and estimated anisotropy ratios $\gamma < 1/10$ this causes only minor systematic errors in determining material parameters influenced by anisotropy, e.g. ξ_{ab}, and negligible effects on the vortex phase diagrams.

Similar to the non-columnar films sets of I-V curves at fixed magnetic field and varying temperature were taken. They show the same principle change in curvature from upward at high temperatures to downward at low temperatures. Accordingly, a scaling analysis was attempted based on VG theory, since only point-like defects had to be considered. In addition to the analysis in section 3.2 special attention was turned to fulfilling the scaling relations 11 and 13 and to collapse the I-V curves onto the two universal functions using Equations 15 simultaneously for all applied fields in the range 0.05 to 1.3 T with field independent glass scaling exponents ν and z. This approach turns out to be necessary to obtain the best possible results for the scaling exponents as well as the glass melting temperatures T_g due to the experimentally limited I and V range of the measurements [66, 67]. As discussed above, a scaling collapse is not conclusive proof of the existence of a true phase transition. Nevertheless, the melting line thus obtained at least serves to delineate the regime of strongly pinned behavior from the area where the vortices behave in a liquid-like manner. This is useful for later comparison to the data obtained with the field aligned along the columns.

In Figure 8 the reduced phase diagram as it resulted from a VG scaling analysis described above is shown. Below the upper critical field which is the uppermost straight line the vortices form a liquid phase with a narrow FFF regime very close to H_{c2} and a TAFF region covering the rest of the liquid phase. This liquid phase is separated from the VG phase by the experimentally determined glass melting line (filled circles). At least close to $T_c(0)$ the melting line should follow a simple power law as in Equation 14. As can be seen from the inset in Figure 8 where the applied field H is plotted versus $T_c(0) - T_g$ in double-logarithmic fashion the data points do indeed follow a simple power law in very good approximation. The exponent derived from this plot is very close to 2. Because exponents derived for similar samples and similar magnetic field orientation were also equal 2 to within $\pm 5\%$ (e.g. sample G) the least-squares fit to obtain the curve in the phase diagram was performed with a fixed exponent equal 2. The resulting glass exponent $\nu_0 = 1$ is significantly different from the theoretically predicted value 2/3. This discrepancy may by due to the fact that the theoretical value was calculated for temperatures near $T_c(0)$, a condition certainly not fulfilled here.

For comparison the transition line for the homogeneous sample C is also plotted in Figure 8 as the dotted line. This line could be almost exactly reproduced by the glass melting line in a sample with layering similar to F, but only marginal columnar structure which was ineffective to produce strongly pinning defects [26]. Although the extended defect structure has been *turned off* due to our deliberately chosen geometry the glass melting line is shifted towards significantly higher temperatures and fields. This could be explained by a combined effect of the extended pinning sites together with the layered structure of these films [26, 68]. The corresponding reduced phase diagram for sample G is very similar to the one shown in Figure 8, indeed the VG melting line can be described by the same power law to very good approximation. This can be well understood by the above mentioned pinning mechanism involving the combined action of the strongly pinning defects and the layering [68] and provides further support for this explanation.

Aligning the applied magnetic field with the orientation of the defect structure should greatly enhance the pinning potential and in turn should be reflected in the phase diagrams. In the case of pinning by randomly distributed point-like defects the pinning force grows only sublinearly with the flux line length $\propto L^{1/2}$ [16], whereas the Lorentz force on the flux line grows linearly with its length. A net pinning force can thus only result if the flux line is made of individually pinned segments with length equal to the single vortex collective pinning length L_{sv} [69, 70]. This is in contrast to the case of extended and correlated pinning sites, such as columnar or coplanar defects, where the flux line can be strongly pinned along its entire length, if the applied field is parallel to the defects. Therefore, one would also expect a glass phase analogous to the VG phase in Figure 8 yet taking up even more space in the H-T phase diagram.

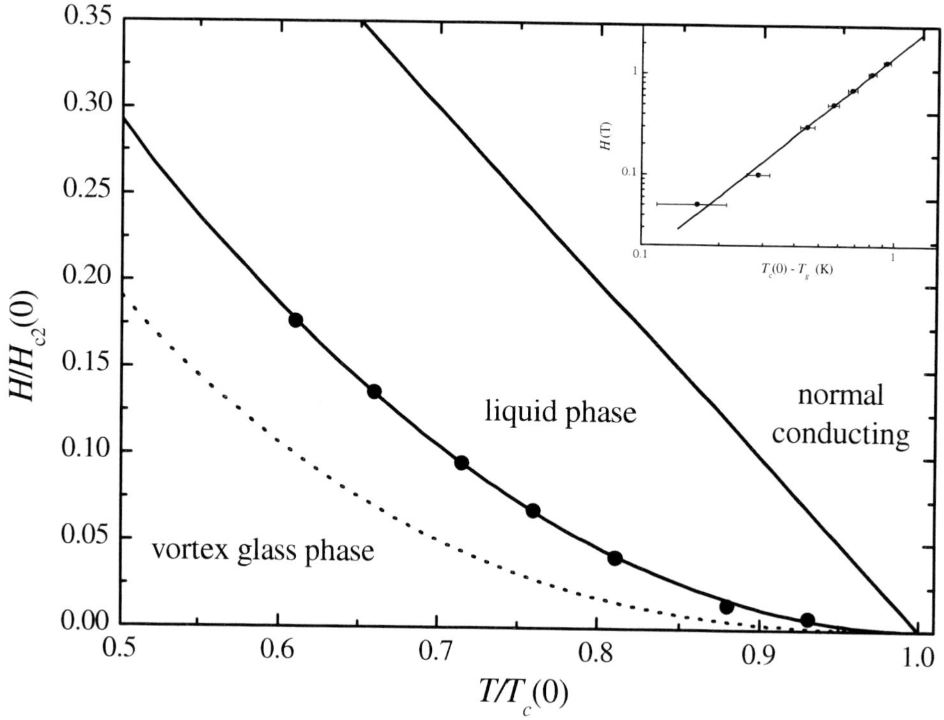

Figure 8: Reduced H-T vortex phase diagram for sample F and magnetic fields applied at an angle $\theta = -23.8°$, i.e. tilted away from the extended pinning sites. The uppermost straight line is the upper critical field $H_{c2}(T)$. Below, the vortices were in a liquid phase with finite ohmic resistance. The experimentally determined data points mark the glass melting temperature separating the liquid phase from the truly superconducting VG phase at lower temperatures. The solid curve is a least-squares parabolic fit to the data points. The inset shows the same data in a double-logarithmic plot of H vs $T_c(0) - T_g$. Here, the solid line has a gradient equal 2, justifying the parabolic fit in the main graph. The dotted curve in the main graph is the transition line in sample C which is identical to the glass melting line in a layered sample very similar to F but with marginal columnar structure [26].

A scaling theory for correlated disorder has been developed by Nelson and Vinokur [21] quite similar to the VG theory, but with some important differences mainly due to the additional anisotropy caused by the disorder. This theory is based on a strong analogy between vortices and 2D-bosons in the presence of a random potential. Hence, the predicted low-temperature glass phase is termed Bose-glass (BG) and the theory itself is known as the BG theory. The theory should be applicable to systems containing columnar defects, but also to those with parallel pinning planes, if the flux lines move transverse to these planes.

The magnetic field is assumed to be parallel to the defects. The first length scale to be introduced is the transverse wandering length $l_\perp(T)$, which is a measure of how far the flux line has *wandered* from its pinning site in the direction transverse to the applied field. As the transition temperature $T_{\rm BG}$ is approached from below, this length scale is expected to diverge as

$$l_\perp(T) \propto |T - T_{\rm BG}|^{-\nu'}, \tag{16}$$

with a static critical exponent ν' different from the corresponding ν in the VG theory. There is a second length scale longitudinal to the applied field $l_\parallel(T)$. In the simplest possible model it is related to the transverse length scale via

$$l_\parallel \propto l_\perp^2. \tag{17}$$

The time scale for relaxations of excitations of size $l_\perp(T)$ is assumed to diverge with a new critical exponent z'

$$\tau_{\rm BG} \propto l_\perp^{z'}. \tag{18}$$

Very similar dimensional arguments like those used for the VG theory result in the new scaling ansatz for Bose-glass scaling

$$E l_\perp^{z'+1} = \mathcal{F}_\pm(J l_\perp l_\parallel), \tag{19}$$

with a pair of scaling functions $\mathcal{F}_\pm$ above and below the transition temperature, respectively. Taking the limits $x \to 0$ and $x \to \infty$, where x is the argument of the scaling function as in the VG theory, one gets similar relations from which to determine the critical exponents and the transition temperature:

$$E = J^{(z'+1)/3} \text{ for } T = T_{\rm BG}. \tag{20}$$

The resistance above $T_{\rm BG}$ should vanish like

$$\rho \propto |T - T_{\rm BG}|^{\nu'(z'-2)} \; (T > T_{\rm BG}), \tag{21}$$

and the glassy behavior below the transition temperature is given equal to Equation 12

$$E \propto \exp\left[-c(J_c/J)^\mu\right] \; (T < T_{\rm BG}) \tag{22}$$

with a possibly different glass exponent μ. The cross-over current densities separating critical from noncritical behavior are given by

$$J_x^\pm \propto (l_\perp l_\parallel)^{-1} \propto |T - T_{\rm BG}|^{3\nu'}. \tag{23}$$

Comparing the above equations with the corresponding Equations for the VG theory (Equations 9 to 13) one can easily see their similarity. As a consequence one cannot distinguish between VG and BG phases by scaling analysis alone. However, the differences between these two vortex phases become quite apparent when tilting the magnetic field away from the extended pinning sites. In the case of the VG phase with randomly distributed point defects all quantities vary smoothly only due to the anisotropy of thin films or layered samples. Due to the additional anisotropy of the defects the BG behavior differs significantly. Two explicit results shall be discussed here.

For small tilting angles away form the defect orientation the flux lines will be *locked* to the defects. This is equivalent to an infinite tilt modulus c_{44}. The BG theory gives for the divergence of c_{44} as the phase boundary is approached from above

$$c_{44} \propto |T - T_{\mathrm{BG}}|^{2\nu'} \; (T > T_{\mathrm{BG}}) \tag{24}$$

and stays infinite for temperatures below T_{BG}. This effect of flux lines locked to the extended pinning sites is sometimes called the transverse Meissner effect, i.e. the transverse magnetic field component H_t will be screened up to a critical value $H_{t,c}$. Another consequence arises for the ohmic resistance above T_{BG}. It should vanish according to the scaling relation [71, 72]

$$\rho(t_{\mathrm{BG}}, \varphi) = |t_{\mathrm{BG}}|^{\nu'(z'-2)} \mathcal{G}_{\pm}(\varphi |t_{\mathrm{BG}}|^{-\nu'}), \tag{25}$$

with $t_{\mathrm{BG}} = (T - T_{\mathrm{BG}})/T_{\mathrm{BG}}$ the reduced temperature with respect to the BG transition temperature, and φ the tilting angle with respect to the defect orientation. An attempt was made to verify Equation 25 for the micro-structured samples of this report, though it turned out to be inconclusive. Possible reasons are the finite film thicknesses and the unavoidable distribution of defect orientations. Nevertheless, we used the BG scaling laws to analyze I-V curves for magnetic fields aligned parallel to the defects. Not only could the columnar structure be seen in the TEM photographs, but also graphs like Figure 2 clearly demonstrate the additional anisotropy existent in those films with columnar structure and the additional pinning potential caused by it. It is also assumed that pinning by the correlated defects is strong enough such that pinning by the still present point defects can be neglected [73].

Figure 9 shows the reduced H-T phase diagram as it resulted after a BG scaling analysis for sample F with magnetic fields applied in the C-direction parallel to the defect structure. Again, special emphasis was placed on universal scaling, i.e. independent of magnetic field H. The enhanced pinning by the extended defects led to a further shift of the phase transition to higher fields and temperatures as compared to the case when the field was tilted away from the C-direction. In order to demonstrate this change, the corresponding VG melting line from Figure 8 is shown as a dotted curve. Furthermore, the data points cannot be well described using a simple power law as in the case of misaligned magnetic fields. This was even more obvious for sample G, see the discussion below.

Instead, the data was fitted using an expression obtained for the BG melting line[5] $T_{\mathrm{BG}}(B)$ and pinning by columnar defects [16]:

$$T_{\mathrm{BG}}(B) \approx \chi T_m(B) + (1-\chi) T_c \left(1 - \frac{B}{\mu_0 H_{c2}(0)}\right), \quad \left(B > \frac{\Phi_0}{\lambda^2}\right) \tag{26}$$

with μ_0 the magnetic permeability, $T_m(B)$ the melting transition in the pure system without defects and χ describing the disorder, which in this notation is $\chi = 1$ for the pure system and $\chi \to 0$ in the presence of strong disorder when $T_{\mathrm{BG}}(B) \to T_c(B)$. Because $T_m(B)$ is unknown for these samples the transition line of the weakly pinning sample C is used. The

[5] Due to our sample geometry with a demagnetizing factor close to 1 and lower critical fields $H_{c1}(0) \lesssim 1$ mT, $B = \mu_0 H$ is a very good approximation for all applied fields in this study.

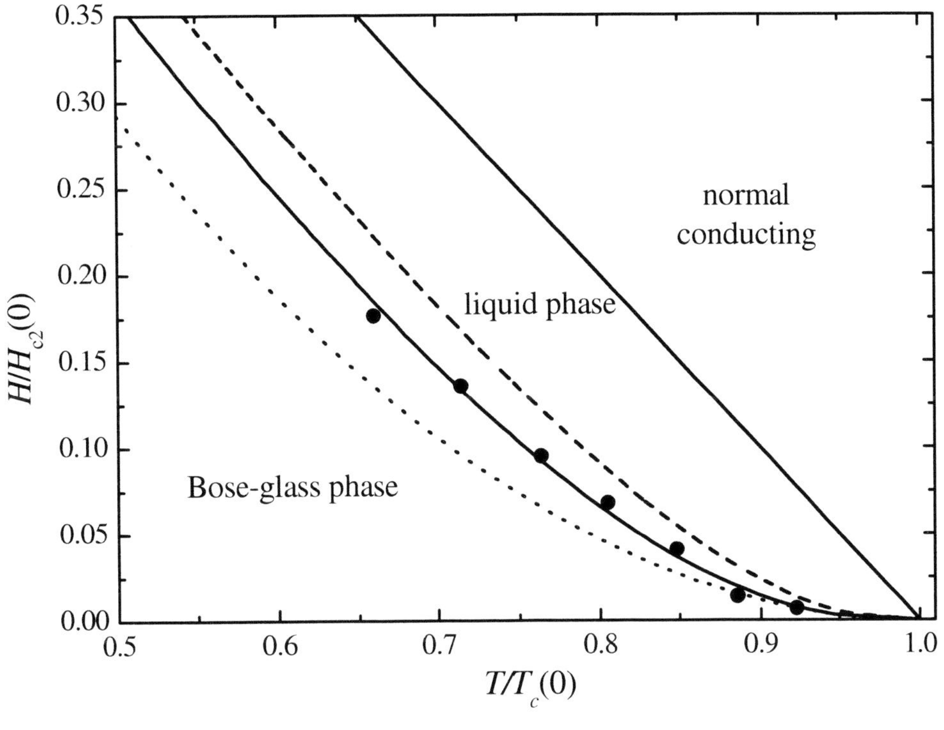

Figure 9: Reduced H-T vortex phase diagram for sample F and magnetic fields applied in the C-direction parallel to the defect structure. As a reference the VG melting line when the field is at large angles to the defects is drawn as the dotted line, also compare with Figure 8. The enhanced pinning by the extended defects led to a further shift of the phase transition line (solid curve) to higher fields and temperatures. Besides, the glass phase is assumed to be a BG phase. The solid line is a least-squares fit according to Equation 26. Also included in this graph is the BG melting line of sample G (dashed curve).

Table 2: Glass scaling exponents as they resulted from BG and VG scaling analyses.

	BG			VG		
	ν' (±0.2)	z' (±0.5)	χ (±0.05)	ν (±0.2)	z (±0.5)	ν_0 (±0.05)
F	1.0	8.7	0.50	1.4	5.1	1.00
G	0.7	8.6	0.38	1.1	6.9	1.00
H	1.3	7.0	0.64	–	–	1.30

derivation of Equation 26 even allows to relate the disorder parameter χ to microscopic details of the columnar pins. However, since here the pinning sites are coplanar in nature, χ was regarded as a phenomenological fitting parameter, only.

The vortex phase diagrams for samples F and G are very similar. As already mentioned above, in the case of misaligned magnetic fields the VG melting lines are identical for both samples within the accuracy of the scaling analysis. The BG melting line in G on the other hand is moved even closer to the upper critical field $H_{c2}(T)$ (dashed curve in Figure 9), but experimental data points are still well described using Equation 26. Unfortunately, we could not characterize the films' layering and columnar microstructure well enough to ascribe this difference in the phase diagrams to either differences in the layering or in the columnar structure. Numerical results for the glass scaling exponents and the disorder parameter are summarized in Table 2.

Before we continue with the discussion of experimental results we would like to make some remarks on the existence or non-existence of low temperature glass phases with zero ohmic resistance. Especially for the case of the VG phase there are still doubts whether the vortices really freeze into a glass phase [22, 23]. As already mentioned the successful collapse of a set of I-V curves onto two universal functions with positive and negative curvature, respectively, is no proof for the existence of a glass phase, because such a collapse can be achieved for a wide range of glass exponents depending on the current and voltage range accessible to the experiment [66, 67]. A second order phase transition requires universal critical exponents, independent of field and temperature and for phase transitions belonging to the same universality class even independent of the superconducting material. By simultaneously fulfilling the scaling relations Equations 11 and 13 for the VG and Equations 21 and 23 for the BG, respectively, for all applied fields we could meet this necessary condition for samples F and G and even sample H as will be shown below. The derived glass exponents are even comparable to results obtained for HTSC, among others see e.g. Refs. [66, 74, 75].

Strachan et al. [22] pointed out an even more stringent condition for the existence of a glass phase as it results from these glass theories. As already mentioned in section 3.2 one should measure positive and negative curvatures for temperatures above and below the transition temperature, respectively, for the same applied current. Due to the extremely rapidly vanishing dynamic resistance at low temperatures, this is an experimentally very demanding condition. The limited voltage resolution denied us to make this additional check. However, further evidence for the existence of glass phases at low temperatures comes from experiments on HTSC. Strong support for the existence of BG phases in the presence of extended defects comes from the observation of the transverse Meissner effect [75] and as a consequence thereof the localization of flux lines in the vicinity of the defects.

An even stronger argument for the existence of a second order phase transition comes from measurements of specific heat steps [76] along a transition line which was identified as the glass melting line.

Interestingly, the universality also seen for misaligned magnetic fields was not observed in the unstructured, non-columnar films. The reason for this observation is unclear, there are a number of parameters which need to be considered, such as the film thickness and details of the pinning potential. There is no doubt, for example, that the columnar films are much more disordered. One parameter that is certainly influencing the existence of a glass phase is the dimensionality of the superconductor, as has already been shown in section 3 and will be shown even more clearly below.

So far, the discussion focused on the vortex phase diagrams of the strongly coupled samples with columnar microstructure. They were always best described as three dimensional systems. Turning to sample H with much less coupled superconducting layers a much more complicated situation emerges, with the effective dimensionality depending on temperature, magnetic field and magnetic field orientation with respect to the correlated defect structure.

At temperatures above $T_c(H)$ sample H is best described as being three dimensional by using the 3D-forms for the fluctuation conductivity [34, 35]. The expectation that the columnar microstructure has no or only negligible influence on the conductivity above $T_c(H)$ is confirmed by consistent results for fields applied in the C-direction and at large angles to it. Significant differences between the two field directions first appear in the TAFF region. In this region R-T curves could be well described assuming an exponential relation of the form $R \propto \exp(-U/k_BT)$ and the magnetic field dependence of the activation energies $U(H)$ could be determined. Figure 10 shows the results for both field orientations. For misaligned fields the interpretation of the data is relatively straight forward. Over two orders of magnitude in magnetic field the activation energy follows a logarithmic dependence $\propto \ln(H^{-1})$. According to Equation 5 this is a sign of two-dimensional behavior. For fields in the C-direction the situation is much less conclusive. Qualitatively, the effect of the extended defect structure can be clearly seen. The activation energies for flux flow are notably increased for magnetic fields up to about 0.6 T. If the pancake vortices remained decoupled, the pinning potential should not change drastically and the activation energies would not be expected to show such a large change. The obvious explanation therefore is a coupling of vortex segments in adjacent superconducting layers mediated by the extended defects. An effect also seen in highly anisotropic HTSC containing columnar defects [77, 78, 79]. Indeed $U(H)$ does approximately follow the $1/\sqrt{H}$-dependence expected for a three dimensional superconductor as shown by the dotted curve in Figure 10. However at very low fields < 0.1 T the experimental results deviate substantially from this power-law prediction and it seems as if they would approach the two-dimensional expectation. In addition at fields ≥ 0.6 T predictions for the 2D and 3D case coincide and based on the experimental data available one cannot conclude in favor of one or the other. Then again, as the magnetic field is increased to higher and higher values the effect of the extended pinning sites is expected to become weaker, eventually leading to a decoupling transition back to pancake vortices [79].

The effects of reduced interlayer coupling are apparent when looking at the I-V curves, as well. At low magnetic fields applied in the C-direction the qualitative behavior of the I-V curves is similar to that observed in the strongly coupled samples, showing a cross-over from upwards bend curves at high temperatures to those bend downwards below a temperature which can be identified as the glass transition temperature. But at fields $H \geq 0.6$ T no I-V curves with negative curvature were measured. For the low-field I-V sets a scaling procedure

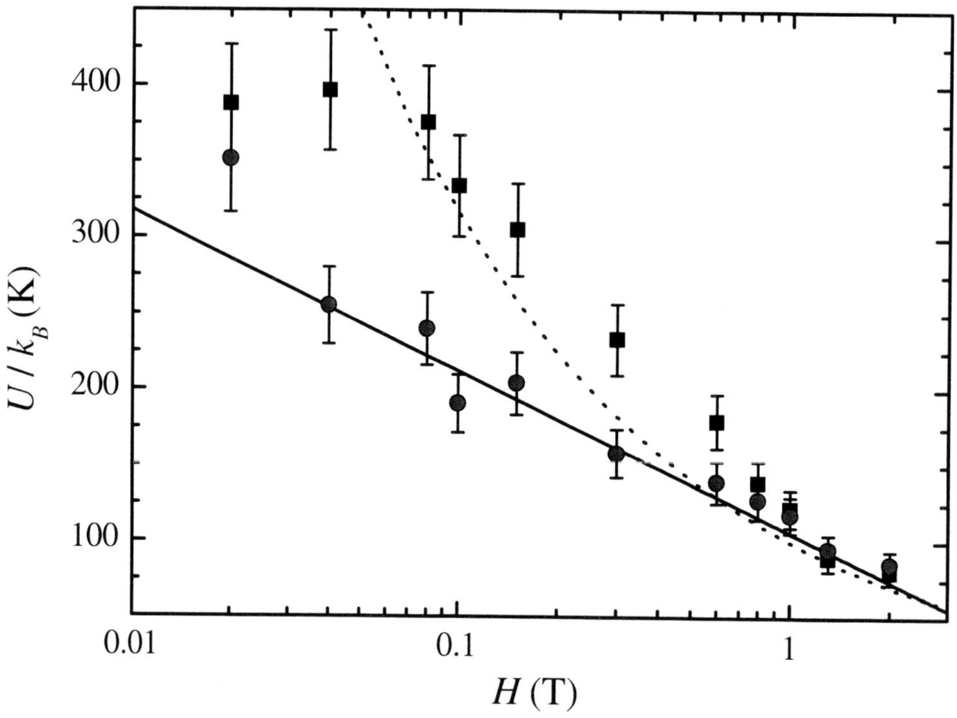

Figure 10: Activation energies $U(H)$ for vortex motion in the TAFF region for sample H and both field orientations. Data for fields misaligned with the extended pinning sites (open circles) can be very well described by a logarithmic dependence on the applied field $\propto \ln(H^{-1})$ (straight solid line) indicating a two-dimensional system. When the field is parallel to the pinning sites (filled squares) activation energies are significantly increased for a substantial field interval demonstrating the strong pinning by these extended defects. Data taken at fields $H \geq 0.1$ T roughly follow a power-law relation $\propto H^{-1/2}$ (dotted curve). This would indicate three dimensional behavior.

analogous to that described above was possible and successful. We also attempted to apply it to the high-field sets. The first problem was to obtain reliable estimates for the transition temperatures. Transforming Equation 21 to obtain

$$[\mathrm{d}(\ln \rho)/\mathrm{d}T]^{-1} = \nu' (z' - 2)|T - T_{\mathrm{BG}}| \quad (27)$$

a transition temperature could be derived from extrapolating appropriately rescaled R-T data. It has to be mentioned that the transition temperatures obtained this way for the high-field data most likely cannot be identified with a glass transition. Surprisingly, using these values as a starting point, resistance and cross-over currents could still be scaled successfully according to Equations 21 and 23, respectively. These results are shown in Figure 11 together with the scaling of respective data from the low-field I-V curves. It is immediately striking that these scaling relations split into two groups at low and high fields. But whereas the low-field I-V curves also show a collapse onto the two scaling functions $\mathcal{F}_\pm$ those taken at higher fields do not collapse nearly as well. This comes at no surprise, because the low-temperature curves with negative curvature are missing.

Alternatively, one could try to analyze the high-field I-V curves within a two- dimensional VG model. The field-dependence of activation energies for TAFF already pointed to a possible 2D phase at higher fields and for a truly 2D vortex system the glass phase should exist at $T = 0$, only [20, 16]. But such an analysis would lead to unreasonable high (≥ 30) and field-dependent glass exponents, almost certainly ruling out such a scenario. Also, so called quasi-2D vortex glass phases [80] cannot resolve the poor collapse of I-V curves and would lead to very unusual glass exponents. Therefore, the most likely description at high magnetic fields is that of a smooth transition into a highly viscous vortex phase comparable to the situation observed in the unstructured samples in section 3.

The above discussion is summarized in the reduced H-T phase diagram shown in Figure 12 for fields applied parallel to the defect structure. As in the previous phase diagrams the upper most line is the upper critical field $H_{c2}(T)$. Below that line the vortices form a vortex liquid which is most likely a liquid formed by pancake vortices moving in two dimensions thus termed 2D vortex liquid. But for a small field interval the vortex segments couple to form extended flux lines along the defect structure. In this region the vortex liquid is best described using a 3D model. At lower temperatures a BG phase is attached to that 3D vortex liquid separated by a second order phase transition. Compared to the transition line in the strongly coupled samples with columnar structure the transition line lies at somewhat lower temperatures. The nature of the high-field low-temperature vortex phase is unknown, we speculate it could be a very viscous vortex liquid. The crossover from this viscous liquid to the more fluid TAFF region is given by the dashed line, a power-law fit to the data points. The exact position of the boundary between the 2D and 3D vortex liquid is unknown as well as between the BG phase and the viscous liquid. They are best estimates based on experimental data, theoretical considerations [16] and comparison with similar results published for Bi2212 [79]. Not depicted in Figure 12 is the 2D-3D vortex liquid cross-over which is expected to take place close to $H_{c2}(T)$ when the coherence length $\xi(T)$ diverges.

For magnetic fields misaligned with the defect structure the phase diagram appears similar to the corresponding diagrams for the strongly coupled samples without columnar structure, except that the flux liquid is probably a liquid formed by pancake vortices and thus two- dimensional. The cross-over line separating the fluid from the viscous vortex liquid is a bit below the glass transition line in the strongly coupled samples with columnar structure and can also be described by a power-law, although with a different exponent ν_0,

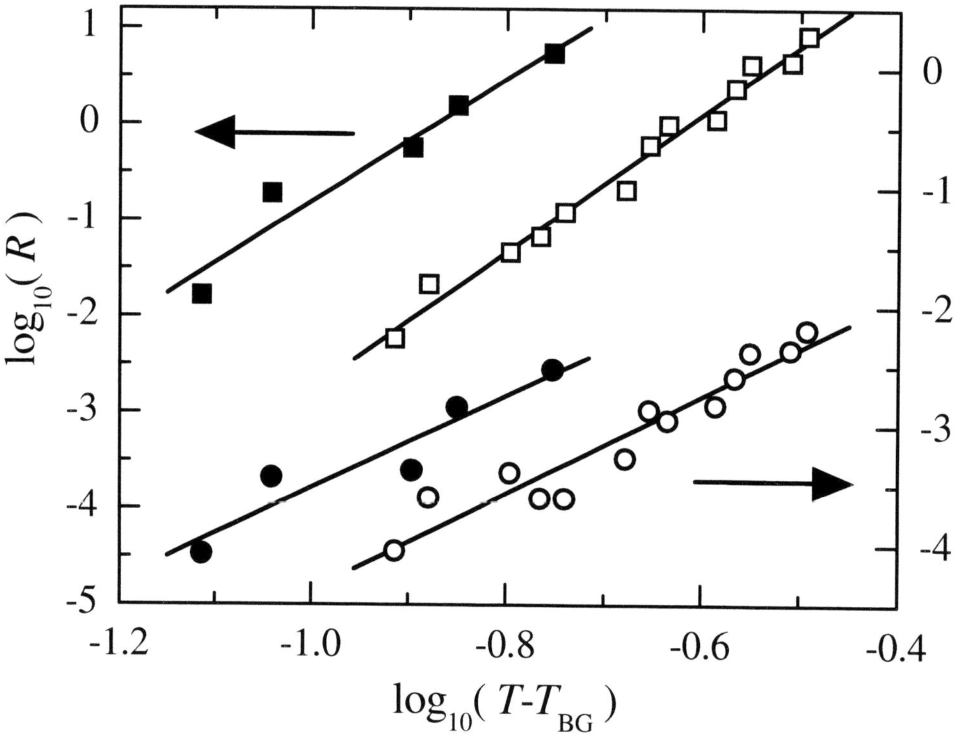

Figure 11: Linear resistances (squares) and cross-over currents (circles) versus $|T - T_{BG}|$ in a double-logarithmic plot for sample H and magnetic fields parallel to the extended defects. The data split into two groups: those at low fields (0.1 and 0.3 T, filled symbols) and another set at higher fields (0.6, 0.8, 1.0, and 1.3 T, open symbols). For both sets the temperature dependence of resistances and currents can be described by power-laws, as shown by the straight lines.

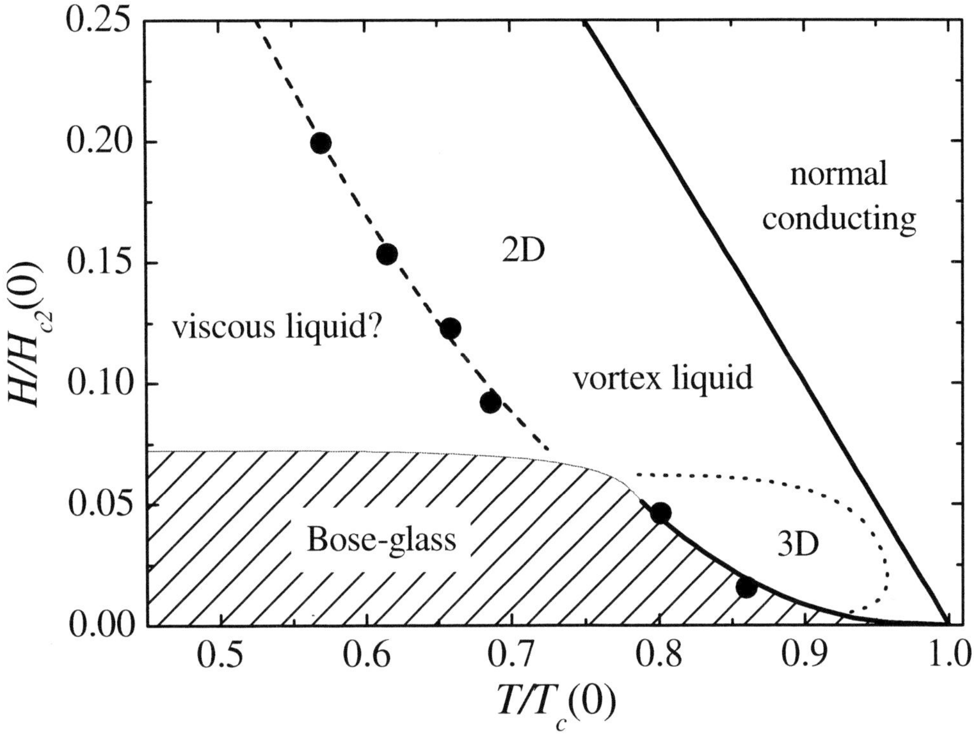

Figure 12: Reduced H-T vortex phase diagram for sample H and magnetic fields applied in the C-direction. The upper most straight line is the upper critical field $H_{c2}(T)$ below which the vortices form a vortex liquid. Sufficiently below $H_{c2}(T)$ this liquid is formed by pancake vortices and thus in a 2D state, except at low applied fields when the pancake vortices recouple along the extended defects. The cross-over between 2D and 3D liquid is estimated and given by the dotted curve. At lower temperatures the 3D liquid freezes into a BG phase via a second order phase transition. The 2D liquid at higher fields most probably undergoes a smooth transition from a fluid to a viscous vortex liquid, only.

see Table 2.

4.2 Vortex Dynamics in the Glass Phase

The dynamic response of the vortices in the glass phase due to the driving force of an applied current is also of great interest. This vortex creep is expected to appear as non-linear I-V characteristics consistent with Equations 12 or 22. The mechanism by which vortex creep takes place is characterized by the glass exponent μ, which may be temperature, field and current dependent. In order to extract the glass exponent from the available I-V data it is most suitable to transform above Equations to obtain

$$\frac{\mathrm{d}(\ln E/J)}{\mathrm{d}J} \propto \mu J^{-(\mu+1)}. \tag{28}$$

Thus, by plotting $\log_{10}[\mathrm{d}(\ln V/I)/\mathrm{d}I]$ versus $\log_{10} I$ the data should result in a straight line with slope $-(\mu+1)$.

The inset of Figure 13 validates Equation 28 for the I-V curves taken for sample H in the BG phase at a magnetic field $H = 0.1$ T and temperature interval $\Delta T = 50$ mK. The extracted exponents μ as a function of temperature below the glass transition $T_{\mathrm{BG}} - T$ are plotted in the main graph of above Figure. Within the experimental accuracy the glass exponents seem to be constant with an averaged value $\overline{\mu} = 0.22$. A constant μ was also observed in Bi2212 with columnar defects [81, 82, 83], although with a different exponent $\mu = 0.33$.

Within the BG model vortex creep is explained by making use of elementary excitations of the flux lines. Examples for such excitations are vortex loops, half loops and kinks [21]. Under the acting Lorentz force due to the finite probing current these excitations lead to a net flux creep rate. Depending on material parameters, pinning potential and applied current one of the excitations can be more favorable than the others. Fortunately, the excitation modes should differ by different glass exponents.

In the presence of extended pinning sites flux line segments may jump to a neighboring pinning site thereby creating a pair of vortex kinks. If the pinning sites have negligible variations in their pinning potential the jumps will be to nearest neighbors actually resulting in I-V characteristics with ohmic resistance. For strong enough dispersion of the pinning energies the flux line segment will not jump to the nearest neighbor, but instead to the next favorable pinning site. Then the vortex motion becomes similar to quantum variable-range hopping (VRH) conductivity in doped semiconductors [84, 85]. Based on this analogy the following glass exponents have been calculated for pinning by columnar [21] and coplanar defects [86, 87], respectively:

$$\mu = 1/3 \text{ (columnar defects)}, \tag{29}$$

$$\mu = 1/2 \text{ (coplanar defects)}. \tag{30}$$

At higher current densities flux creep may be dominated by spreading half-loop excitations. I-V curves should then be characterized by a glass exponent

$$\mu = 1 \text{ (half-loops)}. \tag{31}$$

Comparing the experimental value $\overline{\mu} = 0.22$ with above predictions one has to conclude that none of these excitations can explain the observed I-V curves. The experimental

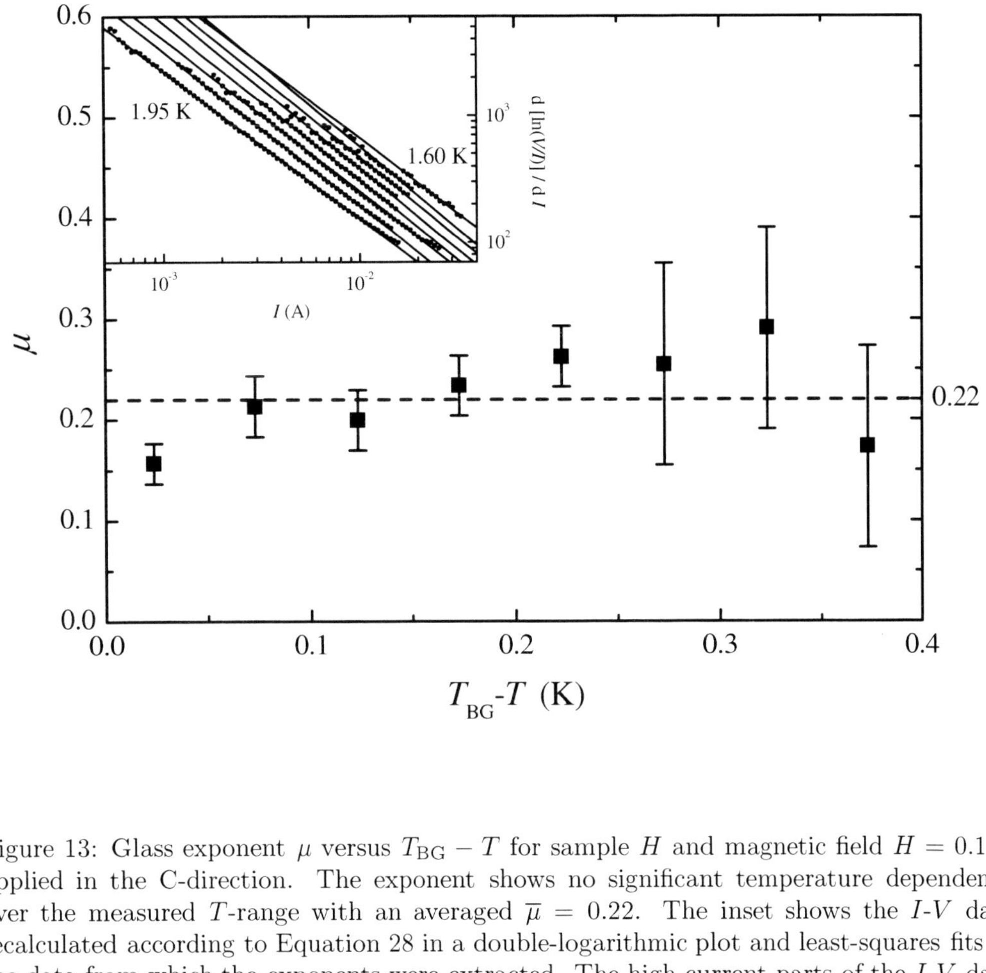

Figure 13: Glass exponent μ versus $T_{\mathrm{BG}} - T$ for sample H and magnetic field $H = 0.1$ T applied in the C-direction. The exponent shows no significant temperature dependence over the measured T-range with an averaged $\overline{\mu} = 0.22$. The inset shows the I-V data recalculated according to Equation 28 in a double-logarithmic plot and least-squares fits to the data from which the exponents were extracted. The high current parts of the I-V data have been truncated where they deviated from the exponential behavior.

value is significantly smaller than the calculated ones, only about half of the anticipated value $\mu = 1/2$ (Equation 30) based on the microstructure with coplanar pinning sites. Unfortunately, the available data for sample H did not allow to extract a possible H-dependence of μ. Although the BG scaling analysis showed a BG phase at the next higher magnetic field $H = 0.3$ T, the vortex system was probably very close to the transition to the viscous vortex liquid. In any case, analysis of the I-V curves according to Equation 28 within the nominally BG phase resulted in very small glass exponents $\mu \simeq 0$.

A totally different temperature dependence of the glass exponent μ was observed in the strongly coupled samples F and G. Due to the BG phase extending up to much higher magnetic fields, it was also possible to determine the magnetic field dependence in these samples. In Figure 14 the results are plotted for sample F. Very similar results were also obtained for sample G and, interestingly, also for the VG phases in both samples when magnetic fields were applied at large angles to the defects. Firstly looking at the field-dependence for fixed $T_{\rm BG} - T$ the glass exponent μ decreases monotonically with increasing field. This is true for the complete depicted temperature and field range[6]. The temperature-dependence in turn exhibits some remarkable aspects and can be divided into two parts. As the temperature is lowered below the glass transition temperature μ increases approximately linearly until about 0.45 K below $T_{\rm BG}$. The slope of this linearly increasing part seems to decrease with increasing field. It is important to note that in the BG phase of sample H the glass exponent is constant for this temperature range. At temperatures below $T_{\rm BG} - T \approx 0.45$ K there is a change to a constant, but field-dependent value of μ. It ranges from about 1.75 at low fields to estimated 0.5 at the highest fields. Clearly, this behavior of μ can not be explained within the above discussed model for flux line excitations and VRH of vortices. And it also differs from results reported for Y123 [88, 89].

An alternative approach to the problem of flux creep in the glass phase is the collective flux creep (CFC) model [90]. It is an advancement of the early Anderson-Kim theory for flux creep [91] including ideas stemming from the weak collective pinning theory [69, 70]. In the original Anderson-Kim theory the energy barriers which the flux lines have to overcome were supposed to be independent of the applied current density. As a consequence the energy barriers remain finite even in the limit of vanishing current density $j \to 0$. That would also result in ohmic resistance and the absence of a glass phase. Indeed, flux lines are one dimensional objects and therefore not only does the hopping distance between favorable pinning configurations depend on the applied current density but also the length of the flux line segment that moves to the new site. Feigel'man *et al.* have shown that this results in a power-law dependence of the energy barriers on the applied current density

$$U(j) \propto j^{-\mu}. \tag{32}$$

Here we have already anticipated that the exponent in Equation 32 can be identified with the glass exponent μ. It follows immediately from Equation 32 that the energy barriers diverge as $j \to 0$ and the existence of a glassy state with vanishing ohmic resistance. In general the smallest independently moving objects are not single flux lines but bundles of flux lines. Additionally, these bundles are elongated in the direction of their movement and form so called superbundles. The interesting parameter, the glass exponent μ, depends on the size of these superbundles. One can distinguish between at least five different regimes

[6] For clarity, data taken at 0.05 T are not shown in Figure 14. At temperatures just below $T_{\rm BG}$ μ values start off above those at 0.1 T. But at $T_{\rm BG} - T \approx 0.2$ K they become smaller and level off between the 0.1 and 0.3 T data. If this is a trend observable at even lower fields could not be verified.

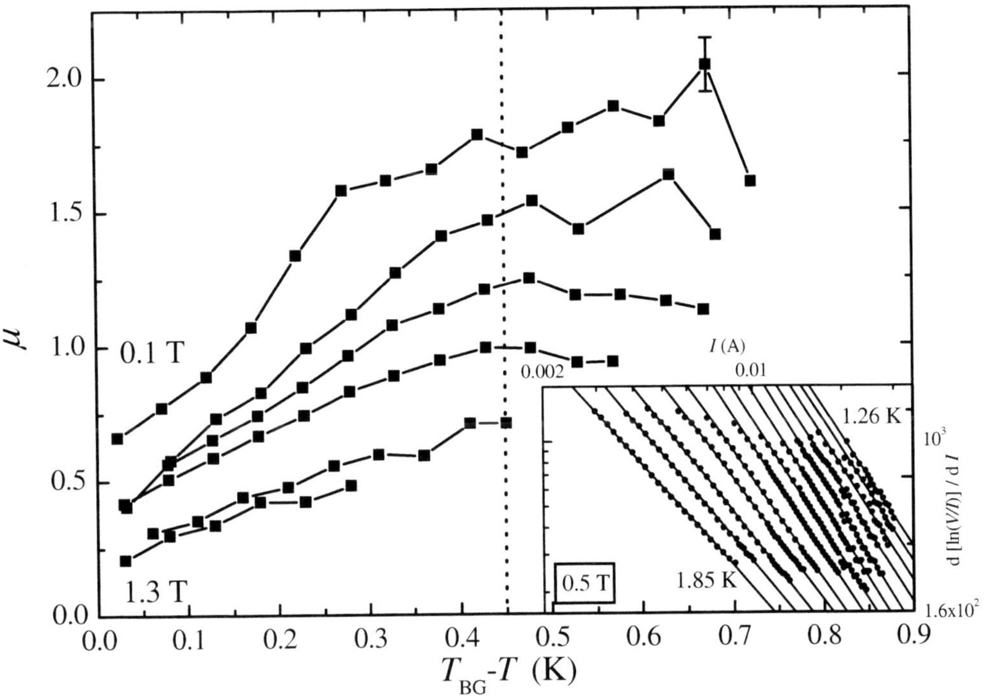

Figure 14: Temperature and field-dependence of the glass exponent μ for sample F and magnetic fields in the C-direction. Field magnitudes are 0.1, 0.3, 0.5, 0.7, 1.0 and 1.3 T from top to bottom. For any given temperature below the BG melting temperature T_{BG} the glass exponent μ decreases monotonically with increasing magnetic field. For a fixed magnetic field the exponent rises when lowering the temperature below T_{BG} until it levels off at a field-dependent value. The crossover to constant μ happens at ≈ 0.45 K below T_{BG} independent of magnetic field. This is marked by the vertical dotted line. The inset shows the original I-V data converted according to Equation 28. The solid lines are power-law fits to the data from which μ values were derived.

with different glass exponents [90, 16]:

$$\mu = \begin{cases} \frac{1}{7} & \text{single vortex} \\ \frac{5}{2} & \text{small superbundles} \\ 1 & \text{intermediate superbundles} \\ \frac{7}{9} & \text{large superbundles} \\ \frac{1}{2} & \text{CDW} \end{cases} \quad . \tag{33}$$

The last value $\mu = 1/2$ results when the hopping distances grow larger than the average vortex separation. This regime is named after an analogy to charge density waves (CDW) in ordinary conductors [92]. From top to bottom above compilation shows the evolution of μ for increasing magnetic field or for decreasing applied current. The boundaries separating above regimes are field, current and temperature dependent and also depend on the pinning potential.

Applying above results to sample F there is a qualitative compliance with the experimental data especially for the low-temperature regime with roughly constant μ. At the relevant temperatures $T \ll T_c$ the temperature-dependence is expected to be weak. Disregarding the single vortex regime CFC predicts decreasing glass exponents with increasing magnetic fields. One can also expect that μ does not change in sharp steps as the vortex system changes from one regime to another, but rather in a continuous way just like the field-dependence observed in sample F. Also the magnitude of μ falls into the theoretically calculated range. Nevertheless, a quantitative analysis is complicated on several counts and reveals some discrepancies. The above values for μ were calculated for weak collective pinning of point-like defects, a condition unjustified especially for magnetic fields applied parallel to the extended defects. Besides, the CFC theory does not account for a thermodynamic glass phase and a glass transition temperature. Accordingly, CFC can not account for the observed temperature dependence as T_{BG} is approached. Last but not least a number of important length scales are known only approximately or have to estimated, such as the collective pinning length.

Nonetheless, an attempt was made to calculate the boundaries between the various superbundle regimes and relate them to the experimentally determined glass exponents. The most important length scale to be estimated is the single vortex collective pinning length L_{sv}. We estimated the single vortex depinning current density at zero temperature $j_{sv}(0) = 5 \times 10^8\ \mathrm{A\,m^{-2}}$, more than one order less than the depairing current density $j_c(0) \approx 7 \times 10^9\ \mathrm{A\,m^{-2}}$. The collective pinning length is related to the depinning and depairing current densities via

$$L_{sv}(0) = \xi(0)\sqrt{\frac{j_c(0)}{j_{sv}(0)}}, \tag{34}$$

giving $L_{sv}(0) = 26$ nm. This in turn allows one to estimate the pinning parameter γ_{pin} at zero temperature and then using

$$L_{sv}(T) \simeq \left[\frac{\epsilon(T)^2\xi(T)^2}{\gamma_{\mathrm{pin}}(T)}\right]^{1/3} \tag{35}$$

one obtains the temperature-dependent collective pinning length. In the last Equation $\epsilon(T) = \Phi_0^2/(4\pi\mu_0\lambda(T))$ is a typical energy scale in weak collective pinning theory and μ_0 the magnetic permeability. $L_{sv}(T)$ grows with increasing temperature but is limited by the film thickness $d \approx 200$ nm, reached at a temperature $T \approx 1.9$ K. Making these assumptions one would have to conclude that all measured μ in Figure 14 were taken in the small superbundle regime. A quantitative analysis of the field dependence of the glass exponent μ within the CFC model is therefore not possible.

Despite these shortcomings we assume the CFC theory to be an appropriate starting point to gain better insight into vortex dynamics in the glass phase even in the presence of strongly pinning defects. An improved model should also account for the existence of a thermodynamic BG or VG phase depending on defect dimensionality. This would be important to explain the decrease of μ as the transition temperature is approached. Within the BG theory the additional length scale introduced is the transverse wandering length[7] $l_\perp(T) \propto |T - T_{\rm BG}|^{-\nu'}$. Near $T_{\rm BG}$ this length will eventually grow larger than all the other length scales and could thereby influence the superbundle size.

5 Summary

We have presented a comprehensive study of superconductivity in amorphous Ta_xGe_{1-x}/Ge multilayered thin films with an emphasis on the influence of the vortex behavior on conductivity properties. The films were extremely type-II superconductors and spanned a wide range from weakly to highly anisotropic. Their superconducting phase diagrams were often remarkably similar to specific HTSC depending on anisotropy and vortex pinning potential. A scaling analysis with the aim to identify a VG phase applied to the films with only weakly pinning point-like defects lacked the universality required for a true second order phase transition. It is thought that in these samples the scaling analysis highlights the crossover from a relatively weakly pinned fluid vortex liquid at high temperatures to a much more strongly pinned more viscous liquid at lower temperatures. For the most anisotropic films with essentially two-dimensional superconducting layers this crossover was absent. Instead their low-temperature vortex behavior was best described as that of plastic flow of pancake vortices.

Moderately anisotropic films additionally containing extended, strongly pinning defects gave support to the existence of a truly superconducting BG phase. Moreover, even for magnetic fields considerably misaligned with the defect structure the scaling analysis showed the universality required for a VG phase transition. A careful analysis of *I*-*V* curves taken within the low-temperature glass phases also allowed for the extraction of the field and temperature dependence of the glass exponent. These results are contrary to reported results for comparable HTSC. We tried to explain the observed temperature and field dependence with the CFC model and pointed out the features an improved model would need to describe adequately.

The more anisotropic sample also containing extended defects exhibited the most complicated phase diagram. For magnetic fields misaligned with the defect structure the phase diagram is similar to those films without extended defects. The scaling analysis lacked universality but indicated a crossover from weakly pinned to strongly pinned vortices. However, the field dependence of activation energies in the fluid vortex liquid indicated a two-dimensional behavior with pancake vortices moving in two dimensions. Turning the magnetic field parallel to the extended defects led to the emergence of a BG phase, but only at

[7]The VG theory introduced the glass correlation length $\xi_{\rm VG}$ above T_g. But one can also define a length scale equivalent to $l_\perp$ measuring the distance a flux line has wandered from a favorable pinning position. This VG wandering length $l_{\rm VG}$ should also diverge as the transition temperature T_g is approached from below.

low magnetic fields. At higher fields the I-V characteristics are similar to the non-aligned case. There are also indications that at low fields the pancake vortices recouple in the vortex liquid and move as vortex lines. The limited BG phase only allowed to determine the temperature dependence of the glass exponent for one magnetic field magnitude. The resulting exponents were constant to within our experimental errors indicating VRH of vortex segments, but the magnitude of the exponents differed from theoretical predictions.

Acknowledgements

We would like to thank Joe Trodahl for his support and many fruitful discussions as well as for critically reading this manuscript. We also acknowledge big support from John Abele who helped in gathering significant amounts of the experimental data. This research was financially supported by the New Zealand Marsden Fund.

References

[1] E. H. Brandt, J. Vanacken, and V. V. Moshchalkov, *Physica C*, **369**, (2002) 1.

[2] D. R. Tilley and J. Tilley, *Superfluidity and Superconducitivity*, Graduate Student Series in Physics (Adam Hilger Ltd, 1986).

[3] F. Dalfovo, S. Giorgini, and L. P. Pitaevskii, *Rev. Mod. Phys.*, **71**, (1999) 463.

[4] M. Tinkham, *Introduction to Superconductivity* (McGraw-Hill, Inc., New York, 1996), second edition.

[5] E. H. Brandt, *Phys. Rev. Lett.*, **63**, (1989) 1106.

[6] S. T. Ruggiero, T. W. Barbee, Jr., and M. R. Beasly, *Phys. Rev. Lett.*, **45**, (1980) 1299.

[7] S. T. Ruggiero, T. W. Barbee Jr., and M. R. Beasley, *Phys. Rev. B*, **26**, (1982) 4894.

[8] P. Koorevaar, P. H. Kes, A. E. Koshelev, and J. Aarts, *Phys. Rev. Lett.*, **72**, (1994) 3250.

[9] W. R. White, A. Kapitulnik, and M. R. Beasley, *Phys. Rev. Lett.*, **66**, (1991) 2826.

[10] O. Brunner, L. Antognazza, J.-M. Triscone, L. Miéville, and Ø. Fischer, *Phys. Rev. Lett.*, **67**, (1991) 1354.

[11] J.-M. Triscone, P. Fivat, M. Andersson, M. Decroux, and O. Fischer, *Phys. Rev. B*, **50**, (1994) 1229.

[12] H. A. Radovan and P. Ziemann, *Physica C*, **315**, (1999) 1.

[13] H. C. Yang, L. M. Wang, and H. E. Horng, *Phys. Rev. B*, **59**, (1999) 8956.

[14] W. R. White, A. Kapitulnik, and M. R. Beasley, *Phys. Rev. Lett.*, **66**, (1991) 2826.

[15] P. Koorevaar, P. H. Kes, A. E. Koshelev, and J. Aarts, *Phys. Rev. Lett.*, **72**, (1994) 3250.

[16] G. Blatter, M. V. Feigel'man, V. B. Geshkenbein, A. I. Larkin, and V. M. Vinokur, *Rev. Mod. Phys.*, **66**, (1994) 1125.

[17] A. Schilling, R. A. Fisher, N. E. Phillips, U. Welp, D. Dasgupta, W. K. Kwok, and G. W. Crabtree, *Nature* (London), **382**, (1996) 791.

[18] M. Roulin, A. Junod, and E. Walker, *Science*, **273**, (1996) 1210.

[19] M. P. A. Fisher, *Phys. Rev. Lett.*, **62**, (1989) 1415.

[20] D. S. Fisher, M. P. A. Fisher, and D. A. Huse, *Phys. Rev. B*, **43**, (1991) 130.

[21] D. R. Nelson and V. M. Vinokur, *Phys. Rev. B*, **48**, (1993) 13060.

[22] D. R. Strachan, M. C. Sullivan, P. Fournier, S. P. Pai, T. Venkatesan, and C. J. Lobb, *Phys. Rev. Lett.*, **87**, (2001) 067007.

[23] I. L. Landau and H. R. Ott, *Phys. Rev. B*, **65**, (2002) 064511.

[24] H. J. Trodahl, H. L. Johnson, A. B. Kaiser, C. K. Subramaniam, B. J. Ruck, and P. Lynam, *Phys. Rev. B*, **53**, (1996) 15226.

[25] J. C. Abele, H. J. Trodahl, B. J. Ruck, A. F. Lopez, L. J. Törnquist, T. R. Lee, and S. M. Robinson, *Phys. Rev. B*, **60**, (1999) 12448.

[26] A. Engel, H. J. Trodahl, J. C. Abele, and S. M. Robinson, *Phys. Rev. B*, **63**, (2001) 184502.

[27] H. van Kranenburg and C. Lodder, *Mat. Sci. and Engineering*, **R11**, (1994) 295.

[28] B. J. Ruck, Ph.D. thesis, Victoria University of Wellington, Wellington, New Zealand (1998).

[29] A. Engel, H. J. Trodahl, A. Markwitz, and V. J. Kennedy, *Modern Phys. Lett. B*, **15**, (2001) 1314.

[30] A. Silhanek, L. Civale, S. Candia, G. Nieva, G. Pasquini, and H. Lanza, *Phys. Rev. B*, **59**, (1999) 13620.

[31] H. Schmidt, *Z. Physik*, **216**, (1968) 336.

[32] R. S. Thompson, *Phys. Rev. B*, **1**, (1970) 327.

[33] K. Maki, *Prog. Theor. Phys.*, **40**, (1968) 193.

[34] S. Ullah and A. T. Dorsey, *Phys. Rev. Lett.*, **65**, (1990) 2066.

[35] S. Ullah and A. T. Dorsey, *Phys. Rev. B*, **44**, (1991) 262.

[36] P. H. Kes and C. C. Tsuei, *Phys. Rev. B*, **28**, (1983) 5126.

[37] T. T. M. Palstra, B. Batlogg, R. B. van Dover, L. F. Schneemeyer, and J. V. Wasczak, *Phys. Rev. B*, **41**, (1990) 6621.

[38] M. V. Feigel'man, V. B. Geshkenbein, and A. I. Larkin, *Physica C*, **167**, (1990) 177.

[39] V. Geshkenbein, A. Larkin, M. Feigel'man, and V. Vinokur, *Physica C*, **162-164**, (1989) 239.

[40] V. M. Vinokur, M. V. Feigel'man, V. B. Geshkenbein, and A. I. Larkin, *Phys. Rev. Lett.*, **65**, (1990) 259.

[41] V. M. Vinokur, V. B. Geshkenbein, A. I. Larkin, and V. M. Feigel'mann, Zh. *Eksp. Teor. Fiz.*, **100**, (1991) 1104, [*Sov. Phys. JETP* **73**, 610 (1991)].

[42] N. Y. Fogel, V. G. Cherkasova, O. A. Koretzkaya, and A. S. Sidorenko, *Phys. Rev. B*, **55**, (1997) 85.

[43] V. M. Vinokur, P. H. Kes, and A. E. Koshelev, *Physica (Amsterdam)*, **168C**, (1990) 29.

[44] A.-C. Shi and A. J. Berlinsky, *Phys. Rev. Lett.*, **67**, (1991) 1926.

[45] A. V. Balatskii and V. M. Vinokur, *Solid State Commun.*, **52**, (1984) 847.

[46] V. L. Berezinskii, *Sov. Phys. JETP*, **32**, (1970) 4936.

[47] V. L. Berezinskii, *Sov. Phys. JETP*, **34**, (1971) 610.

[48] J. M. Kosterlitz and D. J. Thouless, *J. Phys. C*, **6**, (1973) 1181.

[49] J. M. Kosterlitz, *J. Phys. C*, **7**, (1974) 1046.

[50] B. I. Halperin and D. R. Nelson, *J. Low Temp. Phys.*, **36**, (1979) 599.

[51] W. R. White, A. Kapitulnik, and M. R. Beasley, *Phys. Rev. Lett.*, **70**, (1993) 670.

[52] D. Ephron, A. Yazdani, A. Kapitulnik, and M. R. Beasley, *Phys. Rev. Lett.*, **76**, (1996) 1529.

[53] S. Friemel and C. Pasquier, *Physica C*, **265**, (1996) 121.

[54] R. H. Koch, V. Foglietti, W. J. Gallagher, G. Koren, A. Gupta, and M. P. A. Fisher, *Phys. Rev. Lett.*, **63**, (1989) 1511.

[55] P. L. Gammel, L. F. Schneemeyer, and D. J. Bishop, *Phys. Rev. Lett.*, **66**, (1991) 953.

[56] H. Safar, P. L. Gammel, D. J. Bishop, D. B. Mitzi, and A. Kapitulnik, *Phys. Rev. Lett.*, **68**, (1992) 2672.

[57] Q. Li, H. J. Wiesmann, M. Suenaga, L. Motowidlow, and P. Haldar, *Phys. Rev. B*, **50**, (1994) 4256, observation of vortex-glass-to-liquid transition in the high-Tc superconductor Bi2223.

[58] N.-C. Yeh, D. S. Reed, W. Jiang, U. Kriplani, C. C. Tsuei, C. C. Chi, and F. Holtzberg, *Phys. Rev. Lett.*, **71**, (1993) 4043.

[59] P. W. Anderson and Y. B. Kim, *Rev. Mod. Phys.*, **36**, (1964) 39.

[60] A. I. Larkin and Y. N. Ovchinnikov, *Zh. Eksp. Teor. Fiz.*, **68**, (1975) 1915, [*Sov. Phys. JETP* **41**, 960 (1976)].

[61] A. I. Larkin and Y. N. Ovchinnikov, D. N. Langenberg and A. I. Larkin, eds., *Nonequilibrium Superconductivity* (North-Holland, Amsterdam, 1986), 493.

[62] A. I. Larkin and Y. N. Ovchinnikov, *Zh. Eksp. Teor. Fiz.*, **73**, (1977) 299, [Sov. Phys. JETP **46**, 155 (1977)].

[63] A. I. Bezuglyj and V. A. Shklovskij, *Physica (Amsterdam)*, **202C**, (1992) 234.

[64] B. J. Ruck, J. C. Abele, H. J. Trodahl, S. A. Brown, and P. Lynam, *Phys. Rev. Lett.*, **78**, (1997) 3378.

[65] B. J. Ruck, H. J. Trodahl, J. C. Abele, and M. J. Geselbracht, *Phys. Rev. B*, **62**, (2000) 12 468.

[66] P. Voss-de Haan, G. Jakob, and H. Adrian, *Phys. Rev. B*, **60**, (1999) 12443.

[67] P. Voss-de Haan, G. Jakob, and H. Adrian, *Physica C*, **341**, (2000) 1387.

[68] A. Engel, Ph.D. thesis, Victoria University of Wellington, Wellington, New Zealand (2001).

[69] A. I. Larkin and Y. N. Ovchinnikov, *Zh. Eksp. Teor. Fiz.*, **65**, (1973) 1704, [Sov. Phys. JETP, **38**, 854 (1974)].

[70] A. I. Larkin and Y. N. Ovchinnikov, *J. Low Temp. Phys.*, **34**, (1979) 409.

[71] J. Lidmar and M. Wallin, *Europhys. Lett.*, **47**, (1999) 494.

[72] D. R. Nelson and V. M. Vinokur, *Phys. Rev. B*, **61**, (2000) 5917.

[73] T. Hwa, D. R. Nelson, and V. M. Vinokur, *Phys. Rev. B*, **48**, (1993) 1167.

[74] T. Klein, A. Conde-Gallardo, I. Joumard, J. Marcus, C. J. van der Beek, and M. Konczykowski, *Phys. Rev. B*, **61**, (2000) 3830.

[75] S. A. Grigera, E. Morré, E. Osquilguil, C. Balseiro, G. Nieva, and F. de la Cruz, *Phys. Rev. Lett.*, **81**, (1998) 2348.

[76] M. Roulin, A. Junod, and E. Walker, *Physica C*, **296**, (1998) 137.

[77] M. Sato, T. Shibauchi, S. Ooi, T. Tamegai, and M. Konczykowski, *Phys. Rev. Lett.*, **79**, (1997) 3759.

[78] M. Kosugi, Y. Matsuda, M. B. Gaifullin, L. N. Bulaevskii, N. Chikumoto, M. Konczykowski, J. Shimoyama, K. Kishio, K. Hirata, and K. Kumagai, *Phys. Rev. Lett.*, **79**, (1997) 3763.

[79] N. Morozov, M. P. Maley, L. N. Bulaevskii, V. Thorsmølle, A. E. Koshelev, A. Petrean, and W. K. Kwok, *Phys. Rev. Lett.*, **82**, (1999) 1008.

[80] Z. Sefrioui, D. Arias, M. Varela, J. E. Villegas, M. A. López de la Torre, C. León, G. D. Loos, and J. Santamaria, *Phys. Rev. B*, **60**, (1999) 15423.

[81] J. C. Soret, L. Ammor, V. Ta Phuoc, R. De Sousa, A. Ruyter, A. Wahl, and G. Villard, *Sol. Stat. Comm.*, **109**, (1999) 461.

[82] J. C. Soret, V. Ta Phuoc, L. Ammor, A. Ruyter, R. De Sousa, and E. Olive, *Phys. Rev. B*, **61**, (2000) 9800.

[83] L. Ammor, R. De Sousa, J. C. Soret, V. Ta Phouc, A. Ruyter, A. Wahl, and E. Olive, *J. Phys.: Condens. Matter*, **12**, (2000) 4217.

[84] B. I. Shklovskii and A. L. Efros, *Electronic Properties of Doped Semiconductors*, volume 45 of *Springer Series in Solid-State Sciences* (Springer, Berlin, 1984).

[85] N. F. Mott, *Philos. Mag.*, **19**, (1969) 835.

[86] M. C. Marchetti and V. M. Vinokur, *Phys. Rev. Lett.*, **72**, (1994) 3409.

[87] M. C. Marchetti and V. M. Vinokur, *Phys. Rev. B*, **51**, (1995) 16 276.

[88] C. Dekker, W. Eidelloth, and R. H. Koch, *Phys. Rev. Lett.*, **68**, (1992) 3347.

[89] J. R. Thompson, L. Krusin-Elbaum, L. Civale, G. Blatter, and C. Feild, *Phys. Rev. Lett.*, **78**, (1997) 3181.

[90] M. V. Feigel'man, V. B. Geshkenbein, A. I. Larkin, and V. M. Vinokur, *Phys. Rev. Lett.*, **63**, (1989) 2303.

[91] P. W. Anderson, *Phys. Rev. Lett.*, **9**, (1962) 309.

[92] T. Nattermann, *Phys. Rev. Lett.*, **64**, (1990) 2454.

INDEX

#

A

B

C

D

E

F

G

H

I

K

L

M

N

V

W

X

Y